The Clinical Nutrition Manager's Handbook

Solutions for the Busy Professional

Julie A. Grim, MPH, RD, LD,

and

Susan Renee Roberts, MS, RD, LD, CNSC, Editors

eat right. Academy of Nutrition and Dietetics

Cathy Iammartino, Publisher
Elizabeth Nishiura, Manager of Production and Digital Content Development

The Clinical Nutrition Manager's Handbook: Solutions for the Busy Professional
Julie A. Grim, MPH, RD, LD, and Susan Renee Roberts, MS, RD, LD, CNSC, Editors
ISBN 978-0-88091-481-9

The views expressed in this publication are those of the authors and do not necessarily reflect policies and/or official positions of the Academy of Nutrition and Dietetics. Mention of product names in this publication does not constitute endorsement by the authors or the Academy of Nutrition and Dietetics. The Academy of Nutrition and Dietetics disclaims responsibility for the application of the information contained herein.

10 9 8 7 6 5 4 3 2 1

For more information on the Academy of Nutrition and Dietetics, visit: www.eatright.org

Contents

Susan Renee Roberts, MS, RD, LD, CNSC

Cindy Hamilton, MS, RD, LD, Robert S. DeChicco, MS, RD, LD, CNSC,
Laura A. Jeffers, MEd, RD, LD, and Elizabeth Anne Pash, MS, RD, LDN

Contributors and Reviewers

Editors

Julie A. Grim, MPH, RD, LD
Vice President of Operations
Diabetes Health and Wellness Institute
Dallas, TX

Susan Renee Roberts, MS, RD, LD, CNSC
Area Director of Clinical Nutrition
Baylor Health Care System/ARAMARK Healthcare
and
Dietetic Internship Director
Baylor University Medical Center
Dallas, TX

Contributors

Pamela Charney, PhD, RD, CHTS-CP
Program Chair
Healthcare Information Technology and Management
Bellevue College
Bellevue, WA

Vicki L. Crittenden, RD, LD
Assistant Director of Nutrition Services (retired)
Baylor Medical Center at Garland
Garland, TX

Robert S. DeChicco, MS, RD, LD, CNSC
Manager, Nutrition Support Team
Cleveland Clinic
Cleveland, OH

Susan C. DeHoog, RD, CD
Clinical Nutrition Manager (retired)
University of Washington Medical Center
and
Guest Lecturer, Nutritional Sciences
University of Washington
Redmond, WA

Kendal T. Ecker, MS, RDN, LD
Assistant Director of Nutrition Services
Baylor Medical Center
Irving, TX

Nancy Hakel-Smith, PhD, RD, LMNT
Manager, Clinical Nutrition Services
Bryan Medical Center
Lincoln, NE

Cindy Hamilton, MS, RD, LD
Director, Nutrition
Center for Human Nutrition, Cleveland Clinic
Cleveland, OH

Laura A. Jeffers, MEd, RD, LD
Outpatient Nutrition Manager
Cleveland Clinic
Cleveland, OH

Sherri L. Jones, MS, MBA, RDN, LDN, FAND
Improvement Specialist (formerly Clinical Nutrition Manager)
University of Pittsburgh Medical Center Presbyterian Shadyside
Pittsburgh, PA

Elizabeth Anne Pash, MS, RD, LDN
Senior Director of Medical Affairs
Covidien
Mansfield, MA

Marsha K. Schofield, MS, RD, LD
Director, Nutrition Services Coverage
Academy of Nutrition and Dietetics
Chicago, IL

Marsha R. Stieber, MSA, RD, CNSC
Independent Nutrition Consultant
Mesa, AZ

Reviewers

Curtis L. Calder, MBA, RD, CD
Clinical I.S. Analyst
Intermountain Healthcare
Ogden, UT

Liz P. Copes, RDN, LD, CNSC
Assistant Director of Food and Nutrition
North Central Baptist Hospital
San Antonio, TX

Debby Kasper, RD, LDN, SNS
Westmont, IL

Ashley L. Mullins, RD, LD, CNSC
Area Director of Clinical Nutrition
Baylor All Saints Medical Center
Fort Worth, TX

Mary Krystofiak Russell, MS, RD, LDN, FAND
Senior Manager, Medical Affairs
Baxter Healthcare Corporation
Deerfield, IL

Acknowledgments

This book is dedicated to our families for their support and love, to our authors and colleagues for their valuable time and contributions to this project, and to the members of the Clinical Nutrition Management Dietetic Practice Group, who provided ongoing support and enthusiasm for this publication.

Julie A. Grim, MPH, RD, LD
Susan Renee Roberts, MS, RD, LD, CNSC
Editors

Preface

When we go through our training to become registered dietitians (RDs), our exposure to management principles and skills is often minimal. Then, when we find ourselves in a management role, it is not always easy to find practical resources to hasten the learning curve. Sometimes in a managerial role, it is the things we don't know we don't know that can get us into trouble, especially with regard to regulatory compliance and human resources issues.

We all can agree that being a clinical nutrition manager (CNM) is challenging in a number of ways. Juggling a long list of priorities, retaining engaged staff, and complying with ever-changing regulations are just some of the demands that CNMs tackle on a daily basis. Understanding that these and other responsibilities are time-consuming, we created this book with the busy CNM in mind. Whether you are an experienced manager or a novice, all CNMs can benefit from useful, applicable information. This book is tailored to address common issues and problems that you encounter. Additionally, the book features many practical ideas and best practices from a distinguished group of RDs who have experience as managers. It also contains sample forms and checklists to assist you in tasks such as competency assessment, preparing for a regulatory survey, and strategic planning.

Our hope is that the information in this book will make you more knowledgeable, successful, and effective in your role as a CNM—and that it will keep you out of "hot water"!

Julie A. Grim, MPH, RD, LD
Susan Renee Roberts, MS, RD, LD, CNSC

A Note about the Dietitian Credential: RD vs RDN

In March 2013, the Commission on Dietetic Registration (CDR) and the Board of Directors of the Academy of Nutrition and Dietetics determined that individuals who hold the credential registered dietitian (RD) may optionally use "registered dietitian nutritionist" (RDN) instead. Although we chose to primarily use "RD" in this handbook, the information is equally applicable to RDNs.

1

Human Resources 101

Julie A. Grim, MPH, RD, LD

"You give me the right people, and I don't care what organization you give me. Good things will happen. Give me the wrong people, and it doesn't matter what you do with the organization. Bad things will happen."

— COLIN POWELL

Introduction

In health care, as in many service businesses, the most valuable resource is people. Many clinical nutrition managers (CNMs) have little or no experience with the human resources (HR) functions of hiring, counseling, and so on, when they take their first management position. Clinicians are often promoted due to such qualities as their strong technical skills, work ethic, and personal desire for advancement. However, the skills that lead to a registered dietitian's (RD's) promotion might not be the skills necessary to be an effective manager. Promotion to CNM is often an RD's first exposure to management. Navigating labor laws and the hiring process in general can be a challenge, and mistakes can have legal, financial, and emotional costs. It is important to understand the basic HR functions as well as the laws that govern them.

Research shows that sound hiring choices are directly linked to a company's financial returns (1). As a CNM, you may be responsible for hiring and managing RDs; dietetic technicians, registered (DTRs); kitchen supervisors; diet office staff; and possibly tray-line or room-service staff. Becoming a manager does not automatically mean you know how to interview, coach, train, evaluate, or otherwise manage employees effectively. However, all of these skills can be learned, and there are many people available to help you do so. In this chapter we discuss the hiring process,

1

employee management, and how best to partner with your HR team to maximize your effectiveness.

The Hiring Process

Many HR and management skills are best learned from interactions with people, not from reading books. Nevertheless, it is worthwhile to start with a basic understanding of important processes and concepts. Accordingly, this chapter reviews five key components of the hiring process: recruiting, applicant screening, interviewing, checking references, and making the job offer.

Recruiting

The first step in the hiring process is recruiting. Recruitment refers to the process of attracting, screening, and selecting qualified people to interview for a position within your organization.

Working with Human Resources

The role of HR in the recruitment process varies from institution to institution. In some cases, the HR department closely manages the process, from sourcing candidates and completing the screening interview to determining the appropriate salary level and extending the job offer. In other facilities, HR plays a smaller role in this process and you may be responsible for some or all of these steps. It is important to meet with your HR staff before you begin recruiting so you have a clear understanding of their role in the process and yours. The following are important areas to address:

- What methods will be used for recruitment? What resources are available to you and how are costs allocated?
- Who is responsible for verification of a candidate's licensure and registration status?
- What kind of paperwork is involved in opening a position for recruitment and selecting a candidate for hire? For example, your facility may have specific forms, requisitions, or worksheets that you must complete to create the job description, set its pay grade, and get approval for new hires.
- How soon can someone start work after an offer is made? The amount of time typically depends on how long the background check, pre-employment physical (including a tuberculosis test), and employment verification processes take.

Establishing a Recruitment Strategy

When determining your recruitment strategy, it is essential that you know your environment and competition and ensure that the job description posted by HR makes sense and is up to date. For example, if you are recruiting for clerical or patient services staff, consider who is your local competition for such employees and how your institution's pay scale compares to that of the competition for similar jobs.

Candidates for these types of positions may also want to know whether your institution is accessible to public transportation and if public transportation runs when shifts begin and end.

If you are looking to hire RDs or DTRs, potential recruitment resources include the following:

- Dietetic internship directors, DTR program directors, and university faculty—these individuals typically keep in touch with their students and know who is actively and potentially looking.
- Local sales representatives for pharmaceutical companies—they often travel to multiple institutions and know many of the clinical dietitians in their service area.
- Professional associations—many local dietetic associations offer online job posting opportunities as well as free networking opportunities at meetings; additionally, many dietetic practice groups offer the opportunity to share information on open positions at no cost.
- Job sites, such as JobsinDietetics.com or Monster.com.
- Social networking sites—find out whether your facility has a Facebook page and if so, if you can advertise there. Can you use one of the professional networking sites, such as LinkedIn or Yahoo? (See Chapter 9 for more information on social networks.)

You can accelerate your recruitment learning curve by asking other managers at your institution what strategies they have found successful for hiring frontline staff. For example, if the laboratory manager has been consistently successful posting open positions on community college bulletin boards or websites such as Craigslist, can you do the same? If your institution holds or participates in job fairs, find out how you can be included. If there are dietetics programs in your local area, you might wish to recruit undergraduate or graduate students looking for nutrition experience—these students may become valuable employees with a passion to learn.

Talk to your staff and find out how they found out about their jobs at your institution. Current employees can also be a great source of referrals. In fact, many hospitals pay bonuses for employee referrals. If your institution has such a bonus program, find out if your positions are, or can be, included.

Writing the Job Posting

When writing a job posting, it is important to include key information in a succinct format that will get the attention of your desired audience (see sample in Figure 1.1 on page 5). The following are key elements to include:

- Job title
- Company (brief description and why it is a good place to work)
- Overview of responsibilities
- Reason for job opening if applicable (eg, department growth or new project)
- Requirements or qualifications—be sure to distinguish between what is desirable (eg, nutrition support order writing experience) and what is mandatory

(eg, RD credential or licensure, education level, or minimum number years of experience)
- Soft skills, such as communications skills or leadership ability

Applicant Screening

The second step in the hiring process is applicant screening. A well-conducted pre-screening process should save you significant time and frustration in the hiring process, result in a solid list of applicants to interview more thoroughly, and provide some initial insight into those applicants. The following are steps in effective applicant screening:

- Provide your HR department with an accurate position description, including licensure or registration requirements, shift or schedule requirements (such as need to alternate early or late shifts, work weekends, or attend early morning rounds), and soft-skill requirements, such as team skills or strong verbal communication skills.
- Review resumes and cover letters. Cover letters should be well-written, error-free, and succinct summaries of an applicant's qualifications. Resumes should also be error free and well formatted and reflect the skills and experience listed in the job posting. Look for keywords that match the qualities you are seeking and potential red flags, such as long gaps in employment or short tenures at multiple positions ("job hopping").
- For hourly positions that do not require a resume, look for job applications that are complete and error free. Evaluate carefully how well a candidate's skills, education, and experience match the position you have posted, and note if you find any of the potential red flags listed in the previous bullet point.
- Conduct a short phone interview with each promising candidate to help evaluate the applicant's verbal communication skills, probe deeper into his or her qualifications, and identify whether salary expectations are in line with what the position pays, if this is a concern. (Note: In some facilities, this function may be performed by the HR department.)

Preparing for the Interview

The third, and perhaps most challenging, step in the hiring process is the interview itself. Interviewing candidates is an art but also requires certain skills. You have to be a good listener; you need to know how to redirect a conversation; you must be able to distinguish between applicants who simply want the job and the superior candidate who can get the job done; and you have to ensure you are abiding by employment laws and the requirements of your institution.

Understanding the Law

To master the interview process, begin by learning the laws that govern this process. Although sometimes confusing and complicated, employment regulations are

Location:	Regency Medical Center, Dallas, Texas
Posting date:	September 1, 2014
Open position number:	01678
Job title:	**Clinical Dietitian**
Work type:	Full time
Work schedule:	Days
Hiring manager:	Alice Smith, MBA, RD, LD

JOB SUMMARY:

- Provides medical nutrition therapy using evidence-based practice to optimize patient care. Provides consultation to the health care team to ensure efficient and effective nutrition care of patients. Monitors and evaluates patient care and nutrition outcomes on an ongoing basis. Educates patients, health care team members, dietetic interns, and members of the community. Participates in ongoing process improvement activities within the Department of Nutrition Services and the institution.
- Maintains a customer-service, patient-centered approach at all times when fulfilling job duties. Meets the qualifications to provide care for patients in the specific age range of assigned clinical area. Works under the direction of the Clinical Nutrition Manager in the Department of Nutrition Services.

COMPETENCIES AND SKILLS:

- Demonstrates competence in written, oral, and electronic communication skills.
- Demonstrates effective ability to function in an interdisciplinary environment.

EDUCATION AND EXPERIENCE:

- Bachelor's or advanced degree in dietetics or nutrition required.
- Registration with the Commission on Dietetic Registration, or eligibility for registration when hired, required. If eligible for registration, must obtain registration and licensure within 6 months of hire.
- At least 2 years of clinical experience preferred.

WORKING CONDITIONS/PHYSICAL DEMANDS:

Work is typically performed in both inpatient and ambulatory settings.

REGENCY HEALTH SYSTEM:

Regency Health System serves nearly 2 million people in North Texas and has been nationally recognized for innovative practices and quality care. Regency is a not-for-profit health system and a premier teaching institute. Regency was named to the Becker's Hospital Review "100 Best Places to Work in Healthcare" list for 2012.

Regency offers a competitive compensation package beginning day one of hire, including comprehensive medical and retirement program benefits, and more.

We are an Affirmative Action, Equal Opportunity Employer.
TO APPLY: www.regencyhealth.com/employment

Figure 1.1 Sample Job Opening for a Clinical Dietitian

designed to eliminate bias, discrimination, prejudice, and unfair hiring practices, and to ensure that all candidates are judged solely on the basis of their ability to do the job. There are a number of federal Equal Employment Opportunity Commission (EEOC) laws that you should understand. Since a hospital's labor pool is typically larger than 20 employees, the following laws are most likely applicable at your institution (2):

- **Title VII of the Civil Rights Act of 1964**: This law, which applies to employers of 15 or more individuals, prohibits employers from discrimination based on race, color, gender, national origin, or religion.
- **Equal Employment Opportunity (EEO) laws**: EEO rules prohibit specific types of employment discrimination, such as discrimination on the basis of race, color, religion, sex, age, national origin, or status as an individual with a disability or as a protected veteran.
- **Americans with Disabilities Act (ADA) of 1990**: ADA bars discrimination due to physical or mental disability and requires reasonable accommodation of individuals with disabilities during hiring and employment (applies to employers of 15 or more individuals).
- **Age Discrimination in Employment Act (ADEA) of 1967**: ADEA, which applies to employers of 20 or more individuals, prohibits discrimination against employees age 40 years or older in favor of younger employees. There is no upper limit to the age; therefore, mandatory retirement is illegal in most cases.

The US Department of Labor (DOL) administers and enforces most labor laws and is a reliable resource if you wish to know more about the individual statutes.

To avoid any potential violations of the antidiscrimination statutes during the hiring process, it is essential that you understand whether interview questions are legal or illegal (see Table 1.1 for examples) (3). If you are in doubt about whether a question is legal, a good rule of thumb is to ask yourself whether the question relates to the specific functions of the job. If it doesn't, don't ask the question.

In addition to employment law, you must also know your state's licensure laws as well as your hospital's policies related to registration and licensure. Can you hire a candidate who is RD-eligible but does not yet have the credential? Is a license required to practice in your state? In many states, a dietitian must be licensed to practice (4). If you reside in one of these states, is there an option for provisional licensure and, if there is, how long does it take to obtain a provisional license?

Doing Your Homework

Far too often, busy managers (is there any other kind?) do not prepare sufficiently and fail to get the key information during the interview that they need to make an informed decision. Be sure to prepare ahead of time and write out your questions so you do not forget in the interview what you most want to find out about the candidate. According to Davila and Kursmark, managers most often make hiring errors because they do not gather enough information and make improper assumptions. In fact, research reveals that more than 70% of managers spend less than 5 minutes preparing for interviews (1). A CNM describes an HR hiring error of this nature in Box 1.1.

Table 1.1 Examples of Illegal and Legal Interview Questions

	Illegal Questions	Legal Questions
Age	How old are you? When is your birthday? In what year were your born? In what year did you graduate from college/high school?	Are you over the age of 18? Can you, after employment, provide proof of age?
Marital and family status	Are you married? With whom do you live? Do you have children? How many children do you have? Are you pregnant? Do you expect to have a family? What are your child care arrangements? How is your family's health?	This job requires 25% travel. Do you have any restrictions on your ability to travel? Do you have responsibilities or commitments that will prevent you from meeting specified work schedules? Do you anticipate any absences from work on a regular basis? If so, please explain the circumstances.
Religion	What religion do you follow?	Are you able to work Saturdays or Sundays? **Note**: Tread carefully here. If the respondent says that he or she has religious obligations that limit availability, you should indicate that your company makes reasonable efforts to accommodate religious beliefs or practices. However, you are not required to make an accommodation if doing so would create an undue hardship to the business (3).
Ethnic origin	Do you speak Spanish?	What languages do you speak?

Box 1.1 Lessons from the Field: A Hiring Error

"When I was promoted to CNM, my first task was to hire a registered dietitian (RD) to replace me. A good personal friend (also an RD of many years) recommended a friend of hers. This candidate did interview well, but I did not interview others and did not fully investigate her job history. Almost immediately after hiring her, red flags went up—she was bad-mouthing previous bosses, she abused her salaried status, and she became sloppy with her work. I was hesitant to discipline her because I considered her more of a friend than an employee. After she was a no-show for a weekend shift (guess who had to cover!) and then blew off a class she was scheduled to teach, I finally took action and drafted a letter with help from human resources. One week after I gave the letter (which stated objectively the poor performance and what was expected), she just walked off the job. Lesson learned. Just because someone is a personal friend does not mean they are the best candidate for the job, *and* being a manager means sometimes you can't be everyone's friend."

The following steps may be helpful in organizing your interview:

- **Determine the skills/competencies needed for the position beforehand**. Make a list of what you are looking for. For example, if you are interviewing for an outpatient RD, requirements might include experience with motivational interviewing, proven counseling skills, program marketing and development experience, and demonstrable public speaking skills. When interviewing candidates for a diet office supervisor position, you would want to find out about their management skills, employee counseling experience, attention to detail, problem-solving skills, customer service abilities, and knowledge of your particular computerized diet office system, such as CBORD or Computrition. Also determine what soft skills (or "people" skills) the candidate needs to have. These sorts of skills, which may be even more important than technical skills, involve how people relate to each other. Examples include skills in communicating, listening, giving feedback, showing initiative, negotiating, collaborating and cooperating as a team member, solving problems, and resolving conflicts.
- **Write out appropriate interview questions**. Your interview questions should reveal your candidate's technical skills, knowledge, behaviors, likes, dislikes, and key motivators (1). Start with the job description if you are unfamiliar with the job's requirements. Determine what questions will elicit answers that let you know whether or not a candidate has the skills and traits needed for the position. A scripted list of job-related questions will prevent you from straying into illegal question quicksand. Also, preparing questions in advance helps ensure consistency among interviews for the same position. When you gather the same information from all the candidates, you can more objectively compare their suitability for the job.
- **Review the candidate's resume and/or application prior to the interview**. You create a poor impression of your managerial skills if you review application materials in front of interviewees. They may conclude that you are disorganized and do not prepare in advance.
- **Ensure that you can conduct the interview in a private space where you are not easily distracted**. The diet office and the cafeteria are not good places to conduct an interview. If you do not have a private office, schedule a room or borrow an office for the interview.
- **Plan several "ice-breaker" questions**. A few casual questions unrelated to work at the start of the interview can enable you to establish rapport and put the applicant at ease. Questions about weather and traffic are usually safe.
- **Learn from experienced interviewers**. If your interviewing experience is limited, you may want to ask your HR team if you can observe them interviewing or ask them to suggest a manager within your hospital who is skilled at interviewing for you to observe. Another option would be to have someone from HR sit in with you during your first few interviews and coach you.
- **Plan to interview multiple promising candidates, and ask others to help you evaluate them**. Other people can and should help evaluate your pool of candidates. Feedback from others can help you avoid making choices based on the natural bias to choose someone similar to you (5). You may find input from

people who will be colleagues or collaborators with the new hire to be especially helpful.

The Interview

At the start of the interview, set a collegial tone. Let your candidates know that you are glad to meet them and express your appreciation for the time they have taken to interview with you. Use your prepared ice-breaker questions to get the conversation started. Remember, you may be nervous, but your candidates may be even more anxious. It is important to build rapport and set them at ease.

Occasionally, a candidate will volunteer personal information. Take care to not pursue these topics in ways that might run afoul of labor laws or your institution's hiring policies. For example, if your job applicant shares that he or she is arriving to the interview late because his or her child missed the school bus, it is best to avoid comments and further questions about this topic as you do not want to open yourself to potential charges of discrimination based on marital or family status. Instead, move on to your structured questions.

After breaking the ice, explain how the interview will proceed and then try to follow that format as closely as possible. State that you will be taking notes to help you remember, so candidates do not get concerned when they see you writing things down.

The notes you take should be clear and factual. Avoid writing down opinions or interpretations of what you think a candidate said. Focus on the degree to which the candidate meets the competencies. Careful note taking is especially important if you are interviewing many people for the same position, as doing so enables you to distinguish one candidate from another. In addition, these notes serve as your documentation of how you reached your hiring decision. Be aware that your HR department may require that you keep interview notes for a designated period of time in case any questions about hiring practices arise.

Be sure to manage your time. If you've set aside an hour for an interview, do your best to stick with that schedule. However, it is good to be prepared to cut the meeting short and jump to the "wrap up" questions if the interview does not require the full amount of time. Do not waste your time or the candidate's by stretching the meeting out.

As you talk with the candidate, share relevant information about the job. Be sure job requirements and performance expectations are clear. For example, explain whether employees are expected to work on weekends or take calls. Managers often make hiring errors because they do not gather enough information or confirm that the candidate fully understands what the job involves. If you are hiring for a clinical position that requires working every fourth weekend, teaching a weekly evening class, or attending early morning bedside rounds, share that information during the interview and get agreement from the candidate that he or she can accept these responsibilities.

During interviews, focus on hiring the right candidate. Do not rush the interviewing stage just to fill the position, even if you are under pressure to do so. You will potentially be living with the decision for a long time.

Interviewing Methods

There are two common interviewing methods used in health care: (*a*) standard/ psychological/job-related and (*b*) behavioral/situational. Standard/psychological/ job-related interviewing involves general questions related to job qualifications, education, experience, and accomplishments of applicants (see Box 1.2). If an applicant meets requirements and responds appropriately to the interview questions, he or she is judged qualified for the position. Traditional interviewing has been criticized because candidates who are skilled at interviewing can anticipate what the interviewer will want to hear and prepare answers ahead of time.

Box 1.2 Standard Interviewing Questions

Tell me about your experience working on teams.
What has been your greatest work accomplishment and why?
Why have you changed jobs so frequently?
What are your strengths and weaknesses?
What did you enjoy most about your last or present job?
What is the greatest value you bring to your organization?
What have you done to improve your professional skills this year?
What are you looking for in a new opportunity?

Behavioral interviewing uses preselected questions correlated to key competencies and requires that candidates answer by giving specific examples of past behavior (see Box 1.3 for sample questions). This method presumes that the best predictor of future performance is past performance. Many consider behavioral interviewing to be the most accurate interviewing method for identifying performance effectiveness (1). The advantages of behavioral interviewing cited in the literature include the following (1,3,6):

- The technique is inherently nondiscriminatory and focuses on abilities, not disabilities.
- Interviewers avoid asking careless questions and sharply reduce the risk of straying into potentially biased areas of questioning.
- Questions are open-ended and require much more than a yes-or-no response.
- Candidates must give detailed examples that illustrate how they have performed a specific skill or demonstrated a specific competency.
- Interviewers can make hiring decisions based on the proven capabilities of applicants.

Box 1.3 Key Competencies and Associated Behavioral Interview Questions

---

Managing conflict:
- Tell me about a time when you had to manage a conflict or dispute among staff who reported to you or members of a team.
- Describe a time when you worked with others who did not work well together. How did you deal with that?

Coping skills:
- Tell me about a time when you found yourself frustrated by a roadblock. What did you do?
- Tell me about a situation where a crisis occurred and you had to shift priorities and workload quickly.

Ability to work under pressure:
- Describe a time when you were given a job or assignment for which you had no prior training. How did you learn to do it?
- Describe a situation in which you were required to work under pressure and how you reacted.

Adaptability/flexibility:
- Give me an example of a time when your priorities or the priorities of your team were shifted. How did you react?
- Recall a time when you were given very little time to make required changes to a project or procedure. What did you do?

Advanced communication skills:
- Describe an instance when you had to think on your feet to extricate yourself from a difficult situation that arose from miscommunication.
- Tell me about a situation where you overcame objections of other people and convinced them your plan was best.

Peer Interviewing

Peer interviewing is an interviewing process that uses a panel of people within the organization to gain a more complete idea of a candidate's appropriateness for a position. For peer interviewing to be effective, several factors must be in place. First, prepare a decision matrix that identifies for the panel interviewers the key attributes an employee should have for that particular position (see Figures 1.2. and 1.3 on pages 12 and 13). This type of tool ensures the interviews are consistent and helps provide objective, accurate data about the various candidates. Second, select high-performing employees to participate in the peer interviewing process and make sure that they are trained on use of the matrix, the ins and outs of the selection process, performance standards for the position to be filled, improper and illegal questions, and how to ask behavioral questions (7). Your facility may offer training in peer or team interviewing. If so, take advantage of this resource. Third, only present peer teams with candidates after you have interviewed them and determined that they seem qualified for the job. Finally, participating candidates should be sufficiently briefed and informed so that they can prepare for a potentially new interview experience (8).

Diet Office Supervisor: Hiring Worksheet		
Desired Competency	Behavioral Question/Qualification	Scoring Guidelines (1 = poor; 3 = fair; 5 = excellent)
Problem solving	Give me an example of when you solved a tough problem.	
Prioritizing	Think of a day when you had plenty of things to do. Describe how you scheduled your time.	
Initiative	Give me an example of a time you went beyond your boss's normal job expectations in order to get the job done.	
Diligence	Tell me about a time when you had to do a job that was particularly uninteresting. How did you deal with it?	
Technical skills/experience	Minimum: 2 years supervisory experience. Experience in diet office.	
Communication effectiveness	Written and verbal communication prior to, during, and after the interview.	
Professionalism	Poise, professional attire, language, thank-you note sent, etc.	
	Total:	

Figure 1.2 Sample Decision Matrix for Hiring a Diet Office Supervisor

There are several reasons to conduct peer interviews, including the following:

- Peer interviews can help develop a sense of cohesiveness among interviewers.
- Participation in peer interviewing allows employees to have ownership in the selection process. They are truly invested in the success of the new hire.
- When the new hire starts, employees who were involved in the interviews already believe that they can get along with that person.
- Research indicates that peer interviewing enhances employee retention (9).
- Peer interviewing is fairly easy to learn.
- This type of interview gives the candidate (who is also evaluating the company) a chance to interact with your "best and brightest" (7,9).

While peer interviewing has proven to be very advantageous, there are several disadvantages to the peer interview process that, while not outweighing the advantages, should be considered as well:

Outpatient Dietitian: Hiring Worksheet		
Competency	Behavioral Question/Qualification	Scoring Guidelines (1 = poor; 3 = fair; 5 = excellent)
Creativity	What have you done that was innovative?	
Initiative	Give me an example of a time when you went beyond your employers' normal job expectations in order to get the job done.	
Interpersonal savvy	Describe a situation where you tried but were unable to build rapport with someone. Why didn't your efforts work?	
Action oriented	Can you tell me about a time that you seized an opportunity and took the ball and ran with it?	
Experience	RD/LD. Minimum 2 years of experience as outpatient RD. Motivational interviewing, program development, and media skills/experience.	
Professionalism	Poise, professional attire, language, thank-you note sent, etc.	
Communication effectiveness	Written and verbal communication prior to, during, and after the interview.	
	Total:	

Figure 1.3 Sample Decision Matrix for Hiring an Outpatient Dietitian

- The time spent preparing for and conducting peer interviews can become too much for employees when they have other responsibilities.
- Peer interviewing does not work if the team is not high performing and capable of collaboration. You have to make sure you have the right employees doing the interviews. For example, some employees may be determined to reject talented applicants they see as potential competition for promotions.
- Candidates can be intimidated when facing a panel of several people.
- Employees may misunderstand their role in the hiring process and become discontented if you do not follow their recommendations. You must make sure that you clearly tell your employees what impact their input will have on the final decision. Consider how your employees will handle it if you do not select their favorite.
- Candidates may ask the panel touchy questions about management or salary. Train your employees to expect sensitive questions and advise them how to defer those issues to the hiring manager.
- Employees with little experience in interviewing may not be objective in their evaluations. Even experienced interviewers can struggle with this challenge.

As noted earlier, a decision matrix can help objectify the peer interviewing process. Before the interviews begin, review the matrix with the panel members and run through questions that can be used to collect relevant information about the candidates. Shortly after an interview, the interviewers use the matrix to rank the interviewee based on how well he or she answered the questions. The matrix is important because it:

- Makes evaluation of all candidates more objective and consistent
- Ensures the interview team selects the right questions for the attributes identified
- Facilitates the decision-making process and prevents emotional decisions

Telephone Interviews and Other Remote Methods of Interviewing

Telephone interviews are often used as an expedient, less-expensive method of interviewing. They can be very helpful in screening, especially if a candidate is not local; however, they tend to be unpopular with both candidates and managers. If you use telephone interviewing in your recruiting process, be aware that you may not learn as much about the candidate as you would from a face-to-face interview. To obtain the best information possible, telephone interviews should be as structured as face-to-face interviews are structured.

Video conferencing, Skype, and FaceTime are emerging as alternatives to telephone interviews. These options may be worth investigating at your institution.

Ranking and Selection

Once the interviews are complete, you will need to review the completed decision matrix and rank your candidates. It is best to complete the decision matrix on each candidate as soon as the interview is complete, while your notes make sense and the interview is still fresh in your mind. Ideally, all interviewers rate the candidates separately and then get together to discuss their findings, compare their ratings, and tally the scores if a numerical rating system has been used. Ranking competencies in order of importance can help identify the strongest candidate for the position if two or more promising applicants have similar overall scores. No candidate is a perfect match. In addition to interview rankings, you should also consider background and reference checks, salary requirements, information obtained from other sources, and credentials in making your decision.

Reference Checks

The fourth component in the hiring process is the reference check. Before you make a job offer, you or your HR department should check the candidate's references. Some, but not all, HR departments do this as standard operating procedure. Due to liability concerns, many references will not provide much information about previous employees other than verification of their entry and exit dates and possibly the reason for exit and eligibility for rehire. Keep in mind that the same discrimination laws that apply to interviewing also apply to reference checking. Do not ask about marital status, age, disabilities, religion, ethnicity, or other issues related to protected class status.

Do not let your excitement or relief in finding the "perfect" candidate or your impatience to fill the position lead you to make the critical error of skipping reference checks. Even when a candidate's resume and interview responses seem highly credible, you need to conduct due diligence. If you are serious about specific candidates, make sure their work history is accurate, and check at least a reference or two. It is also critical to verify a candidate's licensure and registration status before making a job offer. At a minimum, the reference check should include the following (10):

- Verification of employment dates
- Verification of position or title held
- Eligibility status for rehire
- Reason for separation
- Recommendation for another position/role

Box 1.4 describes what could happen if these steps are not followed.

Box 1.4 Lessons from the Field: Checking References

"I had an employee with a BS in Nutrition who worked in the diet office. Excellent worker; everyone loved her. She kept applying for the local internship and getting rejected. I wrote a letter on her behalf, saying what a great employee she was and that I thought she would make an outstanding dietitian. She got accepted. After she completed her clinical rotations, she came back and asked if I had any dietitian positions open. I hired her for a per diem position. After a few months, the internship director broke the news to me that she had not completed *any* of her classroom assignments for the internship. They gave her a couple of months to complete the assignments, but she did not do so. I had to terminate her employment, as she did not meet the standards for a registration-eligible dietitian. It gave me a *big* lesson on always checking credentials and not going on trust for what someone tells me, even someone I know well."

The Job Offer

The fifth and final step in the hiring process is the job offer. Be sure to work with your HR team to understand your facility's salary guidelines and determine whether your salary range is competitive in the market place. For example, your employer might have data showing what your company and multiple direct competitors pay employees with jobs similar to the one you are filling. The Academy of Nutrition and Dietetics also conducts biannual compensation and benefits surveys for the dietetics profession, which can be a source of regional and position-specific salary trends (11).

Also work with HR to learn how salary negotiations should take place. The availability of online sources of compensation information, such as salary.com, has leveled the playing field between employer and prospective employee when it comes to negotiations and job offers. It is therefore more important than ever to be proactive so you can hire top-quality candidates. If you have the option, be prepared to counteroffer when a candidate asks for more money. However, the reality is that most RD positions are set within the facility budget and CNMs have little flexibility in salary negotiations. If you cannot negotiate on salary, your facility's benefits package may be a selling point to candidates. Be sure that you can articulate its advantages to prospective employees. For example, if your hospital offers a 401K retirement plan and matches up to 5% of employee contributions, let candidates know that this offering is above average and translates to dollars beyond the salary alone. Are you able to offer a sign-on bonus in lieu of a higher initial salary? Do you have a career ladders program that offers the potential for additional compensation? Does your facility pay higher salaries to RDs with advanced degrees or advanced certification such as Certified Diabetes Educator (CDE) or Certified Nutrition Support Clinician (CNSC)? Does your facility pay registration and licensure fees or Academy of Nutrition and Dietetics membership dues? Is there an allowance for professional development or conferences and continuing education events?

Other perqs, such as free parking, subsidized bus or train transportation, reduced rates for health insurance, free or reduced-rate health club memberships, subsidized day care, and flexible scheduling or no weekend work, may all give you the edge over your competition. Tuition reimbursement is an important but often overlooked benefit that might be very enticing to your prospective employee.

Finally, as you prepare to make an offer, make sure you think about its implications for salary equity within your department. Work with your HR team to ensure that the offer is not inappropriately out of line with what other staff members earn.

If you are having a difficult time attracting and hiring quality candidates, do your homework. Where are these desirable candidates accepting jobs, and why? If candidates are choosing sales positions over your offerings, keep in mind that very few hospital positions can compete with the salary and benefits of sales positions. If candidates are electing to work at other hospitals, you may have more leverage. Find out when and how salary budgets are set at your institution. Do you have any outcomes data to show the value of your department? What skills do your RDs have and what are their responsibilities? How long has it been since you last updated job descriptions for your staff? If your RDs are performing tasks typically associated with advanced practice, such as enteral and parenteral nutrition order writing, research, and feeding tube placement, you may be able to get job descriptions revised and regraded. Look at other advanced practice clinician job descriptions, such as those for advanced practice nurses, and talk to other professionals at your institution who have successfully raised salaries to gain ideas.

New Employee Orientation

New employee orientation is one of most important, but most neglected, functions in the workplace. Research suggests that new employees decide within the first 30 days whether they feel welcome in their new work environment. To succeed in their jobs, new employees need to be drawn into the team and the organizational family. Recruitment Solutions found that 47% of employee turnover occurs in the first 90 days (3). An employee handbook and reams of policies and procedures do not comprise a sufficient orientation program. Employees often complain that orientation is boring or overwhelming or that they are left to "sink or swim" after they are hired. As a result, new employees are not productive and may leave the organization within the year.

Typical organizational goals of new employee orientation programs in health care include the following:

- Reduce start-up costs associated with new hires.
- Reduce the new employee's anxiety.
- Reduce employee turnover.
- Prepare the new employee to have realistic job expectations.
- Ensure the employee understands and can meet regulatory agency requirements.

Effective methods to engage new employees include the following:

- Assign your highest performers to "buddy" or mentor new employees.
- Make sure the employee's work space is clean, ready, and comfortable.
- Make sure key coworkers know that the employee is starting, and make sure introductions are made. For example, arrange a group breakfast or lunch on the employee's first day.
- Develop an effective orientation program that starts with the basics and does not cram everything into a one-day session.
- Make the orientation process fun and interesting.
- As a manager, stay involved. Meet regularly during the first 30 to 90 days to evaluate the new employee's progress, clear up any confusion about job responsibilities, and develop your relationship.

The following are necessary components of effective orientation programs in health care:

- Training on all relevant regulatory requirements, such as Health Information Portability and Accountability Act (HIPAA) compliance, fire safety, and patient rights and responsibilities. These topics are usually components of your hospital's orientation program and typically must be completed within 30 days of hire.
- Important department policies.
- Key job responsibilities.
- Skill competency verification. Documentation is typically required within 30 to 90 days of hire. Check with your institution to ensure your process meets its standards.
- Introductions to teammates and other staff the new employee needs to know.
- Regularly scheduled meetings between the new employee and his or her direct supervisor. The goal is to build the relationship between the employee and the manager and evaluate the employee's initial progress. In *Hardwiring*

Excellence, Studor recommends that managers ask the new hire the following four questions after 30 days of employment (7):

◊ How do we compare with who we said we were? In responding, the employee might bring up issues such as real or perceived discrepancies between actual schedules and what hours he or she expected to work.
◊ What are we doing well?
◊ At your previous hospital, what are some things that you saw that you feel could make us better? This question invites the employee to help maximize the department's opportunities for process improvement.
◊ Is there anything that you are uncomfortable with that might cause you to leave?

Common Management Challenges

First-time CNMs often encounter HR situations that are completely new to them. This section covers several issues that many CNMs identified as particularly problematic for them as new managers.

Managing in a Union Environment

In addition to HR issues that are typical in any nutrition department, CNMs managing in a union environment face distinctive challenges. The union contract sets specific parameters for a variety of employment-related issues, such as compensation and benefits, working conditions, job security, disciplinary procedures, employees' rights, management's rights, and contract length. If you are new to the union environment or new to a particular institution with a union contract, you must familiarize yourself with several things. First, learn about the historical and current relationship between the union(s) and management, including past and present grievances, negotiating points during the last contract renewal, and key players involved on both sides. Second, be knowledgeable of the tenets of the collective bargaining agreement that could affect how you address performance management challenges. Learn the meaning of every paragraph that relates to items such as performance management evaluations, scheduling, job tasks, and so on. For example, what options do you have if the diet office staff needs to be trained on a new diet office system? Can you ask them to come in early or work extra hours? When staff or management take issue with a policy or action, people will likely refer to the contract repeatedly to "prove" a point. You will be surprised at the variation in each person's interpretation of the contract, so make sure you know its true meaning. Third, learn to work closely with union representatives as well as management experts working in the staff relations or

HR department. These people can serve as resources who can help you decide how to best respond to myriad situations that may arise. Ask your HR team to identify a department leader who can mentor you in navigating the union environment.

Documentation and communication take on even more importance in this environment. Be sure that you communicate pertinent information regarding any changes, new initiatives, and other relevant matters to union leaders before you share it with the rest of the team. This way, the union can be prepared for any questions or concerns from its members. The steps in the performance management process are similar in union and nonunion environments. In either setting, you usually begin by coaching an employee whose performance is unsatisfactory. Then, if performance does not sufficiently improve, you issue a verbal warning followed by a written warning. If these steps do not work, disciplinary action, such as suspension and termination, is an option. However, there are some important differences to note when you work with unionized employees. For example, a unionized employee typically has the right to have a union representative present during any disciplinary meeting that includes a written warning or suspension. This right to union representation is usually restricted to disciplinary meetings.

By keeping the union informed and involved in the performance management process, you may avoid defensive actions and disputes regarding disciplinary decisions. However, you should not expect that involving and informing the union will mean it necessarily will accept your decision to discipline an employee. The union's role is to appropriately represent the employee, and it may act if the employee's contractual rights seem to have been violated. Be sure to keep complete, factual, detailed, and timely documentation of performance situations and actions. You will need this documentation to justify any performance management decisions if the union initiates proceedings such as grievance hearings or arbitration.

Managing Various Generations

Managers and supervisors in most organizations today are faced with the prospect of managing employees from four generations: those who came of age during World War II, Baby Boomers, and Generations X and Y. Each generation comes to the workforce with its own priorities, preferences, and work styles (see Box 1.5 on pages 20–21) (12). To maximize your managerial effectiveness, you should understand the key motivators of each generation, how they best learn, and how they best receive information. For example, with Xers and Yers being the predominant groups in the workplace today, the traditional management model of "top-down, boss-is-always-right" may not be effective. Many CNMs in the field talk about the increased demands of their Generation X and Y employees for flexible work schedules and input in policies such as the dress code. The issues described in Box 1.6 (see page 21) are common ones for many CNMs today.

Box 1.5 Generational Snapshots

Matures/Traditionalists/Veterans

Who are they?

- Born between 1922 and 1945
- The silent generation, grew up in the Great Depression and WWII
- The smallest group in today's workforce
- The wealthiest group in today's workforce

Values/characteristics:

- Duty before fun
- Respect authority
- Adhere to the rules
- Sacrifice
- Loyalty
- Great faith in institutions
- Demand quality

Baby Boomers

Who are they?

- Born between 1946 and 1964
- The largest generation (77 million) in the United States
- Traditional upbringing, followed by youthful rebellion
- Have entered or are nearing retirement

Values/characteristics:

- Optimism
- Involvement/loyalty to organization
- Strong work ethic
- Limited work-family balance
- Question authority
- Desire quality
- Buy now, pay later attitude
- Continuous learners

Generation X

Who are they?

- Born between 1965 and 1980
- Grew up during Watergate, the PC boom, the Reagan presidency
- Comfortable with technology

(continued)

Box 1.5 *(continued)*

Values/characteristics:

- Skeptical of institutions
- Reluctant
- Respect production over tenure

Generation Y/Millenials

Who are they?

- Born between 1981 and 2000
- Also referred to as the Echo Generation
- Just starting to enter the workplace
- Extremely comfortable with technology

Values/characteristics:

- Realism
- Parental involvement/structured upbringing
- Extreme fun
- Social/confident/inclusive
- Merged families
- Multi-taskers/entrepreneurial
- Work is a means to an end
- Demanding/questioning

Source: Data are from reference 12.

Box 1.6 Lessons from the Field: Working with Younger Employees (Generations X and Y)

"If I had to identify my two biggest issues [as a manager of younger employees], they are the dress code and texting. First, the RDs lobbied to wear scrubs and the request was denied by the administration. Then, they pushed for a business-casual dress code, which we tried but had to do away with because 'business casual' became rumpled and progressed to beach wear.

"The second issue of concern is texting. We have RDs texting when they are unable to work due to illness, rather than calling me on the phone. This is in spite of the fact that our cell phones rarely get service in the hospital so I can't receive their texts. Now we also have to deal with Facebook and Twitter and online shopping at work."

Perhaps the biggest challenge for many CNMs is effectively managing the newest generation to the workforce, Generation Y. Research suggests that Generation Y employees learn best from a "coaching" style of leadership and are looking for a mentoring relationship with their supervisors or their team (13). Business leaders suggest that Generation Y employees can benefit from mentors who can help them understand corporate culture and business decision-making. In return, ask these younger employees to mentor older workers on new trends, such as advances in technology, social media best practices, pop culture, and word-of-mouth marketing (14).

Other recommendations for working with Generation Y include the following (13,14):

- Let them set their goals.
- Don't skimp on the praise.
- Listen to them.
- Don't assume they share your goals.
- Address performance issues quickly. Provide direct, prompt feedback.
- Explain the "why" behind the decisions you make.

Box 1.7 provides a CNM success story with Generation Y.

Box 1.7 Lessons from the Field: Empowering Staff to Find Solutions

"I had a problem with my younger staff continually approaching me with problems, but no solutions. This resolved when I changed my response to the complaints and asked for solutions. I actually found that my staff seemed to feel more empowered and engaged once they realized they have the solutions and can implement them."

Of course, in addition to generational differences, individual employees are shaped by other social and personal factors, which might include gender, race/ethnicity, personality, and thinking style. A hospital needs to provide excellent and efficient service seven days a week, and in this demanding environment a manager cannot possibly cater to every desire of his or her employees regarding working conditions. However, your team will benefit greatly if you aim to accommodate individual differences and provide options when possible in the following areas:

- **Supervision**: Can you individualize the method and degree of supervision (how much or how little) for each employee?
- **Feedback**: What types of constructive criticism and acknowledgement are best for different employees?

- **Technology and equipment**: Can you make available tools that reduce tedious processes and expand your employees' time available for patient care?
- **Scheduling**: Is there room for scheduling flexibility that prioritizes factors other than seniority? For example, can you set up a rotating schedule for covering less-desirable shifts or have teams self-schedule within defined parameters?
- **Work assignments**: How can assignments and tasks be delegated to provide the right balance of opportunity for specific individuals and team growth?
- **Professional development**: Can training and skill-building opportunities be offered in different packages to suit different learning styles? For example, could a training program blend traditional, instructor-led classes (which may appeal more to older employees) and web-based self study (which might particularly excite Generations X and Y)?
- **Communication**: Can your staff effectively communicate across multiple channels, such as print, e-mail, inter- and intranets, phone and voicemail, and face-to-face encounters? What communication methods work best for the individuals being addressed? If you think intergenerational communication styles may be in conflict on your team, consider group discussions with your team about generational differences. During your meetings, ask your team members which "generational" profile best seems to describe them. You may find that some identify with a group older or younger than the generation into which they were born. Ask your team members which of the characteristics attributed to their generation are most important to them.
- **Opportunities for innovation**: Are you prepared to capitalize on the entrepreneurial strengths of employees (such as your Generation Xers) by "outsourcing" challenging problems to special teams? For example, can your staff help develop a marketing plan, choose a new productivity system, or sketch the format to be used for nutrition documentation in the electronic health record system? Consider assigning special projects to small teams composed deliberately of people from several generations, to gain the synergy of their complementary strengths.

Cultural Competence

Cultural competence has recently emerged as part of a strategy to reduce disparities in access to and quality of health care. A culturally competent staff is prepared to tailor health care delivery to meet patients' social, cultural, and linguistic needs. As the CNM, you need to be culturally competent. Furthermore, your team needs cultural competence to work with each other and other health care team members, and, even more important, to provide care effectively to patients with diverse values, beliefs, and behaviors. This topic is addressed further in Chapter 8.

Problematic HR Situations

Unfortunately, many CNMs do not receive training on problematic HR situations. The following sections cover several problematic HR issues that you may encounter in clinical management and offer suggestions and resources for how to address them.

Harassment

Harassment may or may not be sexual in nature. Sexual harassment is a form of sex discrimination that violates Title VII of the Civil Rights Act of 1964 (15). It can occur in a variety of circumstances, and the following are some essential points to understand about it (16):

- Both men and women can be victims of sexual harassment, and both men and women can be instigators. The victim and harasser do not have to be of opposite sexes.
- The harasser can be the victim's supervisor, an agent of the employer, a supervisor in another area, a coworker, or a nonemployee.
- The victim does not have to be the person harassed. He or she could be anyone affected by the offensive conduct.
- Unlawful sexual harassment does not necessarily involve economic injury to or discharge of the victim.
- The harasser's conduct must be unwelcome.

Harassment at work unreasonably interferes with or alters the employee's work performance, or creates a hostile, abusive, or offensive work environment (16). Examples of hostile behavior could include bullying, gossiping about a particular coworker, or excluding coworkers from team activities. To determine whether a workplace environment is "hostile," the following factors are typically examined:

- Whether the conduct was verbal, physical, or both
- How often the conduct was repeated
- Whether the conduct was hostile or patently offensive
- Whether the alleged harasser was a coworker or a supervisor
- Whether others joined in perpetrating the harassment

Examples of inappropriate conduct of a sexual nature include sexually oriented jokes; sexually explicit e-mails, screen savers, posters, cartoons, and graffiti; and unwanted verbal or physical contact. The standard used by civil rights agencies and courts in determining whether a hostile work environment exists is whether a reasonable person, in the same or similar circumstances, would find the conduct offensive (16). A single incident may be sufficient to establish a "quid pro quo" harassment claim, but typically a pattern of conduct is required to establish a hostile work environment.

As a manager, you need to take all steps necessary to prevent harassment from occurring in your department (16). It is critical that you clearly communicate to employees that harassment will not be tolerated. You must set the example by being alert to the behavior of others, by not participating in anything that might be construed as harassment (no matter how subtle), and by stopping inappropriate behavior immediately if you observe it. Carol Merchasin, a noted training consultant in the area of harassment prevention, states that a manager must use caution in the "danger zones, such as comments on personal appearance, jokes, cartoons, and nicknames that demean others on the basis of their race, gender, ethnic origin, religion, age, disability, and sexual orientation" (17).

You must also take immediate and appropriate action when an employee alleges harassment. Find out about your facility's complaint or grievance process, and ensure that your employees also understand the process. Even if no one complains, you need to be alert to conduct that is inappropriate and make sure that you put an end to it (17). The first step is to contact your HR representative for assistance.

Patient Privacy

CNMs need to be knowledgeable of the component of HIPAA that addresses the privacy of protected health information (PHI), understand the policies and procedures that the institution has put in place to comply, and be proactive in educating their staff on how HIPAA pertains to their tasks and responsibilities (18). For example, PHI can be electronic or printed. What does your hospital policy state about students accessing computerized medical records? What patient information is allowed on tray tickets?

Make sure that you and your staff comprehend the requirements for reporting suspected violations. Become familiar with your facility's policy to better understand what suspected violations need to be reported, and to whom. Also be aware that hospitals routinely audit patient's electronic health records to ensure that only appropriate individuals are accessing PHI. Box 1.8 describes a situation in which HIPAA was violated.

Box 1.8 Lessons from the Field: Protecting Patient Privacy

"I had to terminate a dietitian for unauthorized medical record access. Our IT department noted a pattern of medical record access that seemed suspicious. When we investigated, it turned out that an RD was reviewing medical records for her own personal learning on a specific disease because her mother had been recently diagnosed. Even though she had been through HIPAA training, she did not realize her actions were in violation. Because our facility has a zero tolerance policy, I had to let her go. You always think members of your clinical team are professionals and just know these things, but you can't make that assumption."

Fair Labor Standards Act Compliance

The federal Fair Labor Standards Act (1938) established the minimum wage; rules for overtime pay; recordkeeping, which includes certain identifying information about the employee such as name and Social Security number as well as data about the hours worked and the wages earned; and standards for youth employment. The policies are enforced by the US Department of Labor (DOL) (19). In recent years, DOL has expanded enforcement of the act, and multiple health care institutions have been found noncompliant. For example, DOL investigators found that nurses at multiple facilities in a large health care system were owed money because the health care system's timekeeping system automatically deducted time for meal periods whether or not the employees were fully relieved of their duties (20).

Even if appropriate compensation policies and procedures are in place, violations can arise from failures in policy administration and the day-to-day practices of managers and noncompliant employees (20). The DOL may audit an employer at any time. Many investigations are initiated by employee complaints. Employers should be aware that an investigation can expand beyond the initial complaint to a review of all wage and hour practices. Examples of health care violations include the following (20):

- Computerized time systems automatically deduct meal periods even when employees work during meal breaks.
- Employees work before and after their shifts without being paid properly.
- Employees are not paid for attending training sessions.

As a CNM, you must understand the ramifications of the Fair Labor Standards Act for both your exempt and non-exempt employees. It is important to properly distinguish exempt positions from those that are non-exempt. A job title or job description does not necessarily grant exempt status; what matters is the actual work performed (19). Many people believe that all exempt workers are salaried and all non-exempt workers are hourly. That is not the case. How employees are paid does not have anything to do with how they are classified. For example, a non-exempt worker may be paid a salary, but you still have to pay attention to minimum wage and overtime requirements for this employee. The Fair Labor Standards Act website has many tools to assist CNMs in gaining understanding and developing compliance strategies for this law (19).

Summary

The skills required to manage various HR processes are often new to CNMs and may be outside their comfort zone. Therefore, it is vital that you partner with your HR department to understand your role and theirs as well as how they can best support you. Your people are your most important resource. Understanding and gaining competence in the hiring, orientation, and ongoing management of your staff is vital to ensure a highly functioning team that provides safe, timely, effective, and efficient patient care.

References

1. Davila L, Kursmark L. *How to Choose the Right Person for the Right Job Every Time*. New York, NY: McGraw-Hill; 2005.
2. US Equal Employment Opportunity Commission. Laws and Guidance. www.eeoc.gov/laws/index.cfm. Accessed February 2, 2010.
3. Armstrong S, Mitchell B. *The Essential HR Handbook*. Franklin Lakes NJ: Career Press; 2008.
4. Academy of Nutrition and Dietetics. Dietetics Practitioner State Licensure Provisions. www.eatright.org/Members/content.aspx?id=8848. Accessed March 1, 2010.
5. Cottrell D. *Monday Morning Leadership*. Dallas, TX: Cornerstone Leadership Institute; 2002.
6. Yeung R. *Successful Interviewing and Recruitment*. Philadelphia, PA: Kogan Page; 2008.
7. Studor Q. *Hardwiring Excellence*. Gulf Breeze, FL: Fire Starter Publishing; 2003.
8. Frase-Blunt M. Peering into an interview. *HR Magazine*. 2001;46(12):71–77.
9. Pentilla C. Peering in. *Entrepreneur*. 2005;33(1):70–72.
10. Podmoroff D. *How to Hire, Train, and Keep the Best Employees*. Ocala, FL: Atlanta Publishing Group; 2005.
11. *Compensation and Benefits Survey of the Dietetics Profession 2013*. Chicago, IL: Academy of Nutrition and Dietetics; 2013.
12. Banta C, Grim JA. Successful Management Across the Millennium. Presented at Clinical Nutrition Management Annual Symposium. San Antonio, TX, April 1, 2008.
13. Ryan L. Tips on managing generation Y. *Bloomberg Business Week*. www.businessweek.com. Accessed June 13, 2010.
14. Humble L. Preparing for Generation Y. Welcoming Generation Y to the Workplace. November 2007. http://human-resources-management.suite101.com/article.cfm/whats_up_with_y#ixzz0qkVHTSe6. Accessed June 16, 2011.
15. Bowers T. Hostile work environment: A manager's legal liability. http://articles.techrepublic.com/5100-10878_11-5035282. Accessed July 1, 2011.
16. The U.S. Equal Employment Opportunity Commission. *Facts on Sexual Harassment*. www.eeoc.gov/facts/fs-sex.html. Accessed July 1, 2011.
17. Merchasin C, Chapman M, Polisky J. *Case Dismissed! Taking Your Harassment Prevention Training to Trial*. 2nd ed. Chicago, IL: American Bar Association; 2005.
18. Centers for Medicare & Medicaid Services. HIPAA 101 for Health Care Provider's Offices. www.cms.gov/EducationMaterials/Downloads/HIPAA101-1.pdf. Accessed June 13, 2010.
19. US Department of Labor. Fair Labor Standards Act. www.dol.gov/compliance/laws/comp-flsa.htm#applicable_laws. Accessed July 10, 2011.
20. Pear R. Pay practices in health care are investigated. *New York Times*. August 8, 2010. www.nytimes.com/2010/08/10/health/policy/10health.html. Accessed August 1, 2011.

2

Budgeting and Managing Finances

Julie A. Grim, MPH, RD, LD

Introduction

Budgeting provides a method for organizing, communicating, and controlling a health care facility's operational progress toward a budget plan stated in dollar terms. It also provides a mechanism for evaluating financial performance and controlling operations in accordance with the objectives, policies, and plans of the institution (1,2).

New clinical nutrition managers (CNMs) often find budgeting and other financial management processes to be daunting tasks. In fact, some clinicians do not pursue or accept promotions into management positions because they have a fear of managing budgets and other financial responsibilities. However, registered dietitians (RDs) are more than qualified to handle the basic financial calculations involved in budgeting. If you plan effectively, define your work processes, and understand the costs and cost-drivers in your department, you can likely project an attainable and realistic budget. The key to taking the mystery out of the budget process is to become familiar with the timeline, the language, the software or paper forms used, and the methods used at your particular facility. This chapter reviews basic budget vocabulary, types of budgets, common areas of budgetary responsibility for the CNM, common financial tools, and tips for securing approval for the financial resources needed to accomplish the work required in your department.

The Language of Budgeting and Finance

Health care finances seem to have a language of their own. The following are some of the most common terms you will hear in relation to health care finances:

- **Payer**: The entity that pays for an individual's health care. Payers in the health care industry are both public and private. Public payers include federal and state governments—which fund Medicare and Medicaid—and, to a lesser degree, local governments. Private payers are insurance companies. Both public and private payers are often referred to as "third-party payers."

- **Payer mix**: The various types of monies (eg, payments from Medicaid, Medicare, indemnity insurance, or managed care) received by a medical practice or health care institution for patient care.

- **Operating revenue**: The direct income from the provision of patient services, revenue from other operating sources such as sales and services to guests, and revenue from miscellaneous sources, such as rental of hospital space, sale of cafeteria meals, and gift shop sales (total operating revenue). Operating revenue is the primary way hospitals make money.

- **Gross patient revenue**: Total charges billed by the health care facility for patient care delivery.

- **Net patient revenue**: The revenue from patient care delivery remaining after deductions for contractual adjustments and charity care are subtracted from gross patient revenue. Net patient revenue is often reported as the estimated net collectable amounts from patients, third-party payers, and others for services rendered, including estimated retroactive adjustments under reimbursement agreements with third-party payers (1–3). For example, net patient revenue for outpatient nutrition counseling is the amount of money actually received by a hospital for this service after any discounts or contractual allowances.

- **Fixed costs**: Costs that do not vary with the level of patient activity. Typical examples of fixed costs in health care include capital expenditures, most employee salaries and benefits, building maintenance, utilities, and information systems. However, as institutions become more adept at anticipating the number of patient days and the patient census, some costs that have been traditionally defined as "fixed," such as the staffing budget, may be understood as varying with patient activity.

- **Variable costs**: Costs that vary with the level of patient activity. Examples include health care worker supplies, patient care supplies, diagnostic and therapeutic supplies, and medications. Some salaries, such as those paid to part-time and call-in staff, are based on the volume of activity and are included in variable costs. Salaries for managers or supervisory staff are not typically defined as variable costs. For example, the number of hostesses you need to deliver trays may vary based on the patient census, but the salary cost for your tray-line supervisor will stay constant (fixed). Other examples of variable costs include food, the cost for RDs to attend continuing education programs, and membership dues for professional organizations.

- **Fiscal year**: The 12-month period for which a business's financial results and statements are prepared and reported. Many hospitals use a fiscal year that is different from the calendar year, such as July 1 to June 30 or October 1 to September 30.
- **Fixed budget**: Expenses and revenue targets that do not vary with activity levels.
- **Flexible budget**: Projected expenses and revenues that vary as a function of activity level, such as patient census or number of patient days.
- **Productive time**: Hours worked on the job.
- **Nonproductive time**: Hours paid but not worked, such as vacation, time for education, sick days, and holidays.
- **Income statement/profit and loss statement/responsibility report**: A monthly financial report that shows how actual revenues and expenses compare to budget projections.
- **Inpatient day of care** (also commonly referred to as a "patient day" or a "census day," or by some federal hospitals as an "occupied bed day"): The period of service between the census-taking hours on two successive calendar days; the day of discharge is counted as a day of care only when the patient was admitted and discharged on the same day (2,3).
- **Patient days**: The number of adult and pediatric inpatient days of care rendered in a particular time period. This number does not count newborn infants born in the hospital as patients, but it does count days of care for their mothers as well as days of care for infants born in the hospital who are transferred to a neonatal care unit. Patient days count inpatient days for swing beds (beds approved for both acute care and skilled nursing care).
- **Adjusted patient days**. A ratio used to calculate occupancy rates, staff workload, and operating costs per patient. To calculate adjusted patient days, first determine the gross revenue and the number of inpatient days. Adjusted patient days = (Inpatient days × Gross revenue)/(Inpatient revenue).
- **Fixed asset**: An asset that is not consumed or sold during the normal course of business, such as land, buildings, equipment, machinery, vehicles, and other such items. Any asset expected to last or be in use for more than one year is considered a fixed asset.
- **Depreciation**: The process of budgeting for the expense of a fixed asset over its expected length of use, rather than charging the entire cost against one budget period. For example, if a hospital bought new tray-line hot-steam wells for $30,000 and expected them to last 10 years, the hospital might use the straight-line depreciation method (depreciation per year equals the total value of the fixed asset divided by the years of anticipated service or use) to record the expense of the steam wells at $3,000 per year for 10 years (1). Depreciation is often broken down further into a monthly cost for budgeting purposes.

- **Net operating income**: The health care institution's operating income after operating expenses are deducted, but before income taxes and interest are deducted. Also referred to as "the bottom line" or PBIT (profit before interest and taxes).

Types of Budgets

This chapter focuses on the two types of budgets that health care managers typically use: capital budgets (the resources to be allocated to construction, renovation, and equipment-acquisition projects as well as the cash requirements associated with those projects) and operating budgets (detailed projections of all estimated revenue and expenses based on forecasted patient census trends during a given period, which is usually one year). In the review of operating budgets, we discuss two budgeting approaches, zero-based budgeting and incremental budgeting, and review the most common expense and revenue categories associated with operating budgets.

Capital Budgets

Capital expenditures are typically a commitment of resources that will provide benefit for a reasonably long period of time (eg, 2 or more years). Institutions usually set a specific dollar amount (eg, $500 or $1,000) to determine whether a particular purchase is part of the operating budget or part of the capital budget (4) and use the capital budget for items/projects that exceed the specified dollar amount or threshold. Purchases below the threshold are handled in the nonsalary expense part of the operating budget.

It is important to find out what the capital threshold is for your facility. Because the capital approval process is time-consuming and involves many players, some hospitals find it cost-effective to set the capital budget threshold at the high end. A computer is an example of a piece of equipment that sometimes is considered capital and sometimes is not. The purchase of five office chairs at the same time could be considered capital at your institution while the purchase of one would not be.

Capital budgeting typically involves a 3-year cycle. Thus, for any given budget year, managers will be thinking ahead and planning for the next 3 years (4,5). The capital budgeting process may occur at a different time of the year than the operating budget process, and purchasing capital equipment generally takes longer and requires more layers of approval than purchasing items in the operating budget. If you need to make a capital request, be sure to gather sufficient data to justify the expenditure and plan for the potential of a long approval process. Because the capital budget typically is ranked by priority, take care to indicate the priority of your request when you submit it—for example, note whether the expenditure is critical to continued or future operations (sometimes called emergency capital), necessary if funds are available, or desirable but nonessential (4,6).

When you purchase capital equipment, you will probably use a bidding or comparison process where you work with the facility's supply chain, materials management, or purchasing department to obtain price estimates. During the estimation process, bear in mind that items that are more costly to acquire may be less expensive in the long run if they have a lower operating cost, longer life-expectancy, or slower rate of depreciation or are more compatible with other equipment that your department uses. To ensure that you get the equipment that best fits your department's needs, be sure to specify to the supply chain department *why* a particular model or brand of equipment has been selected (eg, compatibility with existing equipment, guaranteed service contracts, availability, durability, ability to handle projected usage, or safety features). If you are purchasing foodservice equipment, you also need to consider the cost of preventive maintenance and repairs, whether the equipment will be serviced in-house or through an outside company, access to and cost of parts, and overall impact of these additional costs on your budget (4,6).

Operating Budgets

Each hospital department typically has its own operating budget, which is counted within the institution's total operating budget. Two types of budgeting methodologies used in heath care to develop operating budgets are zero-based budgeting and incremental budgeting.

Zero-Based Budgeting

Zero-based budgeting is a method of looking at existing programs or services from a cost-benefit perspective. It involves reviewing the entire budget and justifying every expenditure. No existing program or service is entitled to automatic approval. Instead, each service is evaluated to determine whether it is being administered in an efficient manner and an effective manner. According to leaders in the field, the benefits of zero-based budgeting in health care include the ability to gain a greater understanding of actual costs as well as an improved ability to control them through complete analysis and justification of each proposed expenditure (4,6). Unsurprisingly, this approach is growing in popularity in health care because of the challenging financial climate.

Avoidable cost is a concept central to zero-based budgeting. The parties who create the budget investigate what each particular service costs and what the consequences of not spending that money would be (3). For example, if you have offered special meals or take-home gifts for new mothers as a service enhancement/marketing gesture for the past 5 years, you may need to quantify the total cost for that service, provide a numerical measure of the impact of the service on patient satisfaction, and work with the marketing department to attempt to quantify the "good will" value of this particular service. You would then complete a cost-benefit assessment to determine whether the service should be continued.

Zero-based budgeting allows operating managers to gain in-depth knowledge of their operations, and gives senior administration detailed information about the money needed to achieve desired outcomes. However, zero-based budgeting is time-consuming and can be a bit overwhelming to most health care managers, many of whom are clinical specialists with minimal financial training and little familiarity with zero-based methodology. If managers have done any budgeting at all in the past, it was probably the incremental type, which is discussed in the next section.

Incremental Budgeting

Incremental budgeting is the most common form of budgeting in health care. The budget process starts with existing expenditure levels as a base and allows an increase of a certain percentage per budget year. The percentage increase might be tied to inflation or set at a hospital-wide rate.

Under incremental budgeting, the only spending proposals examined during budget creation and justification are those that represent an increase above the base plus an established percentage (6). Incremental budgeting assumes that all currently funded department operations are essential to the ongoing mission of the hospital, are currently being performed in a cost-effective manner, and must be continued during the next budget year.

Incremental budgets can be either fixed or flexible. A fixed incremental budget remains set for a designated time period, such as a fiscal year. A flexible budget will increase or decrease based on a variety of factors related to patient volume. Using a flexible budget enables a department head to use key statistics, such as patient days, to most efficiently align expenditures to patient volume.

Budget Responsibilities for the Clinical Nutrition Manager

As a CNM, you will mostly likely be involved with budgeting for both expenses and revenue. See Figure 2.1 (page 34) for a sample annual budget and chart of accounts for a food and nutrition department.

Expense Categories

CNMs are typically involved in making budget decisions about the types of expenses described in the following sections.

Salaries and Benefits

Salaries and benefits are often the largest component of the expense budget and require the most time and energy in the justification process. It is important to know the following as you evaluate your salary budget for the coming year:

- Your current number of authorized full-time equivalents (FTEs) for the coming year

| Nutrition Department Annual Budget ||
Chart of Accounts Category Description	FY 2014 Budget
Revenues	
Inpatient revenue (guest trays)	$2,100
Outpatient revenue	$106,308
Total patient revenue	$108,408
Cafeteria revenue	$622,872
Intercompany revenue/catering/nourishments	$90,540
Total Revenue:	**$930,228**
Expenses	
Salaries	$260,890
Employee benefits	$52,178
Supplies—office, forms	$1,050
Minor equipment	$0
Supplies—raw food	$161,897
Nutrition supplements	$289
Supplies—general	$1,236
Purchased services	$600
Utilities	$0
Equipment rental	$75
Intercompany charges	$0
Repairs	$1,600
Total Expenses:	**$479,815**
NET OPERATING MARGIN:	**$450,413**

Figure 2.1 Sample Nutrition Department Budget for Fiscal Year 2014

- Whether your staff will be full-time or part-time employees (the distinction between full-time and part-time status affects benefit and overtime costs)
- Hire dates and review periods for your staff (will they be eligible for a raise during the upcoming fiscal year?)
- Regular paid hours, worked hours, time-off hours, overtime hours, and total hours for each employee you oversee
- Productivity standards and benchmarks in place at your facility. Many hospitals have detailed standards for determining productive and nonproductive time by skill level, procedure, or service. It is important to know how your productivity aligns with those benchmarks (see Chapter 6).
- Your institution's approach to budgeting for payroll taxes and fringe benefits. Some hospitals include the cost of payroll taxes and benefits in the average rate of pay. Fringe benefits typically include health insurance, group term life coverage, education reimbursement, childcare reimbursement, cafeteria plans, employee discounts, and other similar benefits. Others define these expenses separately as a direct cost to the department. Still others include benefits as an indirect cost to the department.
- The standard salary increase (if any) built into your facility's overall salary budget and its effect on your department's salary expenses. For example, if the hospital budget allows for a 2% to 3% salary increase, how does implementing that increase affect your department's budget?

When you anticipate salary increases beyond the facility's standard range for raises, you will also need to account for that expenditure in your budget and be prepared to justify the variance. If you anticipate no changes to your business, look at your past history and the impact of performance increases to determine your salary expense for the upcoming fiscal year. However, if your business is likely to change in ways that will affect staffing needs, you must make additional calculations. For example, suppose the facility is adding another patient tower. How many and what types of positions will you need to include in your budget to meet the patient and clinical services needs of those units? If the tower is farther away from food services, how will that impact your delivery time? Will you need additional delivery staff to ensure patients receive food in a timely manner? Other factors that could affect staffing include the implementation of a new menu model, such as room service, or the adoption of an electronic health record (EHR) system that will require additional staff training hours and possibly overtime during implementation.

Food or Tray Costs

Food or tray costs may or may not be in your scope of budgetary responsibility as a CNM. Even if they are not, you should have an understanding of how to budget for changes in this category. Tray cost is affected by several factors, including an inflation factor for the cost of food and paper products and projected patient days for the upcoming fiscal year. Also, remember that fuel costs, environmental conditions, and other factors can substantially affect food costs, as has been the case in recent years for many commodities, such as meat, milk, and corn- and wheat-based foods.

Staying abreast of current food cost trends can help you more accurately estimate costs for the coming fiscal year.

Nourishment Costs

Nourishment costs include the costs for juice, milk, gelatin, and other between-meal snacks for patients. Whether your department incurs nourishment costs or transfers them to the nursing units, you will need to estimate the cost for the next fiscal year's budget. The factors to consider are the same as for food/tray costs: the inflation factor for food; projected patient days; and any factors that could potentially affect labor, such as the relocation of nursing units or facility expansion.

Paper Costs

Paper costs include the costs for tray mats, menus, tray cards, clinical care forms, diet education materials, other disposable paper on patient trays, and so on. This budget line is fairly easy to predict from the anticipated patient volume as well as any potential changes that could positively or negatively affect costs. Examples of changes that could impact costs in this category include new vendor contracts; anticipated increases or decreases in the prices for paper goods; and service changes, such as a transition to an automated diet office system or implementation of a new menu that requires reprinting of all your current menus.

Supply Costs

Examples of supply costs include printer cartridges, diet kits, and office supplies. This budget amount is fairly easy to predict if you do not anticipate any big changes to your current business.

Enteral Formulary

Formulary costs are affected by the number of patient days and the types of formulas you use. When evaluating the number of patient days, think about how institutional changes might affect volume in the coming year. For example, is the facility adding beds in the intensive care unit (ICU), where a higher percentage of your patients will be on tube feedings?

For each formula in the formulary, determine the volume of formula used in the previous year and any potential price increases. Also review your formula contract. How long is your pricing good for? Is your pricing is based on the volume you purchase or on a percentage of purchases made from a primary vendor? If you anticipate that new products will be added to the formulary, project the anticipated usage and start date for each one and estimate its impact on the total cost of formula. If you have an infant formula room and/or donor milk bank, also consider the cost of these products and the type of purchasing agreement.

Dues and Subscriptions

In the dues and subscriptions category, you will budget for professional organization dues, newsletters, and Nutrition Care Manual subscriptions, as well as software maintenance fees for automated diet office systems, diet analysis software, and other ongoing subscription costs.

Continuing Education

To budget for continuing education, you should identify training needs for your staff (eg, web-based or offsite programs), the cost of training, and the cost of associated travel if the training is out of town. If the department pays for certification exams, such as those for Certified Diabetes Educator (CDE) or Certified Specialist in Pediatric Nutrition (CSP), check whether any of your staff are due for recertification and factor that into your forecast.

Equipment Repair

Even if you are not responsible for the equipment repair budget, your supervisor may ask you to project the repair costs for the equipment used in your area of responsibility, such as printers, fax machines, copiers, tray carts, tray-line equipment, and so on. To make these budget projections, review previous repair costs, the age of your equipment, what equipment is still under warranty, and whether the equipment is fully depreciated.

Employee Uniforms

If your department pays for employee uniforms, you need to forecast replacement costs for the number of uniforms allocated to employees annually. Remember, if you are adjusting staff levels, you will need to account for those adjustments in uniform cost as well.

Technology

For the technology section of the budget, consider the modes of communication your team uses, such as pagers/beepers or phones, computers, and software, and estimate the associated support, replacement, and upgrade fees.

Revenue Categories

Revenue forecasting can be challenging because a variety of things can impact revenue. When forecasting revenue, you will need to make certain assumptions. Try to have as much data as possible to minimize the variability of those assumptions.

Outpatient Revenue

When forecasting outpatient revenue, factors to consider include the following:

- Patient volumes from previous year
- Standard facility annual price increases
- Anticipated new services or programs
- Potential changes in physician volume
- Changes in regulations, Medicare fees, or the payer mix that could affect reimbursement rates
- Potential competition that could result in decreased referrals

Charges to Other Departments

Charges to other departments might include charges for patient nourishment, snacks, or catering, as well as charges for RD services, such as cardiac rehabilitation nutrition classes. It is important to find out what your facility includes in this category and whether the budget is in your area of responsibility.

The Budget Justification Process

The budget justification process can be a significant exercise in strategy. All department leaders in your organization are pursuing the same finite pot of money, and the budget committee is likely considering whether any budget requests can be reduced without substantially affecting services (6). The key to success in getting the budget dollars you request is being prepared, both financially and politically. You will need to understand who the key decision makers are as well as the role and impact that your physicians have in this process so you can use that knowledge to your advantage. For example, if you are requesting additional staff in the neonatal intensive care unit (NICU) and the NICU physician director wields power in hospital politics, ask her to put in a good word for you or, if possible, attend the meeting when you present that portion of your budget.

Take care to understand the goals of your organization and identify how your financial requests can help the institution move forward to meet those goals. Current health care priorities include value-based purchasing, chronic disease management and prevention, patient satisfaction, patient-centered care, patient safety, and regulatory compliance. As relevant, use these priorities to frame your budget requests. For example, if your department does not have enough weekend coverage to meet the facility's nutrition assessment and follow-up policies, the facility is at risk of regulatory noncompliance. Assuming that regulatory compliance is a priority at your facility, be sure to bring the potential risk forward in your budget justification. If you are requesting an increase in budget dollars for enteral products because an expensive new product may be added to the formulary, be sure that you can adequately articulate why that product is justified (eg, make the case based on peer-reviewed research, the potential for patient safety improvements, or potential hospital cost savings due to improved patient outcomes, such as decreased time on the ventilator).

As you prepare for the budget justification process, investigate what your competition is doing and try to identify community standards for service and staffing. For example, check out your competition before you ask for funds to implement a room-service program. After you review other menu and service programs, you will be prepared to show that you can provide a program that is cheaper, higher quality, and likely to get better patient satisfaction scores.

Be prepared to negotiate. When you enter your budget justification meeting, you should understand exactly how much money you *really* need to accomplish your goals and where you can afford to make concessions. People rarely get everything they ask for in the budget process. What can you really live with? Many things about the next year are uncertain, and much of it is uncontrollable. Successful budgets are those that will be approved, authorize the needed resources, and protect managers from surprises (7).

Managing Your Budget

Once your budget is approved, the following tricks of the trade can help you successfully manage it throughout the year:

- **Manage labor effectively.** To effectively manage your labor, you must understand and routinely review your productivity measures (see Chapter 6). Do you know how many assessments, tube feeding evaluations, multidisciplinary rounds, and so on, your RDs complete per day? What is your ratio of hosts to patients? Do you know how many patients your outpatient RDs need to see per day to hit budget targets, and do you have a plan for adjusting staffing to account for variations in volume? Additional examples of labor management methods include having a mix of full-time and part-time staff, adjusting your staff schedules based on known admission and census patterns, scheduling staff to work 37.5-hour weeks to minimize overtime, asking for volunteers to take vacation during periods of low patient census, and cross-training staff to perform multiple roles.
- **Master the accrual process.** In your budget's accrual process, are total costs divided evenly by months or allocated specifically for the month when they are due to occur? Knowing the process can help you explain budget variances.
- **Get in sync with your facility's fiscal calendar and the budget cycle timeline.** Since many budget processes have short turn-around times, it is vital that you determine what your role is, what areas you are responsible for, and what you need to prepare ahead of time. Meet with your supervisor or someone in the finance department to gain an understanding of the type of budgeting used and to seek answers to any questions that you may have about your facility's financial statements. For example, if you have an automated diet office, you

will most likely need to pay annual software fees. Know where and when this expense hits your budget.

- **Anticipate budget adjustments throughout the year**. You are not necessarily "home free" when your annual budget has been approved and your department expenses are in line with monthly targets. Your institution may have a history of cutting a certain percentage from its operating budget at a certain time of the year or when the patient census falls to a certain level. Anticipate accordingly and prepare a cost-cutting proposal for such circumstances. By identifying potential decreases in services and their associated impact ahead of time, you have the time to act strategically rather than reactively and can be ready to recommend changes that minimize the effect on your staff or service levels. For example, if the census is down and costs need to be controlled, the facility could suspend or cut the continuing education budget. Anticipating these types of cuts, a savvy CNM might schedule continuing education initiatives for early in the fiscal year to decrease the likelihood that this type of budget adjustment would affect the department.

Pro Formas and Proposed New Services

A pro forma (see Figure 2.2) is a projected financial statement that helps managers and administrators evaluate the potential costs and benefits of new ventures or new strategic initiatives and quickly produce alternative forecasts for different business scenarios or strategies (8). Pro formas, like budgets, are based on various projections, which can change based on a variety of internal and external factors; however, pro formas often cannot be based on the kind of historical data that are used in budgeting. Many institutions require a pro forma before approving any new service or product. For example, you might be required to create a pro forma if you propose a new meal service delivery style; a new restaurant on campus; outpatient services; a dietetic internship or other education program; an automated diet office; or a diabetes self-management training program. Refer to Chapter 10 for more information on revenue generation and business plans, including financial pro formas.

Summary

Like other health care leaders, today's CNMs face numerous fiscal challenges related to the national economic climate, reimbursement reforms, and myriad changes to health care. Effective cost management is therefore a critical job requirement for CNMs. Developing an understanding of your facility's financial language and financial tools is an important step in attaining competence in this area of management. Your annual budget is an important tool for planning and managing the costs in your department and can help you maximize your effectiveness as a leader.

Pro Forma				
Category	Explanation	Fiscal Year 2014	Fiscal Year 2015	Fiscal Year 2016
EXPENSES:				
Clinician salary and 27% benefits	Initial program development and annual updates	$2,440.00	$251.32	$258.85
Clinician salary and 27% benefits	Program management: 2 hours per student per day	$3,050.00	$6,283.00	$9,699.00
Administrative assistant salary and 27% benefits	Program development and ongoing management	$687.15	$152.70	$229.05
Liability Insurance	$20.00 per participant per year	$100.00	$200.00	$300.00
Computer	Allocated laptop for program participants	$1,000.00		
Office Supplies	Copier paper, binders, flash drives	$200.00	$250.00	$300.00
Printing		$250.00	$500.00	$600.00
Preceptor continuing education		$900.00	$1,500.00	$1,500.00
Program marketing	Newsletter advertising, flyers, brochures	$500.00	$500.00	$500.00
Parking/ meals	All participants receive 1 parking voucher and a $6.00 meal coupon per day	$550.00	$1,100.00	$1,650.00
	Total Expenses:	**$9,677.15**	**$10,737.02**	**$15,036.90**
REVENUE:				
Tuition	$2,000 per student per year	$10,000.00	$20,000.00	$30,000.00
	Total Revenue:	**$10,000.00**	**$20,000.00**	**$30,000.00**
	Net Profit:	$322.85	$9,262.98	$14,963.10

Figure 2.2 Sample Pro Forma for Advanced Practice Training Program for Registered Dietitians

References

1. Gunther Lane S, Longstreth E, Nixon V; prepared for the Access Project. *A Community Leader's Guide to Hospital Finance.* 2001. www.accessproject.org. Accessed May 13, 2011.

2. Gapenski L. *Healthcare Finance: An Introduction to Accounting and Financial Management.* 4th ed. Chicago, IL: Health Administration Press; 2007.

3. Iowa Hospital Association Publications. Definition of Hospital and Health System Data Items/Terms. InformationCenter@ihaonline.org. Accessed April 10, 2011.

4. Cleverley W, Cleverley J, Song P. *Essentials of Healthcare Finance.* 7th ed. Sudbury, MA: Jones and Bartlett Learning; 2010.

5. Nowicki M. *Financial Management of Hospitals and Healthcare Organizations.* Chicago, IL: Health Administration Press; 2004.

6. Bary P, Finkler S, Ward D. Zero-based budgeting: the financial evolution and the zero-based budgeting approach. In: *Issues in Cost Accounting for Health Care Organizations.* Sudbury, NY: Jones and Bartlett Learning; 1999.

7. Finney R. *Basics of Budgeting.* New York, NY: American Management Association; 1994.

8. Joy JA. Preparing Financial Projections and Proforma Statements. http://EzineArticles.com/248204. Accessed June 11, 2011.

3

Statutory and Regulatory Issues

Marsha R. Stieber, MSA, RD, CNSC

Introduction

The delivery of safe, high-quality, and cost-effective health care in the 21st century is a challenge for all health care providers, regardless of setting. The myriad legal and regulatory requirements at all governmental and organizational levels can be overwhelming, but every health care provider, including clinical nutrition managers (CNMs), must nevertheless understand and comply with these requirements. For CNMs who direct and manage personnel engaged in the clinical nutrition and/or foodservices components of care, the task of compliance can be immense. Under health care organization accreditation standards, a health care facility demonstrates its compliance with regulatory requirements by providing relevant and acceptable documentation of how each standard is being met. For nutrition care services, it is the CNM's responsibility to ensure that all nutrition care policies, procedures, and processes are consistent with the standards set by both the facility and the accreditation organization (eg, the Joint Commission) and that any required documentation is prepared in the manner and approved format stipulated by the facility. This chapter offers an overview of some of the notable institutions, laws, and regulations involved in compliance and suggests practical steps that CNMs can take to approach legal and regulatory issues of concern for their facility.

Federal Regulation of Health Care Facilities

All CNMs can benefit by becoming familiar with the federal rules, agencies, and organizations most involved in the regulation of US health care facilities (see Figure 3.1 on page 44).

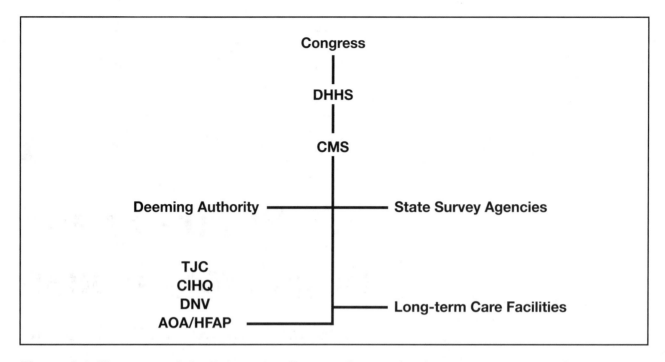

Figure 3.1 Illustration of the Relationship Between Governmental Entities and Survey Agencies. Key: DHHS, Department of Health and Human Services; CMS, Centers for Medicare & Medicaid Services; TJC, the Joint Commission; CIHQ, Center for Improvement in Healthcare Quality; DNV, DNV Healthcare, Inc; AOA/HFAP, American Osteopathic Association's Healthcare Facilities Accreditation Program.

The Code of Federal Regulations

The Code of Federal Regulations (CFR) is the codification of the general and permanent rules published in the Federal Register by the executive departments and agencies of the federal government. It is divided into 50 titles that represent broad areas subject to federal regulation. Each volume of the CFR is updated annually and issued on a quarterly basis (1).

Title 42, Public Health, which is updated as of October 1 each year, is a section of the CFR that is of significant importance to health care providers and organizations (2). It consists of three chapters (I, IV, and V), and each chapter contains numbered parts that correlate with a specific regulatory entity. Of specific importance to CNMs are Chapter IV, Part 482: Conditions of Participation (CoP) for Hospitals, and Chapter IV, Part 483L: Requirements for States and Long Term Care Facilities. In addition, other parts of Title 42, Chapter IV, may apply to CNMs. For example, Part 484 is relevant to CNMs employed within and/or having oversight of registered dietitians (RDs) working in home health, and Part 494 is relevant to CNMs employed within and/or having oversight of RDs working in end-stage renal disease facilities.

Centers for Medicare & Medicaid Services

The Centers for Medicare & Medicaid Services (CMS), a branch of the US Department of Health and Human Services, is the federal agency that administers

Medicare, Medicaid, and the Children's Health Insurance Program according to CFR regulations. CMS also provides information for health professionals, state and local governments, and consumers about these programs (3).

CMS develops Conditions of Participation (CoP) and Conditions for Coverage (CfC) that health care organizations must meet in order to begin and continue participating in the Medicare and Medicaid programs (4). These health and safety standards are the foundation for improving quality and protecting the health and safety of beneficiaries. CMS also ensures that the standards of accrediting organizations recognized by CMS (through a process called "deeming") meet or exceed the Medicare standards set forth in the CoP/CfC. CoP and CfC apply to the following health care organizations:

- Ambulatory surgical centers (ASCs)
- Community Mental Health Centers (CMHCs)
- Comprehensive outpatient rehabilitation facilities (CORFs)
- Critical access hospitals (CAHs)
- End-stage renal disease facilities
- Federally qualified health centers
- Home health agencies
- Hospices
- Hospitals
- Hospital swing beds
- Intermediate care facilities for individuals with intellectual disabilities (ICF/IID)
- Organ procurement organizations (OPOs)
- Portable x-ray suppliers
- Programs for all-inclusive care for the elderly organizations (PACE)
- Clinics, rehabilitation agencies, and public health agencies as providers of outpatient physical therapy and speech-language pathology services
- Psychiatric hospitals
- Religious nonmedical health care institutions
- Rural health clinics
- Long-term care facilities
- Transplant centers

In order for hospitals and other health care sites to receive payment from Medicare and Medicaid, they must undergo site surveys (either by CMS or by another organization that has obtained deeming authority from CMS) and be found compliant with the CMS regulations.

Deeming Authority and Accrediting Organizations

The Balanced Budget Act of 1997 (BBA) and the Balanced Budget Refinement Act of 1999 (BBRA) authorized CMS to establish and oversee a program that allows private, national accreditation organizations to "deem" whether facilities receiving payments from CMS are compliant with certain Medicare requirements. Six areas are deemable:

- Quality assurance
- Antidiscrimination
- Access to services
- Confidentiality and accuracy of enrollee records
- Information on advance directives
- Provider participation rules

To be approved for deeming authority, an accrediting organization must demonstrate that its program meets or exceeds the Medicare requirements for which it is seeking the authority to deem compliance (5). CMS also ensures that the standards of accrediting organizations recognized by CMS through the deeming process meet or exceed the Medicare standards set forth in the CoP and CfC (4).

As of September 2013, CMS has given deeming authority for hospitals to four national accreditation organizations: the American Osteopathic Association's Healthcare Facilities Accreditation Program (AOA/HFAP), Center for Improvement in Healthcare Quality (CIHQ), DNV Healthcare, Inc. (DNV), and the Joint Commission (TJC) (6). Three of these four national accreditation programs have also received deeming authority from CMS for other health care entities in addition to hospitals. AOA/HFAP accredits ambulatory surgical/surgery centers and critical access hospitals (CAHs); DNV accredits CAHs; and TJC accredits ambulatory surgical/surgery centers, CAHs, home health agencies, hospices, and psychiatric hospitals (6).

These national accreditation organizations met the same requirements to attain deeming authority from CMS, but they are not identical in their quality focus and structure. For more information about AOA/HFAP, DNV, and TJC, refer to a comparison matrix, *The Big Three: A Side by Side Matrix Comparing Hospital Accrediting Agencies,* from the National Association Medical Staff Services (7). CIHQ, being the newest of the four organizations, was not in existence at the time the comparison matrix was developed.

The CMS State Operations Manual

CNMs can more fully comprehend the content and context of compliance in a given setting by reviewing the CMS State Operations Manual (SOM) and the accreditation standards of the facility's specified accreditation organization. The CMS SOM is the source for all CoP and CfC. Each type of health care entity has its own set of CoP and CfC, and CNMs should take care to access the appropriate organizational listing when seeking to understand the basis for a compliance activity, its subsequent documentation, and procedural survey review. In particular, CNMs may find a review of the Interpretive Guidelines and Surveyor Guidance sections to be enlightening and informative. In concert with discussions with the facility's compliance department/manager or the appropriate oversight entity, this review may help

CNMs identify possible oversights, misunderstandings, and/or inadequacies in processes or procedures and allow for corrective action before an onsite survey occurs.

At first glance, the SOM is overwhelming in size and content. The State Operations Manual Appendices Table of Contents is a good place to become familiar with the manual as it relates to the CNM's employment setting (8). CNMs employed in hospitals should review State Operations Manual Appendix A: Survey Protocol, Regulations and Interpretive Guidelines for Hospitals Table of Contents (Rev. 89, 08-30-13) (10). CoP §482.28: Food and Dietetic Services contains most standards, interpretive guidelines, and survey procedures related to food and nutrition services. Other CoPs that include relevant nutrition-related standards include the following (9):

- §482.11(c)
- §482.12(a)(1)
- §482.13(a)(2)
- §482.13(e)(10)
- §482.22(a)
- §482.25(b)
- §482.41(a)
- §482.41(c)(4)
- §482.42
- §482.42(a)(1)
- §482.43(b)(3)
- §482.43(d)

Refer to the Quality Management area of the Academy of Nutrition and Dietetics website (www.eatright.org) for many up-to-date practice resources, tools for measuring quality, links to national quality organizations, scope/standards of practice information, and accreditation resources.

Common Compliance Challenges

For many years, CNMs have faced a variety of service-delivery challenges that are partially shaped by changes in accreditation standards related to food and nutrition services. Some changes are driven by modifications in the CMS State SOM content, but others may be caused when enforcement priorities and procedures related to existing SOM content shift.

Scope of Practice

There is no quick and easy way for a credentialed dietetics practitioner to readily understand the myriad statutory and individual factors that structure and impact his or her practice. However, each RD and dietetic technician, registered (DTR) must proactively take steps to achieve such understanding, regardless of employment, practice, and/or service setting. Although "scope of practice" can be a confusing term, RDs and DTRs must understand precisely how the term applies to them as individual practitioners. Practicing outside of one's individual scope of practice, and statutory scope of practice, if applicable, can have serious legal or regulatory ramifications for the dietetics practitioner and/or employer.

The Academy's Definition of Terms List (10) can assist RDs and DTRs in the identification and comprehension of their individual and, if applicable, statutory scope of practice. Box 3.1 (11) provides definitions for these terms and considerations for applying them to an individual practitioner's practice. Of note, each individual credentialed dietetics practitioner (RD or DTR) is responsible and ultimately accountable for practicing solely within his/her statutory, if applicable, and individual scope of practice.

To further assist credentialed dietetics practitioners, as well as the public, other health care professions, governmental agencies at all levels, and many other entities,

---

Box 3.1 Scope of Practice: Definitions and Key Considerations

Scope of practice (statutory):

• Definition: The Academy of Nutrition and Dietetics has adopted the following definition from the Center for the Health Professions, University of California, San Francisco: "Legal scopes of practice for the health care professions establish which professionals may provide which health care services, in which settings, and under which guidelines or parameters. With few exceptions, determining scopes of practice is a state-based activity. State legislatures consider and pass the practice acts, which become state statute or code. State regulatory agencies, such as medical and other health professions' boards, implement the laws by writing and enforcing rules and regulations detailing the acts."[a]
• Key considerations: The scope of practice typically describes the practitioner's practice, qualifications, board representation, and fee and renewal schedule. The scopes may also list specific examples of responsibilities such as taking histories, patient care, education, and training.[b]

Scope of practice (individual):

• Definition: *See* Scope of practice in nutrition and dietetics.
• Key considerations: An individual's scope of practice in nutrition and dietetics has flexible boundaries to capture the breadth of the individual's professional practice. Individuals and organizations must ethically take responsibility for determining the competence of each individual to provide a specific service. Not all registered dietitians (RDs), registered dietitian nutritionists (RDNs), and dietetic technicians, registered (DTRs) will practice to the full extent of the range of nutrition and dietetics practice.[c]

(continues)

Box 3.1 *(continued)*

Scope of practice in nutrition and dietetics:

- Definition: Scope of practice in nutrition and dietetics encompasses the range of roles, activities, and regulations within which nutrition and dietetics practitioners perform. For credentialed practitioners, scope of practice is typically established within the practice act and interpreted and controlled by the agency or board that regulates the practice of the profession in a given state.
- Key considerations: Registered dietitians (RDs), registered dietitian nutritionists (RDNs), and dietetic technicians, registered (DTRs) must comply with the Academy of Nutrition and Dietetics/Commission on Dietetic Registration Code of Ethics for the Profession of Dietetics.[d]

[a]Dower C, Christian S, O'Neil E. Promising Scopes of Practice Models for the Health Professions. The Center for the Health Professions, University of California, San Francisco, 2007. http://futurehealth.ucsf.edu /Content/29/20 07- 12_Promising_Scope_of_Practice_Models_for_the_Health_Professions.pdf. Accessed June 12, 2012.

[b]Scope of Practice Laws in Health Care: Exploring New Approaches for California. March 2008. www .chcf.org/publications/2008/03/scope-of-practice-laws-in-health-care-exploring-new-approaches-for-california. Accessed June 5, 2012.

[c]Revised 2008 Standards of Practice for Registered Dietitians in Nutrition Care; Standards of Professional Performance for Registered Dietitians; Standards of Practice for Dietetic Technicians, Registered, in Nutrition Care; and Standards of Professional Performance for Dietetic Technicians, Registered. The American Dietetic Association Quality Management Committee. *J Am Diet Assoc.* 2008;108:9:1538-1542.e9.

[d]American Dietetic Association/Commission on Dietetic Registration Code of Ethics for the Profession of Dietetics and Process for Consideration of Ethics Issues. *J Am Diet Assoc.* 2009;109(8):1461-146.

Source: Adapted from references 10 and 11 and based on data from the following:

in comprehending and using a scope of practice in nutrition and dietetics, the Academy developed the following groundbreaking documents, which were published in the *Journal of the Academy of Nutrition and Dietetics* in 2013 (11,12):

- Comprehensive Scope of Practice Resources for the Registered Dietitian or Registered Dietitian Nutritionist
- Comprehensive Scope of Practice Resources for the Dietetic Technician, Registered

Prior to the publication of these documents, a singular scope of practice document for RDs and DTRs did not exist. To more fully comprehend the definitions and considerations of the various "scopes of practice," see Box 3.1. Future delineation and publication of focus area Standards of Practice and/or Standards of Professional Performance for the RD and for the DTR will be constructed using the cornerstone Comprehensive Resources documents.

Defining "Qualified Dietitian"

When navigating the maze of what activities can and/or cannot be undertaken by the RD and/or DTR, CNMs must understand how "qualified dietitian" is defined in the CMS State Operations Manual Appendix PP—Guidance to Surveyors for Long Term Care Facilities. A "qualified dietitian" refers to one who is qualified based upon either registration by the Commission on Dietetic Registration or as permitted by state law, on the basis of education, training, or experience in identification of dietary needs, planning, and implementation of dietary programs (13). This definition is also used by the national accreditation organizations that have deeming authority from CMS. RDs may object that people who do not hold the RD credential can be defined as "qualified dietitians." CNMs have flexibility to craft position descriptions to stipulate the RD credential is preferred, and to prefer or require other certifications as part of the position description. Nevertheless, if there are state regulations that supersede such language, those regulations pre-empt its use and inclusion.

Therapeutic Diets and Order Writing

For CNMs, one of the most contentious compliance challenges in recent history involves CFR CoP §482.28(b)(1)—Therapeutic diets must be prescribed by the practitioner or practitioners responsible for the care of the patients (9). This CoP was issued October 17, 2008, with a concurrent effective and implementation date (9), and is of relevance in both long-term and acute care settings.

The CMS State Operations Manual Appendix PP—Guidance to Surveyors for Long Term Care Facilities defines "therapeutic diet" in the following way: "Therapeutic diet refers to a diet ordered by a health care practitioner as part of the treatment for a disease or clinical condition, to eliminate, decrease, or increase certain substances in the diet (e.g., sodium or potassium), or to provide mechanically altered food when indicated" (13). Many credentialed dietetics practitioners might have issues with this definition, but the CNM must ensure that all diets that conform to the definition of a "therapeutic diet" are consistent with this regulatory definition, or ensure that the individual ultimately responsible for complying with the accreditation organization's standards does so.

As noted previously, CoP §482.28(b)(1) requires that therapeutic diets be prescribed by the practitioner responsible for the patient's care. The definition of "the practitioner responsible for the patient's care" is grounded in the CMS State Operations Manual Appendix A—Survey Protocol, Regulations, and Interpretive Guidelines for Hospitals (9). The "practitioner responsible" is most often an MD or DO. However, depending on state law and regulations and the rules of the facility's governing body (eg, the medical executive committee), certain other health care practitioners—including doctors of dental surgery or dental medicine; doctors of podiatric medicine; doctors of optometry; chiropractors; and other non-MD/DO practitioners who meet the definition of physician—may be eligible for appointment to the medical staff (9). Also, the facility's governing body has the authority, in accordance with state law, to appoint some types of non-physician practitioners, such as nurse practitioners, physician assistants, certified registered nurse anesthetists, and midwives, to the medical staff. Furthermore, the governing body may grant a physician or non-physician practitioner who has not been appointed a member of the medical staff privileges to practice at the hospital, as long as those privileges are limited to specific practice activities authorized within the practitioner's state scope of practice (9).

The last statement is a potential opening to expand practice opportunities for qualified RDs. Depending upon their statutory scope of practice, as applicable, and their individual scope of practice, an RD could be granted privileges to perform specified practice activities (such as enteral tube placements) within an institution, providing the RD meets all specified statutory and facility requirements to perform the specified practice activities and attains appropriate documentation showing that the facility has granted privileges to him or her.

Action taken by CMS in February 2013 indicates that a rule change allowing RDs greater latitude in diet order writing is anticipated in the near future. It is important to stay abreast of CMS actions and communication from the Academy on this important issue so CNMs/RDs can provide timely feedback to CMS as well as ensure compliance with current CoP. Note: If the proposed rule change is finalized and allows RDs to attain prescriptive privileges for ordering therapeutic diets, the privileges will be granted on an individual practitioner basis by facility and will not apply across the board to all RDs within that facility or entity.

A wealth of information is available to assist CNMs in understanding the concepts and legal constructs embedded in CoP §482.28(b)(1). The Academy has numerous resources that address order writing (including for therapeutic diets), clinical privileges, and disease-specific and condition-specific nutrition protocols. Refer to the Academy website (www.eatright.org) for links to practice-related resources and information, including selected *Journal of the Academy of Nutrition and Dietetics* articles on diet order writing privileges.

2012 Changes to Requirements for Hospital Participation in Medicare and Medicaid

In May 2012, CMS issued a final rule that revises the requirements that hospitals and critical access hospitals (CAHs) must meet to participate in Medicare and Medicaid programs; the revised regulations became effective July 16, 2012 (14). Responding to an executive order to reduce outmoded or unnecessarily burdensome regulations, CMS addressed numerous issues and concerns in the provision of patient care in hospitals and CAHs in this final rule. Several of the changes may directly or indirectly affect services currently provided by some RDs in a positive or negative manner. Of the 19 provisions listed in the Summary of the Major Provisions, the following six are of significance to credentialed dietetics practitioners, CNMs, and the provision of nutrition services within hospitals and CAHs (14):

- Role of other practitioners on the medical staff
- Nursing care plans
- Orders by other practitioners
- Standing orders
- Verbal orders
- Authentication of orders

Precisely how the content of these six areas can and will affect organizational department and interdepartmental patient care services will depend on the type of facility and the services provided. It is possible that the accreditation standards of deeming organizations may also be altered. Box 3.2 provides additional information about the revised rule.

Box 3.2 Centers for Medicare & Medicaid Services 2013 Revised Rule on Hospital Participation in Medicare and Medicaid: Six Provisions That May Affect Credentialed Dietetics Practitioners

Role of other practitioners on the medical staff:

- Broadens the concept of "medical staff" and allows hospitals the flexibility to include other practitioners as eligible candidates for the medical staff with hospital privileges to practice in the hospital in accordance with state law. Change will clearly permit hospitals to allow other practitioners (eg, APRNs, PAs, pharmacists) to perform all functions within their scope of practice. Medical staff must examine credentials of all eligible candidates (as defined by the governing body) and make recommendations for privileges and medical staff membership to the governing body.
- *May* broaden the independent practice privileges of individual RDs providing services in the facility (eg, enteral tube placement, enteral formula and delivery orders, oral diet progression/digression, nutrient alterations for parenteral nutrition).[a]

Nursing care plan:

- Allows hospitals the options of having a stand-alone nursing care plan or a single interdisciplinary care plan that addresses nursing and other disciplines.
- *May* allow for oral diet and/or enteral nutrition support alterations by RDs without a physician's order, dependent upon the structure, content, and flexibility of the interdisciplinary care plan, and consistency with other facility protocols.[a]

Orders by other practitioners:

- Allows for drugs and biological to be prepared and administered on the orders of practitioners (other than a doctor), in accordance with hospital policy and state law; allows orders for drugs and biological to be documented and signed by practitioners (other than a doctor), in accordance with hospital policy and state law.
- *May* broaden the independent practice privileges of individual RDs providing services in the facility (eg, enteral tube placement, enteral formula and delivery orders); *may* allow the increase/decrease of prokinetic drugs, such as metoclopramide, within approved interdisciplinary care plans/protocols.[a]

(continues)

Box 3.2 *(continued)*

Standing orders:

- Allows hospitals the flexibility to use standing orders and adds a requirement for medical staff, nursing, and pharmacy to approve written and electronic standing orders, order sets, and protocols. Requires that orders and protocols be based on nationally recognized and evidence-based guidelines and recommendations.
- *May* broaden the independent practice privileges of individual RDs providing services in the facility; *may* provide RDs the opportunity to incorporate nutrition-related evidence-based guidelines and recommendations into facility protocols, to include a degree of independent delivery of nutrition care by the RD.[a]

Verbal orders:

- Eliminates the requirement for authentication of verbal orders within 48 hours and defers to applicable state law to establish authentication time frames.
- *May* broaden the independent practice privileges of individual RDs providing services in the facility; *may* provide RDs the opportunity to intervene in delivery of nutrition care, such as an oral diet and/or enteral tube nutrition support, sooner than 48 hours, dependent upon applicable state law(s) and facility protocols.[a]

Authentication of orders:

- Makes permanent the requirement that all orders, including verbal orders, be dated, timed, and authenticated by either the ordering practitioner or another practitioner who is responsible for the care of the patient and who is authorized to write orders by hospital policy in accordance with state law.
- *May* broaden the independent practice privileges of individual RDs providing services in the facility, dependent upon facility policy and protocols, and *may* promote the earlier initiation and provision of patient-specific nutrition care and monitoring.[a]

---

[a]The following conditions apply: RD statutory scope of practice permits such actions, or if there is no statutory scope of practice, RD is not statutorily excluded from performing such actions; RD individual scope of practice demonstrates knowledge and skill competency as delineated by the facility.

Source: Data are from reference 14.

Compliance Guidelines and Suggestions

As the previous review of compliance issues demonstrates, the regulatory landscape is continually changing. Therefore, CNMs must be vigilant to maintain compliance within the facility where they are employed. How does a CNM ensure that all accreditation standards pertinent to clinical nutrition services and/or food services are appropriately and adequately adopted and incorporated, and that procedures are in place to address and maintain compliance? The following steps are essential:

- Identify the applicable accreditation organization, such as the state agency or agencies, TJC, AOA/HFAP, DNV, or CIHQ.
- Read the accreditation standards in their entirety.
- Identify the standards that apply specifically to clinical nutrition services, such as nutrition screening, nutrition care, nutrition education, and nutrition care coordination.
- Identify the standards that apply specifically to other related nutrition services, such as food services and emergency/disaster preparedness plans.
- Identify the standards that apply specifically to staff resources, such as requirements related to hiring, immunization(s), training, performance reviews, and competency documentation.
- Identify the standards that require service coordination with other departments, services, or disciplines, such as nursing, pharmacy, social services, and so on. Many standards are interdepartmental and contain shared aspects of care or service delivery. Address them as follows:

  ◊ Meet one-on-one with the managers or supervisors of these areas and jointly develop, implement, test, analyze, and revise, as necessary, the pertinent coordinated policies and procedures, which should ensure that all entities have components in place to achieve compliance.
  ◊ Become a part of an interdisciplinary team or group of facility managers that meets on a regular basis to identify and address possible compliance concerns.

- Meet one-on-one with the facility's compliance manager or other designated person(s). Do this at least twice a year, if possible, and more frequently, if necessary, to identify areas of strengths and concerns, and to develop, coordinate, and assess action plans to maximize compliance.
- Attend facility meetings/briefings on standards compliance. Take notes and lots of them! Follow through on those items/areas of concern within a reasonable time frame, such as two weeks, or sooner, as dictated by the situation.
- Read facility e-mails/electronic communications/newsletters related to regulations, compliance, documentation, and other need-to-know topics. While this task may seem overwhelming, it is nevertheless the CNM's responsibility.
- Attend and participate in conferences, webinars, and/or other related opportunities, to learn the challenges that other organizations/facilities and CNMs have encountered in addressing standards compliance. Reading blogs and list-servs can also help keep you informed.

- Keep a "resource file" of information, examples, documents, and notes related to standards and compliance components affecting the applicable setting.
- Continuously view the "compliance world" from both the food and nutrition services perspective and the facility-wide perspective.

Nutrition Services Compliance Requirements

Throughout this chapter, a great deal of information has been provided about various accrediting agencies, conditions of participation, and accreditation standards. What is most important is that the CNM focus on the standards relevant to the organization in which he/she is employed or provides contracted services.

Developing Facility and Department Checklists

Over the years, CNMs at many facilities have developed their own facility-specific checklists or guides to help them keep track of all standards specific to nutrition and food services, as well as standards with more interdisciplinary and global content, such as patient education, infection control, and human resources. When developing a facility-specific checklist, start with any guides that the accreditation entity might provide, such as the "Survey Activity Guide for Health Care Organizations 2014" developed by TJC (15). This document provides survey guidance for all the types of accreditations offered by TJC, and the information is applicable to similar organizations accredited by other deeming entities.

TJC's Survey Activity Guide 2014 contains an extensive listing of the myriad documents that site surveyors for the Hospital Accreditation Program will request, including the following (15):

- Performance improvement data from the past 12 months
- Documentation of performance improvement projects being conducted, including the reasons for conducting the projects and the measurable progress achieved (this can be documentation in governing body minutes or other minutes)
- Environment of care management plans and annual evaluations
- Environment of care multidisciplinary team meetings minutes for the 12 months prior to the survey
- Infection control surveillance data from the past 12 months
- An organization chart
- List of departments/units/areas/programs/services within the organization, if applicable
- List of unapproved abbreviations

Other documents that may be requested include the following:

- List of all contracted services
- Complaint/grievance policy
- Medical staff bylaws and rules and regulations
- Medical executive committee meeting minutes

Although CNMs are not directly responsible for maintaining or providing all of the items and documents listed by TJC, they should nonetheless understand how facility-wide compliance and compliance specifically within the nutrition department are interwoven. For some individuals, it is helpful to first view "the big picture" and then slowly break it down into specific components, such as personnel and departmental requirements, that are directly relevant to their compliance responsibilities. As applicable checklists are developed and/or adopted for areas of responsibility, consider the policies and procedures of the entire facility and how the CNM's areas of responsibility may overlap with those other units or departments. Should checklists be crafted using examples from other facilities, peers, and/or publications, they should be carefully reviewed and altered, as necessary, to ensure they are consistent with facility-specific policies and procedures and any existing state requirements.

Personnel Documentation

The CNM is responsible for hiring competent individuals to perform activities in a specified area of nutrition services and ensuring that they continue to develop the knowledge, skills, and competencies required to provide safe and adequate care that meets accreditation standards. In small facilities, a CNM may perform a variety of jobs, such as overseeing aspects of foodservice management and jointly directing clinical nutrition services. In a larger facility, staffing allotments may allow the employment of a variety of individuals with varying knowledge, skills, and abilities and, as required, credentials and certifications. In both circumstances, certain requirements apply and the facility is responsible for specifying and defining for each position both the job responsibility (job description) and the qualifications specific to performance of the activities within the job description. The job description and the specified qualifications should be consistent with the actual job performed. For example, the job description and the specified qualifications for an RD to provide clinical nutrition services and/or clinical nutrition services management would be distinct from the job description and specified qualifications for a DTR, a nutrition services clerk, or a foodservice worker.

All job descriptions and their specified qualifications must be kept up to date and used consistently for all applicable individuals in performance appraisals and reviews. In other words, is the employee performing activities consistent with the applicable job description? If the facility has both employed and contracted individuals providing services, employees and contractors who do the same work should have the same job description and meet the same job qualifications.

Review of employee files is part of the survey process and certain components of employee files must be available at all times. Depending on the facility's policies and procedures, the employee file in the human resources department and the employee file in the food and nutrition services department may require different documents. A checklist can help ensure that the required items are in each employee file.

Human Resources Files

Accreditation surveyors will expect to find the following items in employee files kept by the human resources department:

- Initial employment application as completed by the applicant
- Documentation of all applicable background checks
- New hire orientation (to the facility) documentation, including proof that the employee attended orientation
- Verification of any required license(s)—that is, a copy of each license printed from the primary verification source at time of hire and signed by the specified party (ie, human resources and/or another designated individual)
- Verification of specified and required certifications, such as Basic Life Support (BLS) or Advanced Cardiovascular Life Support (ACLS)

Food and Nutrition Department Files

Within the food and nutrition services department, or designated unit/area, each employee file should contain documentation of the following:

- Orientation to the department, unit, or area in which the employee is *currently* working
- Job description pertinent to the *current* assigned duties with evidence (employee's signature and date) that the job description was reviewed with the employee
- Verification of all *current* certifications that are specific to the job description and/or required (eg, BLS/ACLS, a food handler's card, or nutrition-related certifications specified in the current job description, such as those available from the Commission on Dietetic Registration [CDR], the National Board of Nutrition Support Certification, or the American Association of Diabetes Educators)
- *Current* verification of *current* RD or DTR status from CDR, including date of verification (Note: Prior to offering an RD or DTR candidate a position, his or her current registration status should be verified through CDR.)
- Verification of any required license(s)—that is, a copy of each license printed from the primary verification source at time of hire and signed by the specified party (supervisor, manager, or other designated individual)
- Evidence of specified competency knowledge, skills, and abilities for *current* position(s)
- Performance evaluation(s) signed by required parties (usually the employee and manager) and dated within the last 12 months with documentation of specified competency knowledge, skills, and abilities for *current* position(s)
- Verification of required or specified in-service education

Nutrition-Related Accreditation Standards

In coordination with staff from other pertinent departments or units, CNMs must ensure that facility activities, services, policies, and procedures comply with all accreditation standards and CoP with a nutrition component (eg, assessment and reassessment of patients; or planning, providing, and coordinating patient care, treatment, and services). The essential elements of the standards are fundamentally the same for all accrediting organizations, although the details vary. Several important nutrition-related surveyable areas are discussed in the following sections.

Nutrition Screening, Assessment, and Reassessment

A facility's scope of service must have a written definition of the scale and content of nutrition screening, assessment, and reassessment that includes time frames in which these activities are to be performed. This definition also must identify findings that may lead to more detailed assessment(s). Nutritional risk screening within 24 hours of hospital admission is currently a standard procedure. If there are any concerns as to whether existing nutrition screening, assessment, and reassessment policies and procedures are in compliance with accreditation standards, the CNM should review, in detail, the accreditation organization's standards and discuss those concerns immediately with the appropriate person or department within the organization or facility. Participation in ongoing audits may be recommended.

Facility policies and procedures must define in writing the "triggers" that lead to a more detailed assessment of the patient; the CNM is responsible for the department's formulation of nutrition care policies and procedures that identify conditions and concerns that may indicate a possible need for nutrition education or another nutrition intervention. These policies and procedures should be coordinated with other patient care departments, such as nursing, pharmacy, or social services. The content of the policies and procedures must be facility-specific and tailored to the patient types and units, such as the intensive care unit, within that facility.

Once the policies and procedures have been finalized, approved, and implemented, the CNM must ensure that processes are adequately monitored and that any faults or deficiencies are identified and corrected. Common methods of assessing compliance include monthly chart audit reviews, automated reports from the electronic health record, and attention during initial and annual competency evaluations. If corrective actions, such as staff education or creation of improved follow-up procedures, are taken, the CNM should document the actions to confirm compliance.

Food Services and the Therapeutic Diet/Nutrition Care Manual

To maintain accreditation, facilities must have documented procedures to ensure the provision of safe food and nutrition products to patients (see Chapter 4 for information on quality control in food services). In addition, facilities must have a documented plan in place to provide adequate and appropriate food and foodservice-related supplies to patients, staff, and visitors in a variety of emergency situations. The emergency plan must include procedures to procure, store, prepare, deliver, and dispose of food and one-time-use-only supplies. For the CNM, the provision of adequate and appropriate food (and nutrition) often involves three components: therapeutic or specialized oral diets, oral nutritional supplements, and nutrition support therapies (ie, enteral and parenteral nutrition). Therapeutic/specialized diets and nutritional supplements are available in the food and nutrition services department, but the availability of enteral nutrition products and selected nutrient modular components within the department will be based on an approved formulary and interdepartmental policies and procedures. Provision and delivery of parenteral nutrition support is the domain of the facility's pharmacy department; the nutritional monitoring of this intervention should be an interdepartmental undertaking between the food and nutrition services and pharmacy departments.

The CNM must also ensure that the facility has a readily available therapeutic diet manual or nutrition care manual (an electronic and/or printed version) that can be accessed readily by staff in the food and nutrition services department as well as medical and nursing staff in all patient care areas. Some facilities may also have the manual available in the facility's library, if applicable. At minimum, the manual should contain therapeutic diet information that is pertinent to the facility's patient population and as nutritionally adequate as possible.

Content in the manual should be reviewed annually, or within the timeframe specified by the accreditation entity. Typically, at least one knowledgeable and skilled RD in the food and nutrition services department will analyze the content. The CNM then reviews the analysis before it is presented to the appropriate medical staff entity for evaluation, approval, and signature. An approval signature page contained within each manual can be used to document proof of the annual review. If the facility uses an electronic manual, the approval signature page can be stored in a policy manual.

All therapeutic diets ordered by the physician or other licensed independent practitioner responsible for the individual's care in a facility should be consistent with the diet content/prescription as defined and delineated in the therapeutic diet manual or nutrition care manual. If a patient has a known or suspected food or food-related allergy and/or refuses food or oral nutrition supplementation, the CNM must ensure the availability of food substitutes that are of equal nutritional value and provide these substitutes within a reasonable timeframe, such as at the scheduled meal time or nourishment time, or at a time more preferred by the patient. The facility should develop a standardized list of readily available and applicable food substitutes for a variety of therapeutic diets and food/beverage consistencies, and have this meal/food substitutes list ready for use when a patient requests alternatives to any usually provided foods or beverages. Additionally, accreditation standards require that the facility recognize and accommodate a patient's cultural, religious, and/or ethnic food/beverage preferences within the therapeutic diet order.

Some CNMs, particularly in smaller facilities, are responsible for ensuring that food is procured, delivered, stored, prepared, and served in a safe, timely, and sanitary manner, for scheduled meals and between-meal nourishments. In larger facilities, these activities and responsibilities are usually overseen by foodservice managers and directors.

Staff Education and Credentials

Accreditation standards place a high priority on training and education for facility staff and employees. As noted previously in this chapter, the facility must document that staff and employees are qualified and have the necessary training and credentialing to perform the duties and functions required of their assigned positions. The CNM should require documentation that RDs and DTRs have attained the continuing professional education units (CPEUs) that CDR requires for maintenance of their credential (75 CPEUs every 5 years for the RD and 50 CPEUs every 5 years for the DTR). Additionally, CNMs should closely monitor state-mandated continuing education requirements and verify that employees are meeting those requirements. Be aware that state regulations vary in their continuing education requirements, and the number of CPEUs required by a particular state in a given time frame may differ from CDR requirements.

To diminish the chance that credentials could lapse, procedures should be in place to remind credentialed/licensed employees of their continuing education obligations in a timely manner. Individuals who have let their RD or DTR credential lapse should not be employed in positions requiring proof of current registration, even if they have taken steps to reinstate their credential.

The work of employed individuals who have met the requirements for CDR credentialing but who have not yet taken the appropriate credentialing examination should be closely monitored. A qualified and credentialed staff person (an RD) should cosign medical record documentation by these individuals to confirm that nutrition care interventions/recommendations are appropriate and safe and in compliance with facility procedures and requirements.

Additionally, the CNM should confirm that all employees attend required in-service education and training sessions. Timely and appropriate documentation of attendance should be included in each employee's personnel file.

Patient Education

To be accredited, a facility must provide education to patients. The type of education provided depends on the individual patient's needs, the facility's patient care protocols, and the orders of the physician or other licensed independent practitioner.

All patient education should be provided in a manner that maximizes the patient's ability to comprehend the content. The CNM should ensure that patient nutrition education is provided for a variety of diseases, conditions, and disorders, with the necessary information delivered in a way that is understandable to the patient or to the patient's family member or advocate.

Nutrition education, with the RD as a member of a multidisciplinary team, is often incorporated into facility protocols related to other types of patient education, such as education about medications, treatments, or specific diseases or conditions. Documentation of the education provided, and of the patient's (or family member's or advocate's) comprehension of and anticipated compliance with the information provided, is required. As relevant, the documentation should include evidence about the media used and what efforts were taken to facilitate patient comprehension.

The Survey Process

An onsite survey is an intense, stressful time for all management and staff, including the CNM, even when the facility is prepared and ready for the surveyor(s). Accredited facilities should always be at survey readiness, but an impending survey can magnify the stress level readiness can cause. However, a knowledgeable, skilled, responsible, and responsive CNM can reduce this stress and ensure the survey goes well. To that end, the following tips may help.

Checklists, Checklists, Checklists

As noted previously in this chapter, checklists are extremely helpful in preparation for surveys. Figures 3.2 and 3.3 (on pages 62 and 63, respectively) are examples that may help you create checklists for your specific facility, department, or unit. You can also seek out checklists created by others and modify them to your specific setting.

Effective checklists are specific, relevant, and easy for all users to understand:

- The document should have a clear title and include fields for dates and signatures.
- The items to be checked should be specific and well defined. As appropriate, incorporate the exact wording of the applicable standard, create status boxes to indicate conclusions or outcomes, and include space for comments, such as required follow-up steps.
- To ensure consistent use of a checklist, explain how to mark its status/check boxes. For example, indicate that users can enter a checkmark (✓) or a "Y" for "Yes"; an "N" for "No"; and "NA" for "Not Applicable."
- When creating a "Reminder" or "Don't Forget" checklist for a particular process, be sure to include all items/actions related to the process that must be done or checked.

Once a checklist has been created, set a standard protocol regarding when it is used and by whom. Also, review each checklist periodically. If a checklist becomes outdated, modify or delete it. Retain each completed checklist for at least 12 months and be prepared to provide it to a surveyor in a timely manner, if requested.

Performing Mock Surveys

To prepare your department or unit for an actual survey, conduct mock survey exercises on a regular basis. Provide a list of questions a surveyor might ask employees and contractors who work in a certain area and help them practice their responses. Sample questions might include the following:

- What do you do if the fire alarm sounds?
- What job do you perform? What training did you have to perform this job?
- What do you do if you see an unidentified container in the kitchen and a ticking sound is coming from it?

Personnel File Checklist

Employee Name: _____   **Date:** _____

Instructions: For each item, check that appropriate documentation is on file for the employee. Supervisors should keep the department/unit file current, as needed.

Human Resources (HR) file:

☐   Initial application for employment
☐   Completed background check
☐   Registration and license verification printed from primary source at time of hire (signed by hiring HR consultant or manager)
☐   Verification of other certification(s) at time of hire

Unit/Department file:

☐   Orientation to *current* department/unit
☐   *Current* job description signed and dated by employee
☐   Subsequent verification of certification(s), if required
☐   Subsequent registration and license verification (printed primary source obtained from the license or accrediting agency web site and signed by supervisor/manager, dated prior to expiration)
☐   Initial competency skills check-off for current position
☐   Most recent performance evaluation (last 12 months) with evidence of annual competency skills check-off signed and dated by employee and manager
☐   Verification of in-service education
☐   Documentation of continuing education (CE). Should include topics relevant to the position (eg, if the dietitian works in the neonatal intensive care unit, CE in this area should be completed)
☐   Proof of attendance at New Hire Orientation

Figure 3.2 Sample Checklist for Registered Dietitians' Personnel Files

- What action do you take if a patient refuses a meal because the temperature isn't "right"?
- What do you do if a chemical or unknown solution splashes on your face?
- Do you do nutritional risk screening here? Tell me about it.
- What do you do if you see a patient fall?
- Do you document your actions in the medical record? If so, what do you do and how do you do it?
- Is there a protocol you use to determine which patients you see and when?
- Can you tell me what National Patient Safety Goals are? Can you identify something being done in this facility to meet these goals and tell me about your role in this effort?

Survey Preparation Checklist

☐   Be able to describe/explain the following:

    ☐   National Patient Safety Goals
    ☐   Nutrition screening and assessment policy (should know the time frames)
    ☐   Interdisciplinary interaction
    ☐   Education of patients (how identified, where you document, what you take into consideration)
    ☐   How you know to see patients
    ☐   Performance improvement activities
    ☐   How you are competent to take care of a patient population

☐   Wear badge: It should be facing the right way and visible
☐   Work with diet tech to review all medical records on nursing units to be sure that every patient marked with a positive nutrition trigger has been assessed and that all notes are timely.
☐   All week, every day, monitor the patient food refrigerator on nursing units.
☐   Keep pager with you and on at all times in case the surveyor on the nursing unit needs you.
☐   If spoken to by a surveyor, notify your manager as soon as possible after the interview regarding the questions you were asked and what your answers were.

Figure 3.3 Checklist for Preparing Staff for a Survey

- What is the correct temperature for the dish machine in the "wash" mode?
- What are universal precautions? How are you impacted by them?
- As a CNM/foodservice manager/director of food and nutrition services, how do you know that the employees you supervise are competent to perform their assigned duties and tasks? What steps do you take if there is a concern about their competency?
- How do you assess and document competence in the employees you supervise?

Assess the outcome of each mock survey so you and your staff can build on strengths, identify weaknesses and their causes, and restructure processes and procedures to overcome weaknesses and reinforce strengths.

Postsurvey Follow-Up

After a survey ends, begin preparing for the next one:

- Meet with other managers/supervisors in your department, as well as managerial and supervisory staff from other relevant areas of the facility. Share input and insights about facets of the survey that went well and facets that did not. For those parts of the survey that went well, solicit input about how to maintain or improve performance. If deficiencies were identified, discuss how they can be corrected.

- Attend the post-survey exit interview or exit conference and take notes about concerns that relate to your department. Devise and implement a follow-up plan to respond to those concerns. Have the plan in place within two weeks, if possible.
- Share information gathered at the exit interview with staff. At this time, thank employees and contractors for their involvement and efforts before and during the survey; emphasize the value of teamwork in the survey process; highlight positive aspects and findings of the survey; underscore the negative aspects and findings of the survey; and present initial ideas to improve performance.
- Above all, be open, be honest, and be a leader in setting the stage for staying "survey ready" at all times.

Hospital-Acquired Conditions

The following "never events," or hospital-acquired conditions (HAC), are defined by CMS as events that "could reasonably have been prevented through the application of evidence-based guidelines" (16):

- Pressure ulcers stages III and IV
- Falls and trauma
- Vascular catheter related infection
- Manifestations of poor glycemic control (diabetic ketoacidosis, nonketotic hyperosmolar coma, hypoglycemic coma, secondary diabetes with ketoacidosis or hyperosmolarity)
- Surgical site infections and mediastinitis following coronary artery bypass graft (CABG)

Since these conditions or complications should never occur during the hospitalization of a patient, CMS will not reimburse the hospital for the costs associated with treating them unless their presence is documented on admission.

Malnutrition and weight loss have been shown to play a role in HACs (17). Therefore, CNMs should educate clinical nutrition staff about HACs and partner with nurses, physicians, and other departments (eg, risk management and quality improvement) to optimize the delivery of nutrition interventions to patients at high risk for HACs.

For example, patients on parenteral nutrition (PN) are at high risk for catheter-related infections (18). If PN is being used inappropriately in patients who could tolerate enteral nutrition, the CNM should provide this information to the appropriate physician leaders so they can establish steps to reduce inappropriate PN use. Additionally, the CNM should coach RDs to question and advise against PN use when an evidence-based indication is not present. Peterson et al found that incidence of inappropriate PN use was lowered when RD order-writing privileges were established and RDs had the authority to deny PN when an indication was not present (19).

A nutrition and nursing partnership may help address the incidence of hospital-acquired pressure ulcers (HAPUs), if nutrition screening identifies patients admitted with pressure ulcers and leads to timely interventions to prevent the progression of pressure ulcers. For this reason, some hospitals use the Braden Scale (20), which takes into account many factors, such as mobility, moisture, friction, and nutrition, to evaluate a patient's risk for pressure ulcers (the lower the score, the higher the risk; frequently, a score less than 18 identifies a patient who is at risk). An automatic nutrition consult for those identified at risk may ensure that early intervention and prevention measures will be implemented. Several hospitals have developed integrated protocols or bundles, which incorporate nutrition, to address the multidisciplinary facets of prevention and management of HAPUs (21,22). CNMs should collaborate with nursing and others to determine whether the facility needs to improve procedures related to HAPUs, and, if so, how the nutrition staff can assist in the process.

Summary

Regulations are an integral and indelible part of health care delivery. Individuals charged with ensuring compliance are continually challenged as the rules become narrower in focus, more detailed in content, and perpetually more difficult to incorporate into daily operations. For CNMs, the need to be compliant, safe, and creative in the delivery of food and nutrition services is a given. The methods by which those ends are accomplished are as numerous as the challenges that precipitate them.

References

1. Centers for Medicare & Medicaid Services. Frequently asked questions: What is CMS? https:// questions.cms.gov. Accessed August 6, 2013.
2. Code of Federal Regulations. www.gpoaccess.gov/cfr. Accessed August 6, 2013.
3. Code of Federal Regulations. Title 42. Public Health. www.access.gpo.gov/nara/cfr/waisidx _10/42cfrv5_10.html. Accessed August 6, 2013.
4. Conditions for Coverage (CfCs) & Conditions of Participations [sic] (CoPs). www.cms.gov /Regulations-and-Guidance/Legislation/CFCsAndCoPs/index.html?redirect=/cfcsandcops/16_asc.asp. Accessed January 3, 2014.
5. Centers for Medicare & Medicaid Services. Conditions for Coverage (CfCs) & Conditions of Participation (CoPs). www.cms.gov/CFCsAndCoPs. Accessed August 6, 2013.
6. CMS-Approved Accreditation Programs. www.cms.gov/Medicare/Provider-Enrollment-and-Certification /SurveyCertificationGenInfo/Downloads/CMS-Approved-Accreditation-Organizations.pdf. Accessed December 15, 2013.
7. Meldi D, Rhoades F, Gippe A. The big three: a side by side matrix comparing hospital accrediting agencies. *Synergy.* 2009(Jan–Feb):12–14. www.namss.org/Portals/0/Advocacy/NAMSS_Synergy_JanFeb09 _Accreditation_Grid.pdf. Accessed August 6, 2013.
8. Medicare State Operations Manual Appendix. www.cms.gov/manuals/downloads/som107_Appendices toc.pdf. Accessed August 6, 2013.

9. Medicare State Operations Manual Appendix A—Survey Protocol, Regulations and Interpretive Guidelines for Hospitals. www.cms.gov/Regulations-and-Guidance/Guidance/Manuals/downloads/som107ap_a_hospitals.pdf. Accessed December 15, 2013.

10. Quality Management Committee and Scope of Practice Subcommittee. Academy Definition of Terms List. Updated 05/2013. Academy of Nutrition and Dietetics. www.eatright.org/scope. Accessed December 15, 2013.

11. Academy of Nutrition and Dietetics Quality Management Committee. Academy of Nutrition and Dietetics: Comprehensive Scope of Practice Resources for the Registered Dietitian or Registered Dietitian Nutritionist. *J Acad Nutr Diet*. 2013;113(6 Suppl 2).

12. Academy of Nutrition and Dietetics Quality Management Committee. Academy of Nutrition and Dietetics: Comprehensive Scope of Practice Resources for the Dietetic Technician, Registered. *J Acad Nutr Diet*. 2013;113(6 Suppl 2).

13. Medicare State Operations Manual Appendix PP—Guidance to Surveyors for Long Term Care Facilities Table of Contents (Rev. 70, 01–07–11). www.cms.gov/manuals/Downloads/som107ap_pp_guidelines_ltcf.pdf. Accessed August 6, 2013.

14. US Department of Health and Human Services. Centers for Medicare & Medicaid Services. 42 CFR Parts 482 and 485. Medicare and Medicaid Programs; Reform of Hospital and Critical Access Hospital Conditions of Participation. *Federal Register*. 2012;77(95). www.cms.gov/Regulations-and-Guidance/Legislation/CFCsAndCoPs/Downloads/CMS-3244-F.pdf. Accessed December 18, 2013.

15. The Joint Commission. Survey Activity Guide for Health Care Organizations 2014. www.jointcommission.org/2014_survey_activity_guide. Accessed December 27, 2013.

16. Centers for Medicare & Medicaid Services. Hospital-Acquired Conditions (HAC) in Acute Inpatient Prospective Payment System (IPPS) Hospitals. www.cms.gov/HospitalAcqCond. Accessed January 31, 2012.

17. Fry DE, Pine M, Jones BL, Meimban RJ. Patient characteristics and the occurrence of never events. *Arch Surg*. 2010;145(2):148–151.

18. Matsushima K, Cook A, Tyner T, Tollack L, Williams R, Lemaire S, Friese R, Frankel H. Parenteral nutrition: a clear and present danger unabated by tight glucose control. *Am J Surg*. 2010;200(3):386–390.

19. Peterson SJ, Chen Y, Sullivan CA, Kinnare KF, Tupesis NC, Patel GP, Sowa DC, Lateef O, Sheean PM. Assessing the influence of registered dietitian order-writing privileges on parenteral nutrition use. *J Am Diet Assoc*. 2010;110(11):1703–1711.

20. Braden Scale for Predicting Pressure Sore Risk. www.bradenscale.com/images/bradenscale.pdf. Accessed February 1, 2012.

21. Baldelli P, Paciella M. Creation and implementation of a pressure ulcer prevention bundle improves patient outcome. *Am J Med Quality*. 2008;23:136–142.

22. Delmore B, Lebovits S, Baldock P, Suggs B, Avello EA. Pressure ulcer prevention program: a journey. *J Wound Ostomy Continence Nurs*. 2011;38:505–513.

## 4

Quality Control in Patient Food Services

Kendal T. Ecker, MS, RDN, LD, and Vicki L. Crittenden, RD, LD

Introduction

Quality is an ancient idea. Nearly 2,000 years ago, Lucius Annaeus Seneca (5 BC to 65 AD), Roman philosopher and counselor to Nero, wrote an enduring and familiar message in one of his epistles: "It is quality rather than quantity that matters" (1). Quality control—which is defined as an aggregate of activities (such as design analysis and inspection for defects) designed to ensure adequate quality, especially in manufactured products (2)—is a more recent concept. Today, leaders in every industry have adapted the following principles of W. Edwards Deming, statistician and consultant, and Joseph Moses Juran, quality control authority, to better understand and implement processes to improve quality (2,3):

- Establish objective and measureable standards.
- Monitor processes to compare performance with the desired standards.
- Follow up with corrective actions when goals are not met.
- Involve trained, committed employees in the quality control processes.

As a clinical nutrition manager (CNM), your responsibilities may include oversight of food quality, safety, and sanitation for patient or resident meal services. This chapter therefore focuses on how you can apply quality control ideas in the daily operations of health care food services. It will help you:

- Understand your quality goals.
- Set standards of performance.
- Use meaningful quality control tools for documenting your progress.
- Plan for "corrective actions" (changes that restore a state of conformance with quality goals) (2).

There are rarely any shortcuts to achieving quality. Avoid "quick fixes"—they will not produce consistent results. Stay organized by using tools such as tracking and auditing forms and checklists that help you establish the frequency of monitoring for each process, report results and trends, and ensure that your efforts are consistent with facility policies. Table 4.1 outlines a possible schedule for the quality control monitors discussed in this chapter. Finally, do not be afraid to be adaptable and flexible and try new methods as you work toward meeting your quality goals. Working together with your staff on quality control issues and corrective actions is an excellent way to promote teamwork and commitment to quality. All ideas, no matter how detailed or brief, are valuable. You may be pleasantly surprised with results stemming from an impromptu brainstorming session.

External Surveys and Inspections

To ensure quality control in food services, the CNM must become very familiar with the regulatory environment. All facilities serving food are monitored by a variety of local, state, federal, and other regulatory organizations. The local department of health, the Centers for Medicare & Medicaid Services (CMS), the Joint Commission (TJC), the Occupational Safety and Health Administration (OSHA), and the Omnibus Budget Reconciliation Act (OBRA) are just a few of the various agencies, organizations, and laws that regulate food safety and quality standards in health care. (See Chapter 3 for additional information about health care regulations and facility compliance issues.)

The US Food and Drug Administration (FDA) standards for food safety (www.fda.gov/Food/GuidanceRegulation/default.htm) are a cornerstone for quality control in food services. Achieving these standards will help you prepare your facility for the various regulatory agencies that can pass through your doors, including your local and state health department, TJC, the fire marshal, and CMS. Most inspectors arrive with very little or no advance notice, so continual readiness is a must.

Local Health Inspections

Local health department inspections are often unannounced and can occur annually, biannually, or more frequently. Most restaurant and kitchen scores are easily found online and must be posted in the operation. To show customers that your facility is safe and well managed, you need to obtain top-notch inspection scores and consistently maintain high standards.

Health code requirements vary among cities, counties, and states, so it is important that you understand your local health department's health codes. For example, some city health departments require that every manager receive a certificate from the city stating that he or she has achieved a level of certification or training to manage the kitchen. Other cities may require that only one manager per site obtain this certificate (4). Certification from a recognized food safety course is often accepted by the city as long as the city health department has a record of the completed training on file and has issued the city's approved certificate to the manager. The National Restaurant Association Education Foundation (NRAEF) operates ServSafe (www.ServSafe.com), a widely recognized program based on the FDA food code

Table 4.1 Sample Documentation Schedule[a]

Document	Monitoring Procedure	Review Procedure
Refrigerator/freezer temperature log	Monitor and document temperatures daily at opening and closing of the kitchen.	Review log for completion and take corrective action as needed.
Dish machine temperature log	Monitor and document temperatures daily at each meal period.	Review log for completion and take corrective action as needed.
Pot and pan sanitizer log	Monitor and document sanitation during every meal period or every 4 hours while sanitizer is in use.	Review log for completion and take corrective action as needed.
Meal service standards checklist	Check and document temperatures of food and equipment and evaluate food quality prior to every meal.	Review checklist for completion and take corrective action as needed.
Taste test evaluations	At least two employees participate in evaluation before every meal. Evaluation should be timed to allow for corrective actions before food is served to patients.	Review documentation for completion and take corrective action as needed.
Test meal evaluations	Order 3 test meals a week; include tests of all meals and a variety of diets.	Review results and trends and report monthly summary.
Tray accuracy evaluations	Three times a week, inspect and document a sample of 10 trays; sample should include trays from all meals.	Review results and trends and report monthly summary.
Meal cart delivery	Document during each meal period.	Review for trends and completion.
Timeliness of tray delivery logs	Check and document tray delivery times.	Review logs for trends and completion and take corrective action as needed.
Menu accuracy evaluations	Staff RD should evaluate menus at least once a week; increase frequency if problem or trend is identified.	Review evaluations for completion and take corrective action as needed.

[a]Retain all documentation for 1 year.

and taught by health inspectors and food professionals nationwide (4,5). This course provides around 16 hours of education and ends in a competency assessment prior to certification. Students with a passing grade obtain the ServSafe certification, which is active for 5 years. Other recognized programs for food safety are the National Registry of Food Safety Professionals (www.nrfsp.com), where learners receive a Food Safety Professional (FSP) certification (6), and Prometric (www.prometric.com/foodsafety/default.htm), where learners receive a Certified Professional Food

Manager (CPFM) certificate (7). Check with your employer and state and local health departments to determine which certifications are accepted in your area.

In addition, many cities require that all foodservice employees complete a course in safe food handling. The course is usually several hours long and upon completion the attendee is issued a food handler's card, to be kept on file with the employer (see discussion of employee files in Chapter 3). To prevent issues during an inspection, work with your local health department to determine your location's specific requirements.

Surveys by the Joint Commission

The Joint Commission is an independent, not-for-profit organization that accredits and certifies more than 20,000 health care organizations and programs in the United States (8). This chapter focuses on TJC's food and patient meal service regulatory requirements. See Chapter 3 for additional information about TJC and health care compliance.

Two aspects of a TJC survey can trigger a kitchen visit from a surveyor. One is a medical record tracer (also known simply as "a tracer"), the process in which a surveyor reviews selected patients' experiences during their hospital stay as documented in their medical records. A diet order or other component of the medical record can trigger a follow-up question for the surveyor that leads him or her to review operations in your foodservice department.

The other trigger that leads surveyors to the kitchen is the required environment of care survey, which also involves inspection of storerooms and receiving areas. The kitchen inspection investigates safety for the employees as well as patients/residents, and the surveyor may ask employees questions related to their environmental safety and adequacy of training. In addition to employee safety, surveyors may evaluate the facility's food safety practices and take food temperatures when visiting the kitchen. See Box 4.1 for sample questions that surveyors may ask.

Box 4.1 Sample Survey Questions for Foodservice Workers

Possible medical record tracer questions for foodservice workers:

- How do you know which diet to send the patient?
- Where is your diet manual?
- How do you determine how many carbohydrates to send to a patient with diabetes on a diabetic diet order?

Possible questions from the Environment of Care surveyor:

- What do you do if there is a fire?
- Where are the fire extinguishers and exit signs located?
- What is your department plan in case a disaster occurrs?

Fire Marshal Inspections

The kitchen environment can be a hazardous place, particularly if safeguards are not in place. Your facility must meet local building codes to pass a fire code inspection conducted by the fire marshal. This inspection may check the following:

- Fire alarm and suppressant systems are serviced and tested.
- Exits are clearly marked and unobstructed.
- Items are stored a safe distance from the sprinkler systems.

Note: TJC requires that facilities leave at least 18 inches of open space between the sprinkler deflector and the top of storage (9), but your local building code may require more space. You should verify the various requirements for your facility and abide by the strictest standard.

Other Types of Inspections

Inspectors from CMS or the state health department have similar expectations to those of the local health department inspectors, TJC surveyors, and the fire marshal. Check with relevant agencies for additional details.

Internal Inspections and Audits

In addition to inspections from external organizations, you or your facility may require internal inspections of foodservice operations. A manager cannot personally monitor every aspect of the foodservice operation, but you can use internal inspections in the form of checklists and audits to ensure that your operation is maintaining standards and is ready for external inspectors. Examples of various quality control audits are available throughout this chapter.

Refrigerator and Freezer Temperature Controls

Time and temperature are essential to keeping food safe by preventing pathogen growth (10). Temperatures in all food storage or holding refrigerators and freezers must be monitored and documented daily (11). A good standard of practice is to document the temperatures at the opening and closing of the business. See Figure 4.1 (page 72) for a sample refrigerator/freezer temperature log.

The temperature in freezers should be 0° Fahrenheit or lower, and refrigerator temperatures should be less than 40° Fahrenheit (12). Commercial refrigerators often have a temperature display on the outside of the unit. However, this gauge can malfunction without notice. Therefore, it is prudent to have another, NSF-certified thermometer located inside the unit to confirm the temperature. (For information on NSF certification, visit www.NSF.org.)

Technology to wirelessly monitor temperatures of all of the kitchen equipment is available from multiple companies and can be a terrific quality control tool because it monitors temperatures at all times, not just when an employee records

Refrigerator/Freezer Temperature Log

Temperature Requirements:

Refrigerator: 34–40° Fahrenheit
Freezer: 0° Fahrenheit

- Keep completed Temperature Log on file for 1 year.
- Record temperatures daily.
- If equipment problems occur, contact maintenance department.

Date	Time	Refrigerator Temperature	Freezer Temperature	Corrective Actions (for out-of-range temperatures)	Employee's Name

Figure 4.1 Sample Refrigerator/Freezer Temperature Log

the temperature manually. If your facility is considering this kind of technology, be sure to select a system and service that fit your needs. Cost, warranty, power supplies, out-of-range alerts, customer support, and data management are a few factors that vary among vendors (13). Potential advantages of this type of system include the following:

- Measurements are accurate.
- Monitoring is less time-consuming and simpler than manual checks.
- You can remotely monitor equipment throughout the facility and offsite equipment.
- Temperatures are monitored during all hours, which is extremely beneficial for those times when operations are closed.
- Some interfaces can be programmed to send out-of-range temperature alerts to selected users through multiple avenues, such as pager alerts, text messages, phone messages, or e-mails.
- Data are collected and can be used to review trends in temperature changes.

Disadvantages of wireless monitoring can include the following:

- The technology can be expensive.
- The technology may have requirements that are not compatible with your facility's wireless network.
- Available vendors may not provide customer service suited to your facility's needs.
- Sensors can break or lose power.
- Sensors may send false alarms, even under normal use.

In addition to monitoring and documenting temperatures, foodservice staff should know how to handle food that may have been stored at unsafe temperatures. Be sure that employees have ready access to reference charts with temperature and time guidelines for food safety. Train employees to check these charts to ensure that any food that has experienced time and temperature abuse is not used in the foodservice operation. Food storage charts are available from NSF International (14).

Dishwashing and Warewashing Safety

Sanitation of the equipment and serviceware prevents potentially hazardous microorganisms from cross-contaminating foodservice equipment or food. Used correctly, commercial dish machines properly clean and sanitize dishes and utensils, but you must monitor and document that the manufacturer-specified temperatures are met during the wash, rinse, and sanitation cycles—a clean appearance can be deceiving. Be sure to record temperatures on a log for all cycles during each period of use (see Figure 4.2 on page 74).

Temperatures and the type of sanitizer used also need to be monitored and documented when dishes are manually washed or cleaned using a chemical sanitizing

Dishwashing/Warewashing Machine Temperature Log

Temperature Requirements:

Wash: _____   **Rinse:** _____   **Final rinse:** _____

- Keep completed Temperature Log on file for 1 year.
- Record temperatures once during each meal period.
- If problems occur, contact maintenance department.

Date	Time	Meal Period (Circle One)	Wash Temperature	Rinse Temperature	Final Rinse Temperature	Employee's Name
		B L D				
		B L D				
		B L D				
		B L D				
		B L D				
		B L D				

Figure 4.2   Sample Dishwashing/Warewashing Machine Temperature Log

dish machine. Note that each sanitizer must be at a specific concentration and temperature to be effective (10).

Monitors of Food Quality

Meal Service Standards Checklist

The preparation, holding, and serving of food can affect food quality and temperature. Implementing procedures that monitor the food during each part of its journey will yield consistent results and prevent unacceptable food from being served. The following is a list of items to consider including in your daily meal checklist:

- **Temperature checks**: Employees should check food temperatures after the food is produced; while it is being held for service (if the meal service is extended over several hours, consider hourly temperature checks); and at the point of service (assessment can be done through periodic test meal evaluations).
- **Taste testing**: Employees should sample food after it is produced, before service, and at the point of service. (This process can be completed by a combination of foodservice employees.)
- **Visual checks**: Employees should evaluate the food for correct color, texture, and overall look on the service line. They should also check the plate set up and overall presentation of the meal.
- **Timing**: Employees should document how much time lapses as food moves from one stage to another (eg, from production to serving or storage stages). This helps ensure that the food does not dry out or go stale.

Taste Test Evaluation

The objective of taste testing is to monitor the temperature, taste, quality, and overall acceptability of food prior to meal service. Although food taste and temperatures are monitored throughout the food preparation process, a final taste and quality check must be conducted again just before the food is served. A good practice is to have a team of at least two employees, such as managers, chefs, registered dietitians (RDs), or other foodservice staff, participate in taste testing. See Figure 4.3 (page 75) for a sample format for recording taste test evaluations for food quality. The following tips are useful in conducting taste tests:

- Schedule taste test evaluations to occur no later than 15 minutes prior to assembly of the first meal. If the taste test identifies a problem, there will be time to make last-minute corrections.
- Measure and record the temperature of each food item.

  ◊ Use a calibrated thermometer (see Box 4.2 on page 78). Wipe the thermometer probe with alcohol or another sanitizer approved for food-contact surfaces.

◊ Insert the probe into the thickest part of the food to measure the internal food temperature. Do not allow the probe to touch bones in meat or the side or bottom of the serving pan. Also check the temperature just inside the surface of the food. All parts of the food, not just the thickest part, must meet temperature standards. Surveyors may check a food's temperature in several places, including near the food surface.

- Transfer small samples of each food using a clean serving utensil to a plate used only for sampling.
- To avoid cross contamination, conduct the taste test in an area away from the service area or steam table. Do not allow the serving utensil to come in contact with a sample plate that has already been used for tasting.
- Determine whether quality standards are met or if further modifications, such as adjustments to seasoning or increased cooking time, are required before meal assembly begins. Do not serve any food that does not meet quality or temperature standards.
- Document items that require corrective action and follow up with appropriate staff.

Test Meal Evaluation

Evaluation of test meals lets you monitor menu items for quality compliance with temperature, taste, and appearance standards of a specific meal and diet order (see Box 4.3 on page 78). Begin by planning a monthly calendar (see Figure 4.4 on page 79) with a variety of staff members (eg, managers, production staff, and RDs) assigned to participate. For a good overall viewpoint of meal quality, be sure to vary the meals by day, meal period, and types of diets. Consider adding a process to track and document both positive and negative trends each month.

As you develop your evaluation standards, determine the acceptable time allowed between the start of the meal assembly and the actual time of testing. The time allowed will vary according to the facility's goals for delivery time (typically 20 to 30 minutes maximum after meal assembly begins) and the type of equipment used for holding hot and cold food temperatures. Check with your equipment representative to learn about the temperature-retention capabilities of your facility's meal delivery system (eg, insulated tray, induction heat, convection heat, thermal pellet, hot/cold cart, rethermalization cart).

Test trays are typically delivered to a nursing unit or resident dining room. The visibility of the test meal evaluation outside of the kitchen provides an opportunity for nurses, diet clerks, and other members of the patient care staff to be involved. Encourage them to participate and provide comments and suggestions for improvement. Be sure to also ask them for help identifying problematic meals and diets, such as pureed or sodium–restricted offerings, and include these meals in the test

Taste-Test Evaluation for Quality Control

Date: _____   **Day of Week:** M T W T F S S

Cook: _____   **Supervisor:** _____

Instructions: Use X to mark unacceptable findings.

	Name of Food Item	Temperature	Taste	Appearance
Entrée				
Entrée				
Chopped entrée				
Ground entrée				
Pureed entrée				
Broth, soup, hot cereal				
Vegetable				
Vegetable				
Potatoes				
Gravy				
Other				
Other				
Salad				
Dessert				
Juice/cold beverage				
Coffee				
Milk				

Figure 4.3 Sample Taste-Test Evaluation Form

Box 4.2 Calibrating a Thermometer Using the Ice Point Method

1. Fill a container with ice and add drinkable water until the container is full. Stir the ice-water mixture.
2. Place the temperature-sensing area of the stem or probe of the thermometer into the ice water. Make sure the sensing area is submerged in the water and does not touch the container.
3. Wait 30 seconds, or until the temperature indicator does not move or the digital readout stops. Leave the thermometer in the ice water while calibrating.
4. Bimetallic-stemmed thermometers: Use a wrench or other small tool (some are built into the design of the thermometer) to rotate the thermometer head to 32° Fahrenheit or 0° Celsius.
5. Digital thermometers, thermocouples, and thermistors: Refer to the manufacturer's directions for calibration. Some models may have a reset button.

Source: Data are from reference 10.

Box 4.3 Case Study: Test-Meal Evaluation

Test tray temperatures were excellent except for the milk and juice. When stored in the same refrigerator on the tray line, the milk and juice initially met temperature standards (38° Fahrenheit). However, by the time the patient received the tray 25 minutes later, the beverage temperatures had risen to 49°. The goal temperature is 45° degrees or less.

The first corrective action involved placing all of the cold items away from the hot items on the tray to avoid any possible heat transfer to the milk or juice. Improvements were minimal: milk was still 48° at the time of service. (Remember that corrective actions may not always be 100% effective, but any improvement is better than none at all.)

Next, the clinical nutrition manager reviewed all refrigerator temperatures with the equipment representative and determined that the refrigerator could not be adjusted to a colder temperature. A staff member suggested storing the milk and juice in the walk-in freezer for at least 30 minutes before the start of meal assembly and then transferring the beverages to the tray-line refrigerator. This corrective action had a positive impact. Juice and milk temperatures start at 33° and stay below 45° on the patients' trays.

The lesson learned: Do not be afraid of trying new processes! Solutions are just waiting to be given a chance to succeed.

Monthly Schedule for Test-Meal Evaluation			
Week of	Breakfast	Lunch	Dinner
Sept 1–7	Susan (high fiber)	Ashley (no salt added)	Tony (soft)
Sept 8–14	Alyson (regular)	Dana (pureed)	Kim (full liquid)
Sept 15–21	Gracie (100-gram protein)	Lisa (fiber restricted)	Julie (1,800 ADA)
Sept 22–28	Nora (clear liquid)	Liz (heart healthy)	Laura (vegan)

Figure 4.4 Example of a Test-Meal Evaluation Schedule

meal schedule, too. Consider sending a thank-you note to each test-tray participant and include a small reward, such as a coupon for a free beverage or dessert, to show appreciation for their time and feedback. This extra step of communicating your appreciation will encourage future involvement.

To complete a test meal evaluation, follow these steps:

- Request a test meal with a specific diet order or menu items. Indicate the delivery location of the test meal. If possible, do not indicate that the tray is a test meal.
- Check and record food temperatures of the specified items when they are on the steam table or in refrigeration. (This data may already be recorded on a temperature log.)
- Track the start and finish times of the test-tray assembly and the time the tray is actually tested. At each step, use a sanitized, calibrated thermometer to record food temperatures.
- Evaluate each food in the test meal for the following:

    ◊ Appearance (eg, color, presence or absence of a garnish)
    ◊ Taste (flavor, seasoning, aroma)
    ◊ Texture (eg, is the food overcooked, undercooked, mushy, or dry?)
    ◊ Portion size (are posted portion-control guidelines met?)
    ◊ Accuracy (is the correct food served?)
    ◊ Overall tray appearance (eg, are there any spills, are items in the correct place, are flatware and dishes clean?)

- If a test meal does not meet quality standards, document the need for a corrective action and note the items that do not meet standards. Share this information with appropriate kitchen team members.

Tray Accuracy Evaluation

Tray accuracy audits aim to ensure that the meal served accurately matches the menu description, the portion sizes are appropriate to the diet type, and all expected items are present. The reputation of the nutrition services department depends on patients' perceptions of quality and service. Patients respond well when the meal received is accurate and plates, bowls, food, and service items are attractively, consistently, and conveniently arranged. An inaccurate tray, on the other hand, suggests to the patient that the facility is inattentive to details and lacks concern for the patient. Furthermore, an inaccurate tray often results in a delayed meal. Worst of all, accuracy errors may potentially have adverse health effects if a patient is served food that is contraindicated.

To provide accurate trays, implement the following tips:

- Take photographs or draw diagrams to represent the proper placement of tray items. For example, create a dinner tray diagram with soup, salad, an entrée with side dishes, bread, dessert, beverage, flatware, napkin, and condiments.
- Have new employees refer to the tray diagrams or photographs to learn how to correctly place all items on the meal tray during its assembly. Explain to them that a tray is easier to check for inaccuracies if the diagram is followed and presentation is neat and orderly.
- Post the diagrams and photos in a visible place in the tray assembly area. Other helpful information to post includes a garnish listing for each meal or food item and a portion control guide with the correctly sized serving utensils noted for each menu item.
- Run regular tray-accuracy tests:

    ◊ Plan a monthly testing calendar with a variety of participants (managers, production staff, and RDs) on a rotating schedule similar to the one described in the discussion of the test meal evaluation schedule. The test schedule should include weekend meals, since every meal is equally important.
    ◊ Determine the number of trays to monitor. You could select a percentage of the average number of meals served or choose a specific set number, such as 10 or more total trays at breakfast, lunch, and dinner each week.
    ◊ Check trays for accuracy according to your specific criteria, and record the names of the staff working at each tray assembly period.
    ◊ Determine and document what corrective actions are needed, and share evaluations with relevant members of the staff, including those who assembled inaccurate trays.

See Figures 4.5 and 4.6 for examples of tray-accuracy quality monitoring and a tray-accuracy action plan.

Tray-Accuracy Quality Control Evaluation

Day of Week: M T W T F S S   **Date:** _____   **Meal:** B L D

Monitored by: _____   **Nursing Unit:** _____

Instructions: This form provides space to evaluate eight trays. For each tray reviewed, place an X in the box next to the item if it was not accurate (eg, for cold items, if the cold item was not what the patient selected or not the correct, standard menu item for that meal for an unmarked menu). After eight trays are completed, total the number of inaccuracies for each row.

Accuracy Criteria	1	2	3	4	5	6	7	8	Total number of innaccuracies for each tray component
Cold food items									
Hot food items									
Beverages									
Condiments									
Portion size									
Garnish									
Flatware/napkin									
Neat, no spills									

Tray Assembly Staff:

Starter: _____

Cold food: _____

Hot food: _____

Beverages: _____

Other Comments:

Figure 4.5 Sample Form for Monitoring Tray Accuracy

Tray Accuracy Action Plan

Instructions:

1. Review results of tray-accuracy evaluations with all tray assembly and production staff.
2. Develop an action plan for each issue marked with an "X" on the tray-accuracy evaluation form.
3. Assign a person responsible for follow-up.
4. Determine completion date.
5. Determine a follow-up date to ensure that the issue is resolved. Enter the date when the follow-up check is made and the name of the individual completing the follow-up evaluation.

Tray Issue	Action Plan	Assigned to	Completion Date	Follow-Up to Ensure Issue Is Resolved

Additional Information:

Checker: _____

Figure 4.6 Sample Tray Accuracy Action Plan

Timeliness of Tray Delivery

It is important to assess the timeliness of tray delivery (the time between receiving a request for a meal and when it is delivered to the patient) both to achieve patient and staff satisfaction and to ensure food safety. To monitor timeliness, first choose a realistic delivery-time goal that reflects the variables that can affect delivery times, such as the following:

- **Facility layout**: What is the distance and travel time from the tray assembly site to the most distant location at your facility? Do you have elevators designated for tray delivery throughout the day or only during standard meal delivery times? If elevators are not designated, do meal delivery staff experience elevator delays to some or all delivery locations? Are you providing off-site meal delivery?
- **Menu**: Do you have a traditional menu? Can staff prepare and send menu items promptly, or do you have a room-service menu with some items that require a longer preparation time?
- **Variations in patient census**: Is the demand for meal delivery relatively steady from day to day, or are certain days or meal periods busier than others?
- **Staffing**: Do you have staff specifically assigned throughout the day to prepare and deliver meals?

Once you have determined your delivery goal (eg, 30 minutes from start to finish for room-service delivery), provide a log for your tray assembly staff to use to track individual meal deliveries. Review a random sample of all meal delivery times from the log to determine whether goals are being met. If the delivery goal is not being met, look for trends: are delays occurring when an order is processed, during meal preparation, or in the delivery stage? Follow up with corrective action. Address job performance with specific staff if they are linked at any point in the process to on-going and consistent problems with meal-delivery time standards. Figure 4.7 (page 84) is an example of a tool to monitor the timeliness of tray delivery. See Box 4.4 on page 85 for a case study of how such a tool led to quality improvements.

If you do not provide room service, it is important to coordinate meal delivery times with the medication schedules set by nursing staff (eg, meals for patients with diabetes must be timed to fit with the insulin administration schedule). Also consider the acuity of the patient population, which will affect the amount of nursing assistance needed at meal times, and work with physical and occupational therapy staff to determine the best time for each meal period, especially if patients or residents eat in a dining room with assistance from health care workers. Patients in rehabilitation units need adequate time to complete their daily personal care and therapy activities without feeling rushed before, during, or after meal times. Balancing multiple requests for specific delivery times can be a challenge. Be prepared to make adjustments before finding the best schedule for all involved.

Timeliness of Tray Delivery Quality Control Evaluation

Day of Week: M T W T F S S   **Date**: _____   **Meal**: B L D

Room Number	Time Order Received	Time Tray Left Kitchen	Time Tray Delivered	Total Delivery Time	Exceeds Standard of _____ or Less (✔)	Delivered By

Figure 4.7 Sample Form to Monitor Timeliness of Tray Delivery

> **Box 4.4 Case Study: Improving Tray Delivery Timing**
>
> You have noticed that your most efficient and well-trained hostess is delivering fewer meals and taking longer to deliver them. Nurses and patients are complaining about the slow service. You therefore investigate the complaints as well as the unexplained change in your best employee's performance by using a timeliness of tray delivery assessment for this employee. The results confirm that the meal requests are processed on time and the food leaves the kitchen within the expected time, so the issue of slow service seems to involve the hostess.
>
> When you inspect other variables, you discover that the number of patients in isolation precaution rooms has increased. The hostess must take additional time to properly put on personal protective equipment and follow all required procedures when entering and leaving the rooms.
>
> Having identified the problem and recognizing that it will affect all hosting staff, you plan training that allows employees to practice putting on the disposable gloves and gown. The employees love the competitive game to see who is the fastest and most efficient at "gowning and gloving." The corrective action becomes a win-win for everyone as "practice makes perfect"—and leads to faster meal delivery.

To help staff stay on schedule, make a list of all nursing units, or other delivery locations, with the delivery time goal noted for each meal. Next, determine when meal trays should be picked up from patients and when the cart should be returned to the kitchen. When setting schedules, allow adequate time for patients to finish their meal (eg, one hour from the time the meals are delivered to pick-up time) and be sure to include sufficient turn-around time for the kitchen staff to unload the carts, wash dishes, and sanitize carts before the next meal or start of a new work shift. For each step, choose certain staff to document actual times in a log.

Review the logs, noting the delivery and pick-up times, to determine whether goals are being met. Look for trends, identify corrective actions, and follow up with action plans as needed to meet delivery objectives.

Menu Accuracy

Menu accuracy is critical to accommodate personal, religious, cultural, and ethnic food preferences, monitor compliance with special diet patterns, and prevent serving the wrong foods to patients with noted food allergies or intolerances. An RD or dietetic technician, registered (DTR) should be assigned to complete menu-accuracy checks. He or she should review menus against each patient's written card file notes (non-automated record system) or electronic card file (automated record system, such as CBORD's Nutrition Services Suite) for preferences, allergies, intolerances, and compliance with special diet patterns, such as carbohydrate counting. The RD or DTR may also find it helpful to check comments from the diet office phone message records and patient visitation notes when comparing patient information with the menu.

Printed menus, including any notes or adjustments made by the nutrition services staff, must be easy for the tray assembly staff to read and understand. Be sure to also look for the following criteria when monitoring menu accuracy:

- Patient name, room number, and diet order match information on diet order list (the facility's patient identifiers, such as date of birth, should be included on the menu as required).
- Menu adjustments comply with patient's preferences and/or meal patterns.
- Allergies and intolerances are clearly identified.
- No unapproved menu abbreviations are used.
- All handwritten items are legible.

When monitoring the accuracy of menus, also determine whether substitutions of equal nutritional value are offered when patients refuse the food served, in compliance with the Joint Commission Provision of Care Standard PC 02.02.03, EP 10 (15). Options for substitutions include (*a*) directly requesting a substitute during normal hours of operation; (*b*) obtaining individual food items, such as cheese, milk, soup, or a sandwich box meal, from the available floor stock or pantry on the nursing unit; and (*c*) authorizing food purchases by nursing staff for patients at a food venue open after normal business hours. Be sure to track meal charges and determine which department is responsible for the charges.

The RD or other designated person monitoring the menus should be responsible for immediately correcting menu errors. Corrective action should always resolve errors in the actual meal and provide additional staff education. A copy of the corrected menu should be referenced as a training tool. Figure 4.8 is an example of a menu-accuracy monitoring form.

Patient Satisfaction Surveys

Health care organizations rely on patient satisfaction surveys to provide feedback about the quality of care provided in the hospital setting and to identify opportunities for improvements. When discussing the topic of patient satisfaction surveys with staff, emphasize that they must regard patients or residents and their families as *customers*. Involving all employees in the department, communicating results of surveys, and updating employees on progress toward improvements create excitement and commitment for everyone (16).

To use survey data effectively, the CNM and director must understand the facility's satisfaction survey process. Meet with the administrator at your hospital who is responsible for patient satisfaction data to learn more about the following:

- **The survey developer**: The facility may have developed an in-house survey or chosen to work with one of several nationally recognized vendors, such as Press Ganey, PRC, NRC Picker, or Gallup.
- **Survey questions**: If a survey is still in the planning phase, you may be able to develop specific questions. Different external vendors vary the questions;

Menu-Accuracy Quality Control Evaluation

Day of the Week: M T W T F S S   **Date:** _____   **Meal:** B L D

Person Audited: _____   **Completed by:** _____

Total Nonconformances: _____

Instructions:

1. Review accuracy criteria for each menu reviewed.
2. Place an X in the box for each criterion that does not meet standard.
3. Total the number of Xs in each row for the 6 menus to determine the total number of times each criterion did not meet standard.

Accuracy Criteria	1	2	3	4	5	6	Total Items Not Meeting Standard
Patient name and room number on menu match wording on diet order listing							
Diet order on menu matches wording on diet order listing							
No unapproved menu abbreviations							
Allergies are written on the menu							
Menu adjustments comply with patient's preferences							
Menu adjustments comply with diet order restrictions and/or meal patterns (eg, number of CHOs)							
All handwritten items are legible							

Figure 4.8 Sample Form for Monitoring Menu Accuracy

however, most surveys generally address the degree of satisfaction with some or all of the following topics:

◊ Quality of the meal
◊ Temperature of the meal (Was hot food served hot? Was cold food served cold?)
◊ Courtesy of the person serving the meal
◊ Clarity of explanations of special diets
◊ Staff sensitivity to cultural and religious food preferences

- **Access to and interpretation of survey results**: The vendor may offer online training or the facility may provide education on how to review survey data. Learn how to compare your results with comparable hospitals and become familiar with the mean score (the average score for each question) and the percentile ranking (the proportion of scores in the database that fall below your individual facility's score; this ranking is not an actual score).
- **Incentives**: Are there financial incentives or other forms of reward and recognition for meeting patient satisfaction goals? Are these incentives based on the mean score or percentile ranking? If you are establishing incentive targets for your staff, clearly define them by ranking or score. Ranking allows you to compare your results to the hospital's overall ranking as well as the rankings of other departments.

One important survey tool is the Hospital Consumer Assessment of Healthcare Providers and Systems (HCAHPS; pronounced *H-caps*) survey, which is also known as the CAHPS Hospital Survey. This national survey, sponsored by CMS and the Agency for Healthcare Research and Quality (AHRQ), measures patient satisfaction and perspectives of care and is a key component of the Hospital Value Based Purchasing Program, which establishes standardized quality measures to evaluate and compare hospitals and provides financial incentives to encourage hospitals to improve patient care (see Chapter 5).

HCAHPS results are published online (www.hospitalcompare.hhs.gov) (17), which can help consumers make informed choices when comparing hospitals. The survey questions are provided from 48 hours to 6 weeks after discharge to a random sample of inpatients who were 18 years of age or older at time of admission. Patients receive the survey. Patients receiving psychiatry services (as their primary reason for admission), rehabilitation, or skilled nursing services are not surveyed.

Survey questions focus on the following:

- Communication with nurses and doctors and the responsiveness of hospital staff
- Pain management and discharge instructions about medications
- Cleanliness and noise level of the hospital and the degree of courtesy and respect shown to the patient by staff

Although the HCAHPS survey does not include any questions directly related to food or clinical nutrition care, the nutrition services department can positively influence the patient's perception of the hospital in several ways, including the following:

- **Communication**: Advise all hourly and clinical staff members who have patient contact to keep medical providers and other staff informed about the role of nutrition and food services in patient care. If a patient raises a patient care concern with your staff that should be addressed by another member of the health care team, the employee should convey this concern to the appropriate provider.
- **Responsiveness:** Nutrition and foodservices employees should act quickly when communicating and follow up to make sure the right person is involved in improving the patient's experience. Timely responses to patients' food-related requests are especially important.
- **Medication and discharge instructions**: Well-informed nutrition and food-services employees can help prevent adverse food and drug interactions. The RD's role could include making recommendations concerning insulin administration and coordination of meals; providing updated and easy-to-understand nutrition education materials for patients requiring diet modifications at home; and answering questions as active team members when on patient rounds or following up on a physician's consult order.
- **Pain management**: Staff in the nutrition department should be aware of each patient's overall condition and how pain affects appetite. Employees should be able to identify patients in pain and, as appropriate, postpone visits until they are feeling better.
- **Cleanliness and quietness**: Make sure your staff are trained to speak softly while in patient care areas. Inspect the wheels on meal delivery carts and other mobile equipment—do they squeak and rattle? Be sure that used trays are promptly collected from the patients' rooms and nursing units after each meal, and especially after the dinner meal; do not let such trays accumulate in closets or elsewhere. Work closely with housekeeping, environmental services, and maintenance staff to resolve patients' concerns about the appearance, cleanliness, and proper functioning of hospital rooms, spaces, and equipment.

The nutrition services department must be committed to quality care and service excellence. The following words of advice apply no matter who and where your customer may be (18):

- Rule #1: The customer is always right.
- Rule #2: If the customer is ever wrong, reread rule #1.

Summary

In food services, quality control focuses on the preparation and delivery of safe, tasty, and nutritious food. As a CNM responsible for food services, you must stay informed about various regulatory standards and facility guidelines related to food safety and patient satisfaction; set quality goals for food preparation and tray delivery; monitor and document how well your staff achieves these goals; and respond as needed with corrective actions. Putting standard procedures in place and training your employees to follow them will ensure continued success.

References

1. Famous Advice on Quality Management. www.adviceonmanagement.com/advice_quality.html. Accessed August 8, 2013.
2. Juran JM. *Juran on Leadership for Quality: An Executive Handbook.* New York, NY: Free Press/ Macmillan; 1989.
3   Deming WE. *The Essential Deming: Leadership Principles from the Father of Quality.* New York, NY: McGraw-Hill; 2012.
4. National Restaurant Association/ServSafe. Regulatory Requirements. www.servsafe.com/regulatory. Accessed August 8, 2013.
5. National Restaurant Association/ServSafe website. www.servsafe.com. Accessed August 8, 2013.
6. National Registry of Food Safety Professionals website. www.nrfsp.com. Accessed August 8, 2013.
7. Prometric. Certified Professional Food Manager Program. www.prometric.com/foodsafety/default.htm. Accessed August 8, 2013.
8. The Joint Commission. About. www.jointcommission.org/about_us/about_the_joint_commission_main .aspx. Accessed August 8, 2013.
9. The Joint Commission. *2013 Hospital Accreditation Standards.* Oakbrook Terrace, IL: Joint Commission Resources; 2012.
10. National Restaurant Association. *ServSafe Essentials.* 5th ed. Chicago, IL: National Restaurant Association; 2010:5.4, 5.9, 11.4.
11. Bauer S, Henderson T, Summers S, Brown G. *Refrigerator and Freezer Safety.* Extension Service West Virginia University; 2001:1-4. www.wvu.edu/~exten/infores/pubs/fypubs/136.wl.pdf. Accessed August 8, 2013.
12. NSF International. Safe Food Handling. www.fsis.usda.gov/wps/wcm/connect/83f3fe0d-636e-4025- 8646-a06c1e3d1c90/How_Temperatures_Affect_Food.pdf?MOD=AJPERES. Accessed November 26, 2013.
13. Cadoret W. Steer clear of common temperature monitoring pitfalls. *Pharm Purchas Prod.* 2011(June);(supplement):S1-S3. www.pppmag.com/article/914/June_2011_Temperature_Monitoring /Steer_Clear_of_Common_Temperature_Monitoring_Pitfalls. Accessed August 8, 2013.
14. NSF International. Shopping and Storage. www.nsf.org/consumer/food_safety/shopping_storage .asp?program=FoodSaf. Accessed August 8, 2013.
15. The Joint Commission. *2012 Hospital Accreditation Standards.* Oakbrook Terrace, IL: Joint Commission Resources; 2012:PC-22.
16. Puckett R. Quality management: American Society For Healthcare Food Service Administrators. In: *Food Service Manual for Health Care Institutions.* 3rd ed. New York, NY: Wiley; 2004:69–100.
17. Hospital Compare website. www.medicare.gov/hospitalcompare. Accessed August 8, 2013.
18. Capezio P, Morehouse D. *Taking the Mystery Out of TQM: A Practical Guide to Total Quality Management.* Hawthorne, NJ: Career Press; 1993:249.

## 5

Quality Management and Improvement

Nancy Hakel-Smith, PhD, RD, LMNT

Introduction

This chapter focuses on the topic of quality management and improvement, which is at the forefront of 21st century health care reform. To help clinical nutrition managers (CNMs) better understand the evolution of quality improvement (QI), the chapter begins with an overview of some of the driving forces in the health care quality movement. The remainder of the chapter describes QI methods and tools available for QI projects.

Drivers of Health Care Quality

The Joint Commission

As discussed in Chapter 3, the Joint Commission (TJC) is one of the key accreditation organizations for health care facilities (1). Operationalized by TJC in 1999, ORYX is a standardized set of core performance measures used in the accreditation process to evaluate the quality of health care delivery at facilities (2).

Centers for Medicare & Medicaid Services

The Centers for Medicare & Medicaid Services (CMS) has developed a number of QI initiatives, including the Hospital Value-Based Purchasing (HVBP) program, also known as Hospital Compare, which establishes standardized quality measures to evaluate and compare hospitals (3,4). A portion of CMS reimbursements to facilities is based on how their performance meets this set of quality measures. The two key components to this program are the Clinical Process of Care measures and the Hospital Consumer Assessment of Healthcare Providers and Systems (HCAHPS) survey, which measures patient experience of care (see Chapter 4 for more information on HCAHPS) (5).

Some of the HVBP measures related to discharge planning, readmissions, central line infections, and hospital-acquired conditions can involve nutrition care (6). Registered dietitians (RDs) can therefore demonstrate enhanced value to their institutions by becoming involved in improvement initiatives. (See Chapter 3 for more on this topic.)

CMS has also implemented a meaningful use (MU) program that pays incentives for effective and appropriate use of electronic health records (EHRs) to eligible professionals, hospitals, and critical access hospitals. See Chapter 9 for more information on MU.

Institute of Medicine

Established in 1970 as the health arm of the National Academy of Sciences, the Institute of Medicine (IOM) is an independent, nonprofit organization that works outside of government to provide unbiased and authoritative advice to decision makers in health care and the public (7). It is driving quality by educating health care professionals on ways to improve their health care systems.

The IOM has released three reports assessing the quality and safety of health care. The first report, *To Err Is Human: Building a Safer Health System,* was released in 1999 (8). This report focuses primarily on safety and recommends that health care organizations reduce errors in their systems that contribute to unsafe conditions for patients. The second report, *Crossing the Quality Chasm: A New Health System for the 21st Century,* was released in 2001 (9). In this report, the IOM states that "Quality problems are everywhere, affecting many patients. Between the health care we have and the care we could have lies not just a gap, but a chasm." This report extends the concept of quality beyond patient safety to include additional problems, such as overuse, underuse, and misuse of resources. The report issues a call for action to "improve the American health care delivery system as a whole, in all its quality dimensions, for all Americans." The third report, *Health Professions Education: A Bridge to Quality* (2003) (10), focuses on core competencies for clinicians.

IOM's Six Aims for Health Care Quality and Rules to Achieve Them

In its 1999 and 2001 reports, the IOM developed a vision for an improved health care system in which health care meets six aims: it is safe, timely, effective, efficient, equitable, and patient-centered (see Table 5.1) (9). The IOM advised that all clinicians in all health care settings should focus on these six aims and called for leadership in education, practice, and research to drive quality improvement efforts. Additionally, the IOM proposed that institutions put these aims at the center of initiatives to change organizations and redesign systems of care to achieve safer, higher quality care and reduce medical-related errors.

Table 5.1 The Institute of Medicine's Six Aims for Improving Health Care Quality

Aim	Description
Safe	Avoid injuries to patients from the care that is intended to help them.
Timely	Reduce waits for both the recipients and providers of care.
Efficient	Avoid waste, including waste of equipment, supplies, ideas, and energy.
Effective	Provide care based on scientific knowledge to all those who could benefit and refrain from providing care to those not likely to benefit (avoid overuse, underuse, and misuse).
Equitable	Provide care that does not vary in quality because of personal characteristics such as gender, ethnicity, geographic location, and socioeconomic status.
Patient-centered	Provide care that is respectful of and responsive to individual patient preferences, needs, and values and ensure that patient values guide all clinical decisions.

Source: Data are from reference 9.

Table 5.2 on pages 94–95 provides examples of how each aim relates to the performance of CNMs and RDs (9,11,12). When designing improvement activities, CNMs need to consider TJC and CMS standards as well as the IOM's six aims.

The IOM also put forward a set of ten new rules (see Table 5.3 on page 95) that health care leaders should use to guide the redesign of health care systems to achieve the six aims of safety, timeliness, efficacy, efficiency, equitability, and patient-centeredness in health care (9). By applying these rules, facilities can bridge the gap between what patients expect and how providers currently perform. The federal Affordable Care Act (ie, the health care reform act) has adopted many of these rules as a way to model value-based purchasing (VBP).

Table 5.2 Applying the Institute of Medicine's Six Aims for Improving Health Care Quality in Clinical Nutrition

Aim	Examples of Performance for RDs	Examples of Performance for CNM Leaders
Safe	• Use the Nutrition Care Process to organize the decision-making process when providing patient care. • Identify patient problems/diagnoses based on analysis of current clinical nutrition knowledge and practice. • Decide, select, and implement evidence-based nutrition interventions (10). • Use a standardized language for nutrition diagnoses, interventions, and outcomes to facilitate communication among RDs and between RDs and other health care providers (11). • Anticipate patient needs to make care seamless (eg, information is communicated across the continuum of care or when patients are transferred from one staff member to another or from one setting to another). • Use proper hand-washing techniques. • Work as an interdisciplinary team to meet patient care needs.	• Ensure that standards are established and staff are educated in standards to guide practice. • Ensure that the Nutrition Care Process and standardized language are accurately used and documented to (a) enhance the continuity and safety of patient care; (b) provide information suitable for computerized patient records and clinical research; (c) evaluate the effectiveness/outcomes of nutrition interventions; and (d) ensure reimbursement of clinical nutrition services. • Provide/expand use of information technology for RDs to ensure quick access to evidence-based resources. • Lead change for a culture of safety, and prepare clinicians for the changes in health care delivery. • Ensure that staff are competent in the IOM's five core competencies.
Efficient	• Apply standards of practice/care consistently, with no variation in the process (standards include all hospital- and department-specific procedures). • Avoid wasting time, ideas, energy, equipment, and supplies (ie, operate productively and efficiently at all times and manage services in a financially responsible manner).	• Ensure staffing plan is developed with appropriate number and type of staff. • Continually evaluate productivity to ensure services are operating in a financially responsible manner. • Develop a dashboard for timely feedback on performance measures to evaluate and track performance and quality of care/services. • Use a Plan-Do-Study-Act model to identify processes where improvement changes can be made in daily work.
Effective	• Provide evidence-based nutrition interventions (ie, integration of best clinically relevant research with clinical expertise and patient values) to all who can benefit and refrain from providing services to those not likely to benefit (avoid overuse, underuse, and misuse).	• Ensure evidence-based clinical standards are established. • Ensure quick access to evidence-based information/resources.

Aim	Examples of Performance for RDs	Examples of Performance for CNM Leaders
Equitable	• Provide care that does not vary in quality because of personal characteristics unrelated to the patient's condition or to the reason for seeking care. The quality of care should not differ because of such characteristics as gender, race, age, ethnicity, income, education, disability, sexual orientation, or location of residence.	• Educate staff to value differences and to achieve cultural competency. • Validate staff's cultural competency.
Patient-centered	• Provide care that is respectful of and responsive to individual patient preferences, wants, and needs. • Ensure patient values guide all clinical decisions. • Base care on continuous healing relationships, which directly affect what information is obtained, and subsequently the accuracy of the diagnostic judgment, care plan, and outcomes. • Inform/educate patients of treatment choices and risks, and involve patients and families in decision making about their treatment.	• Lead the development and implementation of strategies for improving care of patients at the bedside. • Study patient outcomes. • Study patient satisfaction with clinical nutrition services.

Source: Data are from references 9–11.

Table 5.3 Ten New Rules for the 21st Century Health Care System

Rule	Example
Care based on continuous healing relationships	Patients should receive care 24 hours a day, 7 days a week, independent of face-to-face visits.
Customization based on patient needs and values	Patients should receive care that is customized/individualized.
The patient as the source of control	Patients should exercise the degree of control they choose over health care decisions that affect them.
Shared knowledge and the free flow of information	Patients should have unfettered access to personal medical information.
Evidence-based decision making	Patients should receive evidence-based care.
Safety as a system priority	Patients should receive care that is safe.
Continuous decrease in waste	Patients should receive care that is cost effective.
Anticipation of needs	Patients' needs should be anticipated.
The need for transparency	Patients and families should have access to information to make informed decisions and information describing the system's performance on safety, evidence-based care, and patient satisfaction.
Cooperation among clinicians	Patients should expect cooperation and communication among clinicians and institutions.

Source: Data are from reference 9.

IOM Definitions of Core Competencies

The IOM's 2003 report, *Health Professions Education: A Bridge to Quality* (10), emphasizes that the redesign of health care delivery systems requires that all health professionals develop new or enhanced skills and roles. The report stresses that all health care professionals should be educated in the following five core competencies:

- Providing patient-centered care
- Working as members of interdisciplinary teams
- Emphasizing evidence-based practice
- Applying quality improvement approaches
- Utilizing informatics

Implementing the IOM Vision in Dietetics

To achieve the IOM's vision of the ideal health care system of the 21st century, CNMs need to understand and value the importance of applying the following strategies:

- Frame practice around the six QI aims outlined by the IOM.
- Develop a QI plan for measuring all six aims.
- Identify their role in helping RDs master the five competencies called for by the IOM.

The IOM's recommendation that all clinicians attain a different set of competencies than were developed in the 20th century is of great importance in dietetics practice. CNMs, RDs, dietetics educators, and the profession as a whole must ask, "Do current dietetics education programs fully prepare RDs for the scope of practice envisioned by the IOM for the 21st century?" Although the IOM identifies competencies that all health care professionals need, there are no established criteria to guide the development of teaching strategies or to evaluate practitioners' competencies in these five areas. One approach to this challenge has been described by Cronenwett et al (13). These authors clarified how each competency applies in nursing by using statements of knowledge, skills, and attitudes (KSA). The authors' goal was to describe competencies that all nurses, including advanced practice nurses, need to have to continually improve the quality and safety of the health care systems in which they work. However, when Cronenwett et al shared the KSAs for the five competencies with undergraduate nursing faculty for feedback, the faculty reported that they were not teaching those competencies to students (13). The authors also shared the KSAs with new nursing graduates, who reported that they lacked learning experiences related to the KSAs, and they did not believe their faculties had the competencies to teach some of the content.

Table 5.4 presents examples of KSAs that shape the IOM's five competencies for RDs (13,14). CNMs can use these examples to train staff or evaluate an RD's competency in the five areas. Faculty members can use the KSAs to develop teaching strategies and curricula for undergraduate and graduate programs in the future.

Table 5.4 Examples of Knowledge, Skills, and Attitudes for Registered Dietitians to Develop the IOM's Five Competencies

Competency	Knowledge	Skills	Attitudes
Patient-centered care	Describe how diverse cultural, ethnic, and social backgrounds function as sources of patient, family, and community values.	Elicit patient values, preferences, and expressed needs as part of clinical interview, implementation of care plan, and evaluation of care.	Value seeing health care situations "through patients' eyes."
	Describe strategies to empower patients or families in all aspects of the health care process.	Assess level of patient's decisional conflict and provide access to resources.	Recognize that patient expectations influence outcomes of pain and suffering.
	Examine barriers to active involvement of patients in their own health care processes.	Assess own level of communication skill in encounters with patients and families.	Value active partnership with patients or designated surrogates in planning, implementation, and evaluation of care.
Interdisciplinary teams	Describe impact of own communication style on others.	Demonstrate awareness of own strengths and limitations as a team member.	Acknowledge own potential to contribute to effective team functioning.
	Discuss effective strategies for communicating and resolving conflict.	Solicit input from other team members to improve individual as well as team performance.	Respect the centrality of the patient/family as core members of any health care team.
	Describe examples of the impact of team functioning on safety and quality of care.	Follow communication practices that minimize risks associated with hand-offs among providers and across transitions in care.	Value different styles of communication used by patients, families, and health care providers.
Evidence-based practice (EBP)	Describe EBP to include the components of research evidence, clinical expertise, and patient/family values.	Participate effectively in appropriate data collection and other research activities.	Value the concept of EBP as integral to determining best clinical practice.
	Differentiate clinical opinion from research and evidence summaries.	Base individualized care plans on patient values, clinical expertise, and evidence.	Appreciate the importance of regularly reading relevant professional journals.
	Discriminate between valid and invalid reasons for modifying evidence-based clinical practice based on clinical expertise or patient/family preferences.	Read original research and evidence reports related to area of practice.	Value the need for continuous improvement in clinical practice based on new knowledge.

(continues)

Table 5.4 *(continued)*

Competency	Knowledge	Skills	Attitudes
Quality improvement	Describe strategies for learning about the outcomes of care in the setting in which one is engaged in clinical practice.	Seek information about outcomes of care for populations served in care setting.	Appreciate that continuous quality improvement is an essential part of the daily work of all health professionals.
	Explain the importance of variation and measurement in assessing quality of care.	Use quality measures to understand performance and to evaluate the effect of change.	Appreciate how unwanted variation affects care.
	Describe approaches for changing processes of care.	Design a small test of change in daily work (using an experiential learning method, such as Plan-Do-Study-Act).	Appreciate the value of what individuals and teams can to do to improve care.
Informatics	Explain why information and technology skills are essential for safe patient care.	Navigate the electronic health record.	Appreciate the necessity for all health professionals to seek lifelong, continuous learning of information technology skills.
	Identify essential information that must be available in a common database to support patient care.	Document and plan patient care in an electronic health record. Use information management tools to monitor outcomes of care processes.	Value technologies that support clinical decision making, error prevention, and care coordination.

Source: Data are from reference 13.

When considering options for improving the core competencies in dietetics, the dietetics profession may benefit by studying the examples of other health care disciplines that have restructured their clinical education programs to better prepare practitioners. Many health care professions now require advanced degrees to enter practice. For example, pharmacy, audiology, physical therapy, and some advanced nursing practice specialties, such as nurse anesthetists, require a practice doctorate as the terminal degrees for practice (15).

The Academy of Nutrition and Dietetics, in collaboration with the Council on Future Practice, the Accreditation Council for Education in Nutrition and Dietetics (ACEND), the Commission on Dietetic Registration (CDR), and the Academy's Education Committee, held a summit in 2011 to explore a future vision for educating, developing, and advancing dietetics practitioners (16). The Council on

Future Practice final Visioning Report, published September 9, 2012, has defined advanced practice (17). Furthermore, CDR has been collaborating with ACEND and the Academy to develop and offer advanced practice residency programs across the spectrum of dietetics practice (17,18). Implementing residencies for RDs who complete an advanced practice degree program could help practitioners transition into advanced practice roles. These steps are important to begin to move the profession to the forefront of practice.

Advanced practice degrees may help RDs ensure that they stay current and master higher level competencies (19,20). RDs with higher level competencies are better prepared to meet the increasingly complex demands of patient care and to advance science in ways that benefit patients.

To prepare RDs for the future, CNMs need to develop and foster working relationships with other CNMs, university educators, other health care providers, and medical facility administrators, and collaborate with these partners to identify the various needs of health care organizations, educators, students, and dietetics practitioners. Additionally, CNMs may wish to consider the following:

- How can CNMs collaborate with universities to offer programs such as nutrigenomics to their staff and design potential collaborative research projects?
- In what roles should CNMs hire RDs who have a doctorate or experience in an advanced practice residency?
- How can having advanced practice RDs expand or advance clinical nutrition services?
- How can the CNM begin to use the KSA examples for the five competencies presented in Table 5.4 to teach and evaluate practitioners?

Institute for Healthcare Improvement and the Robert Wood Johnson Foundation

Founded in 1991, the Institute for Healthcare Improvement (IHI) is an independent not-for-profit organization that works with health care systems to accelerate improvement of health care worldwide. It primarily focuses on goals adapted from the IOM's six improvement aims for the health car e system.

Transforming Care at the Bedside (TCAB) is a QI program that was developed by the Robert Wood Johnson Foundation and IHI in 2003 (22). Additional information on TCAB is provided in Chapter 8.

The Role of Clinical Nutrition Manager Leadership in the Quality Improvement Movement

CNMs have a vital role to play in leading and driving improvement efforts in their organizations to achieve goals related to quality care and patient safety. To prepare for this role, CNMs must be educated in QI methods, measures, and tools and understand how the IOM reports, including the six aims and five core competencies, can guide their decisions about improving clinical and administrative systems.

CNM leaders should ensure that every member of their team is educated in both the skills needed to engage in QI efforts and the components of the IOM reports.

As leaders, CNMs should foster an environment that encourages frontline team members to bring forward their observations and ideas to help determine which care processes need to be improved. Frontline team members need to understand their roles and their responsibility for patient safety and QI efforts (one of the IOM core competencies). CNMs who do not feel confident that they can successfully lead QI efforts should explore the training and education opportunities offered by their organization.

Finally, to lead systemic change, CNMs must have knowledge of systems-thinking principles. While CNMs are responsible for continual improvement of processes within their own system, they must also understand how improvements or changes in their departments may affect other areas of the organization. When forming a QI team, be sure to invite health care professionals from other departments because they see the system from different perspectives and may have concerns about aspects of the process improvement project that you should know about.

Designing a Quality Improvement Program

As leaders of health care quality, CNMs must design and implement QI programs that define, measure, and report about quality while demonstrating compliance with accreditation and regulatory standards (see Chapter 3). The IOM defines quality as "the degree to which health services for individuals and populations increase the likelihood of desired health outcomes and are consistent with current professional knowledge" (9). Another, broader definition of quality is "doing the right thing, at the right time, in the right way, for the right person—and having the best possible results" (23). The goal of your QI program will be to achieve these concepts of quality in clinical nutrition and patient care.

Methods for Quality Improvement

The first step in designing a successful QI program is to identify a QI model or method that you will use. There are several QI methods that you can successfully apply to direct improvement initiatives. Before choosing a model, check with your facility's QI department or your supervisor to find out whether your organization has already adopted an improvement model, and whether the organization provides training in how to use that model. You should also inquire about any required QI processes and the timeframe for reporting results. You may also wish to ask your QI department for examples of well-done projects from other departments to emulate when getting started. Projects from ancillary services, such as speech pathology, physical therapy, and pharmacy, may be especially helpful as these departments often face challenges and opportunities similar to those you encounter in clinical nutrition. The following sections describe examples of methods for CNMs to use to help guide process improvement projects.

Plan, Do, Study, Act Model

The Plan, Do, Study, Act (PDSA) model (Figure 5.1 on page 102) (24,25) is a simple yet powerful tool that has been used by hundreds of health care organizations to accelerate improvement. The model has two parts. First, three fundamental questions are addressed:

- What are we trying to accomplish?
- How will we know that a change is an improvement? (ie, How will change be measured?)
- What change can we make that will result in improvements?

Box 5.1 on page 103 provides sample answers to these questions in the area of clinical nutrition. The second part of the model is a four-step cycle that serves as a guide for testing a change in the real work setting to determine whether the change is an improvement.

The PDSA model is easy to learn and use for improving clinical and administrative processes. CNMs can use this model to develop and test solutions (25). Once a problem or an opportunity for improvement has been identified, your next steps are as follows (24):

1. **Form a team.** Choose members who are knowledgeable about the process, including employees from other departments that may be affected by the process.
2. **Set aims**. Answer the first PDSA question: "What are we trying to accomplish?"
3. **Establish measures**. Answer the second PDSA question: "How will we know that a change is an improvement?"
4. **Select a change**. Brainstorm an answer to the third PDSA question: "What change can we make that will result in improvements?"
5. **Test the change**. Begin by conducting a small pilot study.
6. **Implement the change**. If the pilot test suggests that the change is an improvement, expand the test(s) and gradually incorporate a larger sample.
7. **Spread the change**. When you are confident that the change is an improvement and should be adopted more widely, implement it in all units.

Box 5.2 on pages 103–104 provides an example of a process improvement project that applied the PDSA model to improve the initial nutrition screening process performed by nursing within 24 hours of admission.

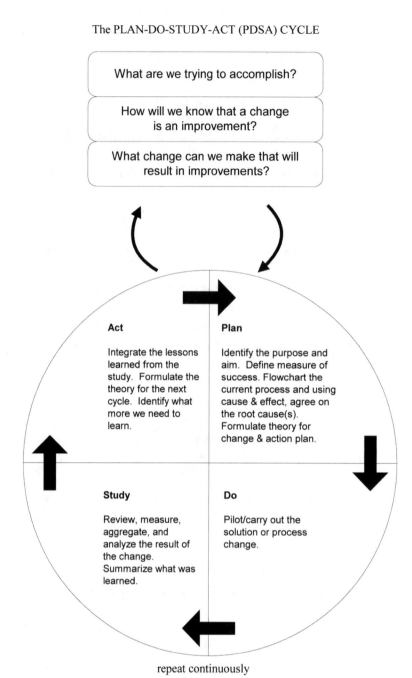

Figure 5.1 The Plan-Do-Study-Act Model for Improvement. Adapted from Langley G, Nolan K, Nolan T, Norman C, Provost L. *The Improvement Guide: A Practical Approach to Enhancing Organizational Performance.* San Francisco, CA: Jossey-Bass; 1996. Adapted with permission of John Wiley & Sons, Inc.

Box 5.1 Tips for Answering the Three Fundamental Plan-Do-Study-Act Questions for Improvement

1. **What are we trying to accomplish?** Answering this question sets the **aim** for the improvement effort that will guide and keep the effort focused. The aim statement should be time-specific and measurable (ie, what do you want to change and by how much). The Joint Commission's standards or the Institute of Medicine's six aims can be used to help develop the aims. For example: Ensure that patients receive timely nutrition assessments in our hospital.

2. **How will we know that a change is an improvement?** Answering this question requires developing **measures** to evaluate if the change led to improvement. Decisions at this point include: What needs to be counted? Who will do the counting? What data collection tools or education are needed? The measure(s) should relate to the aim. For example: For patients requiring a nutrition assessment, the percentage of patients' nutrition assessments completed per your facility's policies and procedures and standards of patient care.

3. **What change can we make that will result in improvement?** Answering this question requires using the Plan-Do-Study-Act model to develop possible changes and interventions. For example: For the aim of ensuring that patients receive timely nutrition assessments, the team could look at the workflow in the process for nutrition assessments. Using a flow chart, they could sketch out the workflow process to analyze the various steps in the process to determine whether they are arranged and prioritized to complete the assessment per standard. Then they could brainstorm to identify ways to change the workflow so that the process is more efficient.

Box 5.2 Using the Plan-Do-Study-Act (PDSA) Cycle to Improve the Nutrition Screening Process

A large Midwestern medical center implemented nutrition screening as a component of the initial patient assessment completed by nursing in the electronic health record (EHR). Clinical nutrition services (CNS) and nursing identified nutrition screening criteria. These criteria were incorporated into the initial patient assessment (eg, unintentional weight loss greater than 10 pounds in the last 3 months). When a nurse answers "yes" to any of the nutrition screening criteria, an automatic electronic consult request is sent to the CNS office.

The registered dietitians (RDs) developed a data collection form and gathered baseline data to assess whether the identified nutrition screening criteria resulted in appropriate nutrition consult referrals. For 4 weeks, the RDs collected data on all nutrition consults they received. Then the RDs determined and recorded each patient's nutritional risk level (eg, at nutritional risk or at minimal nutritional risk).

The RDs received an average of 70 nutrition consults each week. Sixty-seven percent of these consults represented patients later found to be at nutritional risk. Therefore, 33% of the consults received were inappropriate. In other words, the RDs were spending their time reviewing patient records and performing nutrition assessments on patients who did not require RD interventions at that time. The RDs classified these patients at minimal nutritional risk and delegated them to the dietetic technicians, registered (DTRs) to provide nutrition services.

(continues)

Box 5.2 *(continued)*

An opportunity was identified to improve performance to meet the Joint Commission standard of completing a nutrition screen within 24 hours of admission. This opportunity was addressed using the PDSA cycle. A process improvement team, which included nurses as well as RDs, was created for this project, and this team established the following aim statement: "To increase the number of appropriate nutrition consults referred to RDs to 90% within 2 months." The team also identified a measurement of improvement (the number of appropriate nutrition consults received divided by the total number of consults received) to evaluate whether a process change led to improvement in accordance with the six quality aims established by the Institute of Medicine (IOM).

In the Plan phase, the team studied and discussed the following:

- The findings of the baseline data collected by the RDs (percentages of nutrition consults that were appropriate or inappropriate)
- The screening criteria currently used and rationale for that criteria
- Nutrition consults that were inappropriate
- Research studies providing evidence of more effective screening criteria, presented by the RDs to justify recommendations to revise the current criteria

After reviewing and discussing the current screening criteria and the evidence for revising the criteria, the RDs recommended deleting some of the criteria, adding new criteria, and rewording other criteria.

The team predicted that changing the screening criteria would increase the number of appropriate referrals for nutrition consults. The team agreed that changing this process would improve service in terms of at least five of the six IOM quality aims: safe, timely, efficient, effective, and patient-centered care. The team agreed that these changes would be tested. The team also assigned the RDs to educate nurses on the revised screening criteria prior to collecting data.

In the Do phase, nursing staff were educated on the revised screening criteria. Then the initial patient assessment database in the electronic health record (EHR) was updated to include the revised screening criteria. The RDs collected data for 4 weeks.

In the Study phase, the process improvement team met after the 4-week testing period to review and discuss the results. An average of 70 nutrition consults were received per week. The number of appropriate nutrition consults (in which the RD determined the patient was at nutritional risk and required a comprehensive nutrition assessment) increased to a weekly average of 94%.

In the Act phase, the team agreed that the implementation of the changes led to the desired improvement. The team decided to continue with the revised screening criteria and collect data for another 4 weeks. If gains are maintained during this time, staff will collect data on a quarterly basis to evaluate whether gains are being maintained. The team will meet again only if the results of the data collection show a change in direction or new standards require a change in the screening criteria.

Note: If the results of this process improvement project had not resulted in improvement, a second PDSA cycle would have occurred.

Other QI Methods

Other QI methodologies include Lean, Six Sigma, and Transforming Care at the Bedside (TCAB). The Lean methodology aims to remove waste and error from processes. Senior leaders drive this QI method, which is focused strategically on organizational, rather than project-based, improvement. The Lean methodology involves five steps to maximize value-added activities (26):

1. Identify features that create value.
2. Identify the sequence of activities called the value system.
3. Make the activities flow.
4. Let the customer pull the product or service through the system.
5. Perfect the process.

The Six Sigma method for measuring improvement uses a five-phase DMAIC process:

1. Define opportunities.
2. Measure performance.
3. Analyze opportunity.
4. Improve performance.
5. Control performance.

TCAB focuses on engaging frontline staff and unit managers, an approach that sets it apart from traditional QI programs (22,27,28). For more information on TCAB, see Chapter 8.

Any of these QI models can be used successfully in clinical nutrition. As noted earlier in this chapter, before you choose a model, you should find out whether your organization has already adopted one. If your organization has done so, there are likely many people in the organization who can support you through the QI process. If your organization does not have a QI model, choose the one that will allow you to accomplish your objective and is simple to implement.

Selecting Quality Measures

Measurement is a critical part of testing and implementing changes in practice or performance; it is how you determine whether changes comply with defined standards and actually lead to improvement (29). Using measures for quality improvement involves three basic steps (30):

1. Identify problems or opportunities for improvement.
2. Select and use appropriate measures to obtain a baseline assessment of current practices.
3. Use the measures to reassess or monitor the effect of improvement efforts on performance.

Donabedian has created a framework for defining, assessing, measuring, and evaluating the quality of health care through examination of three areas of care (31):

- **Structure measures** assess the physical and staffing characteristics of caring for patients.
- **Process measures** asses the delivery of health care services by clinicians and providers.
- **Outcome measures** indicate the results of care.

TJC and other groups embraced this structure-process-outcome model of quality assessment, and it is still in use today. Box 5.3 provides examples of structure, process, and outcome measures that CNMs can apply to clinical nutrition services. The IHI (32) outlines the following three types of measures, which are similar to Donabedian's:

- **Outcome measures** (perspective of the customer or patient): How is the system performing? What is the result?
- **Process measures** (focus on the workings of the system): Are the parts/steps in the system performing as planned?
- **Balancing measures** (looking at a system from different directions or dimensions): Are changes that are designed to improve one part of the system causing problems in other parts of the system?

Box 5.3 Examples of Structure, Process, Outcomes, and Balance Measures for Clinical Nutrition Services

Structure measures:

- RDs with certification
- Staff competency
- Staffing levels (how many RDs per patient at nutritional risk)
- Nutrition Care Process
- Policy and procedures
- Enteral formulary
- Clinical guidelines/standards

Process measures:

- Percentage of patients screened within 24 hours
- Percentage of nutrition assessments completed within 24 hours
- Number of nutrition diagnoses identified for patients at nutritional risk

(continues)

Box 5.3 *(continued)*

Outcomes measures:

- Percentage of goals met for patients receiving ≥90% of recommended tube feeding estimated needs
- Percentage of goals met for patients consuming ≥75% of estimated needs
- Nutrition Care Process implemented accurately
- Policy and procedures implemented accurately
- Clinical guidelines/standards implemented accurately

Balance measures:

- When transitioning to a closed system for enteral feedings, make sure that formula waste does not increase (eg, make sure that change in formula strength and type does not result in liter bags being thrown out)

Quality Improvement Tools

After selecting a QI model and measures, you will need to decide on the best tool(s) to facilitate the project. Examples of tools that are available to help analyze, understand, and improve existing processes include the following (33):

- **Cause-and-effect diagrams** are graphic tools used to explore and display all the possible causes for a particular effect. Such diagrams define the sources of variation in the process and help identify the problem. Figure 5.2 (see page 109) shows how one CNM used a cause-and-effect diagram to identify the reasons patients were receiving inadequate enteral feeding in the intensive care unit (ICU).
- **Pareto diagrams** help identify the few most important factors that contribute to an effect and, therefore, warrant the most attention.
- **Run charts and control charts** identify and display trends in data over time. A run chart is a single line plotting some value over time. It can help you spot upward and downward trends and it can show you a general picture of a process. A control chart also plots a value over time but, in addition, includes an upper and lower statistical control limit. The control limits help QI teams assess the difference between normal process variation and true improvement (34).
- **Flowcharts** provide a graphic representation of the sequence of steps in a process. They are particularly valuable when the process targeted for improvement has many steps and many participants. Flowcharts ensure a shared understanding of workflow, identify components of the process that are error-prone (particularly at decision points and at handoffs to other departments), and then identify ways to improve the work flow. The flowchart in Figure 5.3

on page 110 illustrates workflow from nutrition screening through the steps of the Nutrition Care Process.

- **Histograms** are a type of bar graph used to display variation in continuous data, such as time, weight, size, or temperature.

Another tool of value to CNM leaders is the QI dashboard. It is a one-page graphic (that looks similar to a car's dashboard) of real-time quality and safety measures that can be used to monitor and improve the quality of all dimensions of organizational performance, including those related to TJC and CMS standards and the IOM's six aims. This tool automatically collects data from multiple sources, which means CNMs can use it to easily and efficiently access and analyze key performance indicators and evaluate whether progress is being made toward goals. Most organizations use some kind of dashboard; contact your facility's information technology department to find an expert who can help you develop a dashboard for your needs.

When developing a dashboard, make sure that it identifies measures that reflect your facility's key processes and outcome measures and are in line with your organization's mission and needs. One way to structure a dashboard is a "clinical compass" approach (35). Envision the dashboard as a compass with four quadrants. As a whole, the compass serves as a guide to maintain perspective on all performance areas, and each of the four quadrants represents a type of outcome for which key performance indicators are measured and displayed (see Table 5.5 on page 111 for examples that could be used in this type of dashboard).

Dashboards can be of great value for improving quality of care, patient safety, and clinical outcomes. For example, information displayed on a dashboard could help you monitor and communicate the percentage of patients at nutritional risk, the percentage of at-risk patients assessed within 24 hours, and the number of staff hours needed to provide nutrition care for these patients. Another type of dashboard display could help you monitor the top nutrition problems and interventions used, outcomes of the nutrition interventions provided, and the revenue generated from ICD codes for malnutrition.

Selection Criteria for Quality Improvement Projects

You can use the following criteria when selecting QI projects:

- Is the process aligned with the mission, vision, and strategic direction of the organization?
- Is the process important to both external and internal "customers" such as patients, payers, regulators, and senior leadership?
- Is the process associated with less-than-ideal outcomes?
- Is there an accepted standard to use as a goal for a process improvement project?
- Is the process safe, timely, effective, efficient, equitable, and patient-centered (IOM's six aims)?

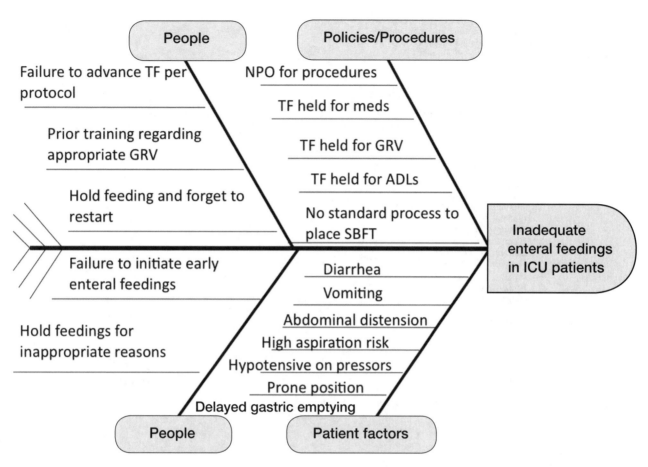

Figure 5.2 Cause-and-Effect Diagram. Abbreviations: TF, tube feeding; NPO, nil per os (nothing by mouth); GRV, gastric residual volume; ADL, activities of daily living; SBFT, small bowel feeding tube; ICU, intensive care unit. Reprinted with permission from Roberts S, Grim J. ICU Enteral Feedings. ABC Baylor Quality Improvement Presentation. Baylor Health Care System; 2009.

- Is there a nutrition component in quality measures that are publicly reported and mandated by:

    ◊ TJC/ORYX core measures, such as those related to acute myocardial infarction, pneumonia, or stroke (2,36)
    ◊ Measures in CMS's public reporting project, such as those related to heart failure or surgical care improvements (3,37,38)
    ◊ CMS measures related to hospital-acquired conditions, such as stage III and stage IV pressure ulcers and manifestations of poor glycemic control (38)

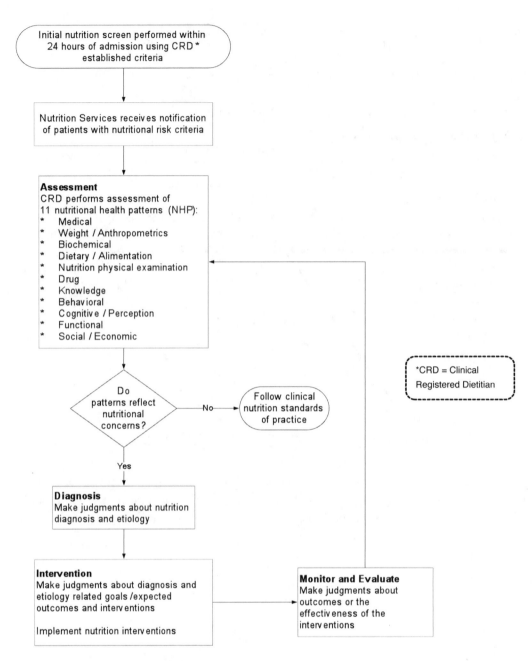

Figure 5.3 Flowchart Illustrating the Role of Registered Dietitians in the Nutrition Care Process

Table 5.5 Examples of Key Performance Indicators for a Four-Quadrant Dashboard for Clinical Nutrition Managers

Quadrant	Indicators
Clinical outcomes	• Percentage of patients at nutritional risk • Percentage of patients assessed within 24 hrs • Percentage of patients with nutrient-based lesions compared to patient census • Percentage of patients with ICD diagnosis for malnutrition • Percentage of patient outcomes met
Functional status and well-being outcomes	• Percentage of patients able to shop for food or have someone to help them at discharge • Percentage of patients able to prepare meals or have someone to help them at discharge • Percentage of patients receiving discharge education
Patient, employee, and physician satisfaction outcomes	• Percentage of patient satisfaction with overall nutrition care • Percentage of patients who do not feel they are engaged in the decision making regarding their care • Percentage of RD satisfaction • Percentage of physician satisfaction
Financial and resources outcomes	• Percentage of patients at nutritional risk to RD ratio • Percentage of RD hours in direct patient care per day • Productivity, salaries, and costs

Source: Data are from reference 35.

Summary

For the new CNM, the QI process can be challenging. To design a successful QI program, you will need to be familiar with the major initiatives for quality improvement (such as those from TJC, CMS, and the IOM) and identify a QI model/method, QI measures, and QI tools that are appropriate to the facility's resources and needs. Before choosing a QI model, find out whether your organization has already adopted an improvement model and can train you to use that model. Learn which standards your organization is held accountable for, and make sure that any changes you propose are aligned with the organization's mission, vision, strategic direction, and defined standards. Once you have identified a problem or an opportunity for improvement, proceed through the steps that will help you implement a change and evaluate and document its impact: form a team, set aims, establish measures, select and test changes with a pilot study, expand testing to a larger sample, and spread the successful changes widely. Choose tools, such as a dashboard, that support your QI efforts. With such an approach, you can be a leader in your organization's efforts to achieve goals related to quality care and patient safety.

Acknowledgments: The author would like to thank Janice Fitzgerald, RN, and Dr Judith Warren, RN, for their contributions to this chapter.

References

1.   The Joint Commission. About. www.jointcommission.org/AboutUs. Accessed August 9, 2013.

2.   Facts about ORYX® for Hospitals (National Hospital Quality Measures). August 2011. www.joint commission.org/assets/1/18/ORYX_for_Hospitals_1_25_11.pdf. Accessed August 9, 2013.

3.   Centers for Medicare & Medicaid Services. www.cms.gov. Accessed August 9, 2013.

4.   Centers for Medicare & Medicaid Services. Frequently asked questions: What is CMS? August 23, 2001. https://questions.cms.gov. Accessed August 9, 2013.

5.   HCAHPS Fact Sheet. May 2012. www.hcahpsonline.org/files/HCAHPS%20Fact%20Sheet%20 May%202012.pdf. Accessed September 27, 2011.

6.   Centers for Medicare & Medicaid Services. Meaningful Use. www.cms.gov/Regulations-and-Guidance /Legislation/EHRIncentivePrograms/Meaningful_Use.html. Accessed November 10, 2013.

7.   Institute of Medicine. About. www.iom.edu/About-IOM.aspx. Accessed August 9, 2013.

8.   Institute of Medicine. *To Err Is Human: Building a Safer Health System.* Washington, DC: National Academy Press; 2000. www.iom.edu/Reports/1999/to-err-is-human-building-a-safer-health-system .aspx. Accessed August 9, 2013.

9.   Institute of Medicine. *Crossing the Quality Chasm: A New Health System for the 21st Century.* Washington, DC: National Academy Press; 2001. www.iom.edu/Reports/2001/Crossing-the-Quality-Chasm-A -New-Health-System-for-the-21st-Century.aspx. Accessed August 9, 2013.

10. Institute of Medicine. *Health Professions Education: A Bridge to Quality.* Washington, DC: National Academy Press; 2003. www.iom.edu/Reports/2003/health-professions-education-a-bridge-to-quality .aspx. Accessed August 9, 2013.

11. Academy of Nutrition and Dietetics Evidence Analysis Library. www.andevidencelibrary.com. Accessed August 9, 2013.

12. *International Dietetics & Nutrition Terminology (IDNT) Reference Manual.* 4th ed. Chicago, IL: Academy of Nutrition and Dietetics; 2013.

13. Cronenwett L, Sherwood G, Barnsteiner J, et al. Quality and safety education for nurses. *Nurs Outlook.* 2007;55(3):122–131.

14. Cronenwett L, Sherwood G, Pohl J, et al. Quality and safety education for advanced nursing practice. *Nurs Outlook.* 2009;57(6):338–348.

15. American Association of Colleges of Nursing. The Essentials of Doctoral Education for Advanced Nursing Practice. 2006. www.aacn.nche.edu/dnp/pdf/essentials.pdf. Accessed August 9, 2013.

16. Boyce B. Future Connection Summit on Dietetics Practice, Credentialing, and Education: the summit at a glance. *J Am Diet Assoc.* 2011;111:1584-1589.

17. American Dietetic Association. *Council on Future Practice Visioning Report.* www.eatright.org/Members /content.aspx?id=4294967345. September 5, 2012. Accessed November 26, 2013.

18. Dodd J. American Dietetic Foundation. *ADAF Matters Newsletter.* Spring 2011.

19. Christie BW, Kight MA. Educational empowerment of the clinical dietitian: a proposed practice doc- torate curriculum. *J Am Diet Assoc.* 1993;93:176–176.

20. Skipper A, Lewis NM. Using initiative to achieve autonomy: a model for advanced practice in medical nutrition therapy. *J Am Diet Assoc.* 2006;106:1219–1225.

21. Institute for Healthcare Improvement. About IHI. www.ihi.org/about/pages/default.aspx. Accessed August 9, 2013.

22. Robert Wood Johnson Foundation. The Transforming Care at the Bedside (TCAB) Toolkit. Chapter 1: TCAB's History and Results and TCAB Video. www.rwjf.org/qualityequality/product.jsp?id=30053 &parentid=30052&grparentid=30051. Accessed September 27, 2011.

23. Agency for Healthcare Research and Quality. Your Guide to Choosing Quality Health Care. http:// archive.ahrq.gov/consumer/qnt. Accessed November 26, 2013.

24. Institute for Healthcare Improvement. How to improve. 2012. www.ihi.org/IHI/Topics/Improvement /ImprovementMethods/HowToImprove. Accessed November 10, 2013.

25. Langley G, Nolan K, Nolan T, Norman C, Provost L. *The Improvement Guide: A Practical Approach to Enhancing Organizational Performance.* San Francisco, CA: Jossey-Bass; 1996.

26. Bennett L, Slavin L. Continuous Quality Improvement: What Every Health Care Manager Needs to Know. www.cwru.edu/med/epidbio/mphp439/CQI.htm. 2002. Accessed August 9, 2013.

27. Robert Wood Johnson Foundation. The Transforming Care at the Bedside (TCAB) Toolkit. Section 6: Additional Resources. www.rwjf.org/qualityequality/product.jsp?id=30063. Accessed August 9, 2013.

28. Robert Wood Johnson Foundation. Frequently Asked Questions about TCAB. www.rwjf.org /qualityequality/product.jsp?id=30059&parentid=30052&grparentid=30051. Accessed August 9, 2013.

29. Institute for Healthcare Improvement. Knowledge Center: Measures. www.ihi.org/knowledge/Pages /Measures/default.aspx. Accessed August 9, 2013.

30. Agency for Healthcare Research and Quality. National Quality Measures Clearinghouse. Tutorials on Quality Measures: Uses of Quality Measures. www.qualitymeasures.ahrq.gov/selecting-and-using/using .aspx. Accessed August 9, 2013.

35. Donabedian A. Evaluating the quality of medical care. *Milbank Memorial Fund Quarterly.* 1966; 44:166–206.

32. Institute for Healthcare Improvement. www.ihi.org/knowledge/Pages/HowtoImprove/Scienceof ImprovementEstablishingMeasures.aspx. Accessed November 10, 2013.

33. Varkey P, Reller K, Resar R. Basics of quality improvement in healthcare. *Mayo Clin Proc.* 2007;82(6): 735–739.

34. Carey R, Lloyd R. *Measuring Quality Improvement in Healthcare. A Guide to Statistical Process Control Applications.* New York, NY: Quality Resources; 1995.

35. Hakel-Smith N, Warren JJ. Using Information Technology: Revealing Expert Knowledge from Clinical Nutrition Practice. Panel presentation at Food and Nutrition Conference and Exhibition of the American Dietetic Association, Chicago, IL. October 6, 2008.

36. History of CMS/JCAHO Measure Alignment. www.qualitynet.org/dcs/BlobServer?blobkey=id&blobn ocache=true. Accessed November 15, 2013.

37. Centers for Medicare & Medicaid Services. Hospital Public Reporting Quality Measures. www.cms .gov/Medicare/Quality-Initiatives-Patient-Assessment-Instruments/QualityMeasures/index.html. Accessed November 15, 2013.

38. Centers for Medicare & Medicaid Services. Hospital-Acquired Conditions (Present on Admissions Indicator). www.cms.gov/HospitalAcqCond/06_Hospital-Acquired_Conditions.asp. Accessed August 9, 2013.

Additional Resources

Academy of Nutrition and Dietetics. Quality Management. www.eatright.org/quality. Accessed July 19, 2013.
Hager MH. The federal case for quality: implications for dietetics practitioners. *J Am Diet Assoc.* 2005;105:1063–1065.

Lacey K, Pritchett E. Quality management and the dietetics professional. Nutrition Care Process and Model: ADA adopts road map to quality care and outcomes management. *J Am Diet Assoc.* 2003;103:1061–1072.

Learning the language of quality care. *J Am Diet Assoc.* 1993;93:531–532.

Letort N, Boudreaux J. Incorporation of continuous quality improvement in a hospital dietary department's quality management program. *J Am Diet Assoc.* 1994;94:1404–1408.

Porter CP. A new emphasis on healthcare safety, quality, and cost containment: how will this affect dietetic practice? *J Am Diet Assoc.* 2004;104:1667–1670.

## 6

Productivity and Time Management

Susan C. DeHoog, RD, CD

Introduction

National clinical staffing standards do not exist at this time. Therefore, it is a challenge for clinical nutrition managers (CNMs) to determine staffing needs. To create a viable staffing pattern, CNMs must analyze their facility's acuity, activities, and time standards. The goal of this chapter is to provide you with an understanding of some of the methods and tools used to measure, evaluate, and justify clinical nutrition staffing.

Acuity, productivity, and time management studies can help determine the clinical staffing requirements needed to provide daily nutrition care coverage efficiently and cost-effectively. Health care facilities must consider adopting staffing models that utilize acuity as the foundation for determining the appropriate personnel for the clinical nutrition department. The patient population today is aging and an increasing number of patients have more complicated co-morbid diseases that require a large amount of resources, including nutrition care. Staffing that reflects both patient acuity and service volume promotes patient safety and high-quality nutrition care. Acuity-based staffing can increase patient satisfaction and provide job satisfaction for clinical nutrition staff and other members of the health care team.

CNMs should focus on the following areas when assessing staffing needs: the facility's mission and vision, the population served, and operations. Assessment of department services should focus on clinical services, including the mix of staff competencies and skills, the technology used in the department, additional staff responsibilities (such as teaching and research), and the relationship between food services and clinical nutrition services. Productivity and time management studies can help validate clinical nutrition staffing needs. Benchmarking helps justify clinical staffing.

Benchmarking

Hospitals participate in benchmarking programs to help them compare their performance with the performance of other similar facilities (eg, level 1 trauma centers or freestanding children's hospitals), typically in the key areas of cost and quality. Such benchmarking programs provide varying levels of specificity in terms of types of performance compared. Performance is evaluated for the facility as a whole, as well as at the department and subdepartment levels (1–3).

A facility may elect to collaborate with one or more of the high-performing facilities in its benchmarking group. This collaborative approach will help the CNM determine ways to provide care and services at a high-performance level. Presumably, lessons learned will be applied in the CNM's own facility.

There are two general levels of benchmarking data: inputs and outputs. Inputs include staffing (measured in paid and/or worked hours or full-time equivalents [FTEs] paid) and expenses (labor, nonlabor, and total). Outputs include service volumes, quality measures, discharges, revenue, and hospital days.

Benchmarking data are gathered from a variety of sources, including budget reports, payroll reports, and self-reports of productivity and nutrition consults. Nutrition care data are consolidated into a single reported number of "consults" for all direct and indirect care with a standard length of time defined for one consult (generally 15 or 30 minutes). Benchmarking data reporting sheets record time in 15-minute increments, thus making it important to conduct time management and productivity studies in corresponding time increments (1–3).

Benchmarking measures of performance and functionality can be compared to outstanding practices from other like facilities. Areas that can be measured are quality, staffing, and time. Benchmarking also involves performing a financial analysis of costs, which includes staffing, and comparing the results in an effort to assess overall competitiveness and productivity. Quality nutrition outcomes are not being measured at this time (1–3).

The results of the data collected are used by upper management (the hospital administration) to compare their facility to similar facilities. Results also allow departments to discuss and develop plans on how to make improvements or adapt specific best practices (1–3). It is important for CNMs to determine which benchmarking program their facility is participating in and to understand the reporting process and how the data are used.

The first step for the CNM in the benchmarking process is to define standard time factors for each clinical activity the staff provides so the number of consults can be measured. It is imperative to capture all activities performed, including each step in the Nutrition Care Process (NCP). When possible, you should use a time study for this step. Figure 6.1 demonstrates how staff can track their performance for 1 week. The data may be in total units of service (using 15 minutes as the base) or standard times. A spreadsheet can be used for weekly, monthly, and quarterly summaries. Use of standard time factors allows staff to report only the number of each completed activity per month (3). For inpatient services, the total for each direct patient care activity completed by all staff is multiplied by the standard time factor for that activity to determine the total time spent for each activity. The time totals for each direct care activity are then added together to calculate the total direct care time. Indirect time (eg, time on rounds, time in meetings, time spent in community meetings) must also be measured and is often reported as actual time spent. Total direct time and indirect time are added together and divided by the number of minutes per consult (eg, 15, 30, or 45 minutes) to calculate the total activities or "consults" reported for benchmarking (1–3). In ambulatory care, direct and indirect care times are also converted to "consults." However, direct care is generally calculated using the number of units of medical nutrition therapy (MNT) provided. MNT units will therefore need to be converted to the number of equivalent "consults" as defined by the benchmarking program, as will indirect time (1,3). The total number of outpatient consults is often combined with the total from inpatient care, since benchmarking programs often report performance based on adjusted discharges. Adjusted discharges incorporate both inpatient and outpatient expenses, volumes, and revenue (1,2).

Benchmarking Log

	Screening	Assessment	Reassessment	Documentation	Rounds	Education	Patient Care Conferences
Monday							
Tuesday							
Wednesday							
Thursday							
Friday							
Saturday							
Sunday							
Total Minutes							

Figure 6.1 Collection Form for Benchmarking

Patient Population Mix

To determine the appropriate staffing levels for the clinical nutrition department, you should understand the patient population mix—ie, the characteristics of the population served that are relevant to staffing decisions. Patient population evaluations may include acuity level, average length of stay, types of diagnosis, conditions treated, services, and procedures.

To identify your facility's patient population mix, you can develop a nutrition acuity profile for patients admitted to the hospital during a defined period or periods of time and then project this mix to the entire fiscal year (3). This acuity profile aims to capture not only the number of patients who need nutrition care but also the degree of complexity of the required nutrition services. You should therefore determine how the facility categorizes patients in terms of nutrition complexity levels (eg, high-complexity vs low-complexity patients or high-, moderate-, or low-risk patients) and then work with your staff to track the number of patients from each category admitted to the facility during a short period of time, such as 2- or 4-week interval. Sampling can be repeated one or more times, if desired, and data from multiple sampling periods can be combined (3–5).

The goal is to determine the average percentages of patients admitted for each nutrition complexity level, with the total of all percentages adding up to 100%. The estimated nutrition complexity percentages are then multiplied by the budgeted admission levels to determine the number of admissions at each patient nutrition level expected during the coming fiscal year.

A patient population mix study can involve a prospective or retrospective chart study. For a prospective study, the clinical staff keeps a detailed record for patients receiving nutrition interventions. For a retrospective study, medical records personnel identify patients after discharge and determine from the records submitted by the clinical staff the percentage of patients who received nutrition intervention during a particular time period, as well as their diagnoses, lengths of stay, ages, and genders. The number of patients assessed by each registered dietitian (RD) and/or dietetic technician, registered (DTR) is noted. Figure 6.2 offers an example of a monitor for identifying a patient population mix. This type of study allows the staff to quantify the percentage of high- and moderate-complexity patients and determine whether selected variables can be used to create a profile of patients at nutritional risk. Such studies can also be used to determine where the high-complexity patients are concentrated (unit location). All components have implications for time management, productivity, and staffing (3).

After determining the patient population mix, determine the average number of direct clinical nutrition services required for patients at each nutrition-complexity level. Ideally, the clinical nutrition staff records the type and quantity of nutrition care activities performed for each patient admitted during the data collection period for the patient's entire length of stay. The result is an average of services per patient at each complexity level. For example, the average high-complexity patient might require an initial nutrition assessment, three follow-ups or monitoring and reassessments, and one complex education intervention (3).

Time factors for each nutrition care activity, which are determined from a previously completed time management study, can be used to convert per-patient

Patient Population Mix Monitor					
Admisson Date	Patient	Medical Record Number	Diagnosis	Feeding Modality	Discharge Date
3/29/14	Doe	1234	Short bowel obstruction	TPN	4/11/14
4/01/14	Smith	5678	Liver transplant	Oral	Pending
4/11/14	Jones	1111	Sepsis	TPN	4/22/14
4/11/14	Brown	2222	COPD	Oral	4/24/14

Figure 6.2 Sample Monitor for Patient Population Mix

average activities to average total time requirements per patient for each nutrition complexity level. Again, consider the example of the high-complexity patient and calculate the average time for nutrition care. If the average high-complexity patient requires an initial nutrition assessment (defined as 45 minutes), three follow-ups or monitoring and reassessments (20 minutes each), and one complex education intervention (45 minutes), the patient would require a total of 2 hours and 30 minutes (2.5 hours) of nutrition care (3).

Once the number of minutes required to perform a total activity is determined, that number can be converted into relative value units (RVUs). In the clinical setting, the volume of services translates into dollars (expenses and revenues). RVUs measure the volume of clinical services provided and can be used as a tool to determine how departments or facilities perform relative to comparable departments or facilities. For example, criteria from each NCP step might be assigned the following RVUs for high-complexity patients, where 0.10 RVU equals 10 minutes:

- Screening: 0.10 RVU (if done by nutrition services)
- Comprehensive nutrition assessment: 0.45-0.60 RVU
- Follow-up: 0.30 RVU
- Education: 0.30-0.60 RVU

The dietetics practitioner determines which criteria accurately reflect the care given. The RVU is assigned to the type of care and the daily frequency of the care. It is important the values remain consistent. As the number of minutes required for care increases, the number the RVUs assigned also increases as a reflection of the higher acuity level (3,6). For example, patients in an intensive care unit (ICU) may be on ventilators, have blood gases drawn several times a day, have medical statuses that are susceptible to change (eg, organ dysfunction), or have multiple lines, drains, and/or fistulas. Compared to patients in other units, ICU patients therefore require more time for nutrition assessment and nutrition intervention. Suppose the clinical staff requires 0.6 RVUs for the initial assessment of the ICU patient and sees the patient for follow-up every other day during a 6-day stay in the ICU. The total time devoted to this patient should be: 0.6 RVU + (0.3 RVUs × 2 follow-up visits) = 1.2 RVUs (2 hours). Time management studies will help determine the time allowed in direct patient care in the ICU. If the clinical nutrition staff spends 60% of their time in direct patient care because they have teaching or research responsibilities, each would be able to manage 12 ICU patients per week.

Acuity Level

Once a facility's patient population profile has been identified, the clinical nutrition staff can conduct an acuity analysis that follows the NCP. A patient acuity measurement system categorizes patients according to the amount of direct patient care they require. Acuity goes beyond a time management study to examine the care activities required, the time required for each activity, and the frequency with which the activities must occur to provide quality care. In nutrition care, acuity is an important factor for documenting nutrition productivity and determining staffing needs based on the patient population mix, thereby ensuring that available staff are efficiently and effectively assigned to the appropriate nursing units (7). A 2- to 4-week acuity level evaluation should be performed annually to determine staffing for the budget process (3).

An acuity system provides multiple benefits. The information derived from the system can be used to establish the nutrition personnel budget, and the data can help accurately forecast the costs of nutrition care services. By identifying the acuity of the patients, acuity-based staffing requirements can be documented and used to support staffing decisions. For example, acuity might be defined in the following four levels (3,5):

- **Level 1**: Minimal amount of time and dietitian expertise is required.
- **Level 2**: Moderate amount of time and expertise is required. Generally tasks may be delegated to the dietetic technician, if available.
- **Level 3**: A high level of time and expertise is required. Very few tasks can be delegated.
- **Level 4**: An extensive level of expertise and time is required. No delegation of nutrition intervention or counseling to others.

Figure 6.3 is an example of an acuity measurement for comprehensive/complex nutrition care. Acuity records for comprehensive care should be completed daily for each high-complexity patient until discharge, until he or she no longer requires a nutrition diagnosis, or until he or she has a Do Not Resuscitate order. Documentation of nutrition care should not necessarily stop when the complexity of care shifts from high to low. In these circumstances, the clinical nutrition staff may still be involved in the care of the patient. By following the patient until discharge, the full

Weekly Patient Acuity Record

Date: _____   **Patient:** _____

Diagnosis: _____   **Feeding modality:** _____

Instructions: Record the number of RVUs per day for each task. In the final column, provide the total weekly RVUs for the task. Use the final row to document total RVUs for the patient per day and week.

	Mon	Tues	Wed	Thurs	Fri	Sat	Sun	Total RVUs
Screening								
Initial assessment								
Intervention								
Documentation								
Monitoring								
Reassessment								
Discharge planning								
Education								
Total daily RVUs								

Figure 6.3 Acuity Measurement for Comprehensive Care

scope of tasks, care times, and frequency of care is established, which means the acuity study can estimate the time needed for all the tasks (3).

Productivity and Time Management Studies

When planning productivity and time management studies, these questions need to be addressed:

- What steps are needed to identify the patient population?
- Are clinical staffing needs determined by what is available or by what is needed?
- What steps are needed to implement a productivity study?
- How will the outcomes be measured?
- How do acuity and complexity affect clinical staffing needs?
- How do particular tasks, the time they take, and their frequency relate to staffing needs?

Productivity Studies

Productivity studies facilitate intelligent and informed decisions regarding comprehensive nutrition care. To contain costs, clinical staff must document that procedures and services are both efficient and effective. Goals of productivity studies are to discover all tasks being performed, estimate and/or validate the time each task takes, and obtain objective data to find appropriate staffing ratios. As the typical number of patient days declines and criteria for insurance reimbursement change, the focus on doing things correctly intensifies. An evaluation of current practices is therefore an integral part of the effective nutrition care program. Evaluations of current practices may indicate specific areas where role changes could improve the quality of the nutrition care provided. Findings from a productivity study may lead to the reassignment or elimination of clinical activities (3-5).

Clinical productivity can be defined qualitatively or quantitatively. Qualitative measure requires comparing services to accepted standards of care. Quantitative measure requires the selection of a method to collect data, usually in the form of a time management study. Time estimates can be obtained through time sampling procedures to define "normal" times for the performance of a specific task and/or NCP step. Clinical productivity studies should have an identifiable beginning and end; characterize activities, not skills and knowledge; be performed by individual staff members; differentiate between activities that involve different kinds of knowledge and skills; be neither too broad nor too specific; and be expressed in clear, unambiguous statements that mean the same thing to all staff. The clinical productivity process is defined as the ratio of inputs to outputs (3,5).

Setting Up the Study

An effective productivity study engages staff in the initial stages of determining productivity codes and establishing the estimated time/RVUs that each task requires. It is important that the RVUs remain consistent (3,6). This information becomes part of the time logs that staff members keep during the study.

All tasks need to be sorted into activity types so they can be quickly documented. For example, Table 6.1 lists clinical productivity codes for the RD and DTR. It is divided into patient care, support activities, and nonproductive time. Evaluating care in these three categories may offer a simple way to compare the performances of staff members or compare productivity at your facility with productivity at other facilities. Time estimates obtained through time sampling procedures can determine "normal" (or average) times per activity. The RVU, in conjunction with uniform definitions, enables reporting of qualification and output comparison. RVUs can reflect the scope of care required in both high- and moderate-complexity levels of nutrition care. The results provide information regarding the productivity of the entire clinical staff as well as each individual (4).

Each staff member must understand his or her code lists and how to complete time logs. A trial period study could be conducted prior to the actual study to make sure all staff are using the logs the same. Figure 6.4 (pages 124–125) presents a productivity log that tracks 15-minute increments as the benchmarking units of service. The log allocates space for 10 hours. The activity codes are printed on the

Table 6.1 Examples of Clinical Productivity Codes

Code	Description
Initial	Chart review
	Patient interview
	Diet history/food preferences
Medical rounds	Rounds
Reassessment	Chart review
	Monitoring/Evaluation
	Reformulating a care plan
	Documentation
Support services	Patient care conferences, phone calls, e-mails
	Quality improvement
	Literature review
	Project work
	Personnel evaluations
	Student/intern precepting
	Teaching of residents and nurses
Nonproductive	Coffee breaks, personal calls, waiting for elevator, etc

log to maintain uniformity. It has a space for work not accomplished. The work not accomplished should represent task/activities not meeting the established standards of care. To save time when the analysis begins, the logs must be kept daily and the number of squares for each code recorded (3).

Data Collection

The timing of the productivity study is important. The activity needs to be planned around a time when the facility is in normal census/circumstances—ie, do not choose the week of the Christmas holidays or the week you go live with a new electronic health record. The study should initially run at least 3, if not 4, weeks. This duration helps you evaluate the number of times a task/activity is typically repeated and will ensure that sufficient data about weekend activities are collected. Then the study can be done quarterly for a period of 1 week. A similar productivity study can be done in the clinic area at the same time. During this period of data collection, it is important to document the nursing unit total census. That data will establish the nutrition complexity of each nursing unit. Figure 6.5 (see page 126) is a data collection form that can be used during the productivity study. It also can be incorporated into the time management form. During the collection time, the daily census should be kept for each nursing unit covered by the clinical staff and then recorded on the clinical productivity log (3).

Productivity Log

Name: _____
Date: _____

Position: _____
Type of unit covered: _____

Day of week: _____

Task	Hour 1	Hour 2	Hour 3	Hour 4	Hour 5	Hour 6	Hour 7	Hour 8	Hour 9	Hour 10	Total units of service
Screening											
Initial assessment, high complexity											
Initial assessment, moderate complexity											
Initial assessment, noncompromised											
Reassessment, high complexity											
Reassessment, moderate complexity											
Reassessment, noncompromised											
Calorie counts											
Patient education											
Patient care activities											
Communications											
Students											
Projects											
Support activities											
Total:											

Figure 6.4 Sample Clinical Productivity Log

DAILY STATISTICS

Unit Census

	Total
# high-complexity patients	
# moderate-complexity patients	
# noncompromised patients	

Tasks Due Today

	Total Due and Done	Total Due and <u>Not</u> Done
High-complexity assessments		
Moderate-complexity assessments		
Noncompromised assessments		
High-complexity reassessments		
Moderate-complexity reassessments		
Noncompromised reassessments		
Patient education		

Instructions: For each hour of the day, record the time spent performing each task by entering a "1" in each small box (unit of service) for each 15-minute increment. In the Daily Statistics section, use the Unit Census to record the daily number of patients on the unit. Use Tasks Due Today to document initial assessments, reassessments, and patient education that should have been done according to the standards of practice. Use the column for Total Due and Not Done to document essential patient care left at the end of the day that should have been done according to the standards of practice.

Nursing Unit Nutrition Complexity Census				
Unit: _____		Date: _____		
Total Census	High-Complexity	Moderate-Complexity	Noncompromised	Unknown

Figure 6.5 Form for Recording Nutrition Complexity by Nursing Unit

Evaluation of the Data

The data for the entire evaluation period should be separated by the clinical position and by the individual person. The data can be entered into a computer program, such as a spreadsheet, by each staff member. The program can be designed to give the percentage of time spent in patient care and other activities by each person and the total time spent by each type of position. The program should be designed around the FTEs allocated. The analysis will show the individual's percentage of time in patient care, and the average FTEs allocated to daily care. The total FTEs can demonstrate what staffing is actually needed by incorporating the work not accomplished and any hours beyond expectations (eg, an 8-hour paid work day versus an actual 10-hour day without monetary compensation for 2 hours). The efficiency of each staff member must be considered (3).

The evaluation should assess weekdays separately from the weekend. When analyzing the weekend time, the level of care needs to be evaluated and the ability to achieve standards for providing care as defined in policies needs to be assessed. If activities are moderate or basic care, the staff assigned to the weekends should reflect that level of care. Consideration should be given to regulatory standards that require the same level of care 7 days a week in a facility. Standards of care of the nutrition department will mandate the staffing on the weekend. For example, once the patient is identified at nutritional risk, most regulatory agencies require a nutrition assessment be completed and documented in the patients' medical record within a certain timeframe (which is usually determined by the facility but must be justified). This should be considered when determining if onsite RD staffing is required both Saturday and Sunday or if on-call status is an option for 1 or more weekend days (3).

Evaluation of professional time includes the following:

- Average amount of time for NCP steps conducted in the patient's presence.
- Average amount of time for NCP steps not conducted in the patients' presence.
- The amount of time spent in support services.

- All categories of time spent by each staff member, each job classification, and as a total. Each staff position must be evaluated by job assignment(s). For example, an ICU dietitian could spend more time assessing high-complexity patients, and therefore manage fewer patients, than a dietitian covering a medical and surgical area.
- Cost of the service determined by the output/input formula.

The time spent in the NCP can be compared to the RVUs assigned. This could validate the RVUs or suggest that "short-cutting" is occurring due to lack of staff. When short-cutting occurs, the quality of care must be evaluated. This can be done through a quality improvement study.

Study Results and Outcomes

Results of the productivity study can help determine and identify specific tasks/activities needed to fulfill patient care responsibilities related to the established standards of care or mission statement, and to whom the activity should be assigned. Tasks/activities that involve flexibility and judgment require greater knowledge and comprehension. Results may have the following outcomes:

- Reduction and/or increase of FTEs
- Better use of support personnel (ie, technicians or clerks)
- Redesign of job descriptions
- Reevaluation of priorities in view of current staffing levels
- Cost-control measures
- Evaluation of peak admission days and appropriate adjustments to staffing

Results may reflect a need for flex scheduling, which puts the nutrition staff on the assigned work area at the most conducive time for patient care and interaction with other members of the health care team. Flex time can decrease overtime. If a staff member works more than the hours assigned, the time should be flexed out within a given period of time. The time should not be accumulated and flexed out by a whole day of work. Time not flexed may be lost, depending on the specific facility's human resources rules (3).

The outcome of the study can justify maintaining the current staffing level or justify more staffing to meet the mission statement of the department and facility and meet the established standards of care. When analyzing the data, look for inefficiencies in indirect and nonpatient care activities. Inefficiencies may include time spent in rounds that may not be necessary, attending patient care conferences that do not have a nutritional implication, and wasting time in unnecessary socialization. After analyzing the data, decisions can be made to eliminate activities or reassign them to basic care.

For the sake of simplicity, the estimation of time/frequency assumes the intensity is the same for each patient and each day of the week. The admission data will determine the intensity. For example, admissions/intensity may be greatest on Tuesdays, Thursdays, Fridays, and Saturdays. Schedules should be adjusted to accommodate the needs of the patients. Patterns of admission and discharge days must be taken into consideration in order to staff effectively. For example, let's assume the RDs at your facility are 100% efficient with their time and 80% of their time is spent in direct patient care activities. If your productivity studies show that each member of the staff has one new high-complex patient admitted per day, the time allocated would be 0.6 RVU (1 hour) for admission plus 3.24 RVUs (5.4 hours) for follow-up care. If the time allocated for follow-up care is determined to be 0.3 RVU (30 minutes), each staffer could care for approximately 12 patients daily (1 new and 11 follow-ups). The time and number of patient care activities would have to be adjusted accordingly if there were more new admissions than anticipated (3).

Existing systems used to determine the number and type of nutrition staff may not be appropriately based on the number and types of tasks required for patients who are nutritionally compromised. Therefore, it is imperative to evaluate current staffing levels and nutrition care requirements.

Time Management/Staffing Models

A time management/staffing model can help you justify staffing requirements to the facility's management personnel (see Figure 6.6). The model should demonstrate that patient care staffing is determined by patient acuity, census, and case mix, with the goal of providing daily nutrition coverage efficiently and cost-effectively. Clinical staffing should be based on the identified levels of care and must consider established department policies and volume of admissions. For example, when the screening criteria identify patients to be at high or moderate complexity, the policy may require that a qualified RD or DTR provide nutrition care according to the NCP and department standards. Reassessment policies must be considered. For example, unstable patients may require nutrition assessment every 2 or 3 days whereas stable high-complexity patients may be re-evaluated every 4 to 7 days. Weekend staffing requirements must be evaluated for maintaining quality nutrition care and department policies.

In determining professional staffing needs, the first step may be to develop a nutrition care matrix to determine the work hours for patient care, as follows:

- Determine the levels of care and who provides the care in each level, as designated by patient population.
- Determine the number of patients in each level.
- Determine the percentage of time allocated to each level of care.
- Determine the percentage of time spent with each patient.
- Determine the acuity levels.

The next step is to determine the work hours available:

- Estimate time for patient care.
- Estimate time for support activities.
- Estimate nonproductive time.

Time Management Model for Clinical Nutrition Department

Policy: Screen/assess patients within the first 24 hours of admission and reassess with documentation every third day.

Time factors:
- Screening: 10 minutes (if done by clinical nutrition)
- Assessment: 45-60 minutes
- Reassessment: 30 minutes

A full-time RD works an 8-hour day with 70% time in the direct Nutrition Care Process. For example:

Patient care: 5.6 hours
    1 new patient: 1 hour
    Follow-ups: 4.6 hours (8-9 patients @ 30 minutes each)
Rounds, conferences, etc: 2.4 hours
Total: 8.0 hours

<u>Staffing Model</u>
Bed size: 400
Occupancy: 80% (320 patients)
    Patients at nutritional risk: 50% (160 patients)
        High-complexity patients: 80% (128 patients)
        Moderate-complexity patients: 20% (32 patients)
Number of admissions per day: 60
    Patients at nutritional risk: 30
        High-complexity patients: 24
        Moderate-complexity patients: 6
Number of screens per day: 60 (5-10 hours)
High-complexity assessments per day: 24 (24 hours)
Follow-ups per day: 36 (18 hours)
Total hours per day: 47–52 hours

Figure 6.6 Example of a Time Management Model

Figure 6.7 (page 130) shows a 10-hour time management log that tracks activities in 15-minute increments, which aligns with the benchmarking units of service. The activity codes are printed on the log to maintain uniformity. There is space for work not accomplished, which may represent activities not meeting the standards of care. The log needs to be used daily and the number of squares for each code recorded. This saves time when the analysis begins. The log is not intended to capture all daily activities. The productivity log (Figure 6.4 on page 125) serves that purpose (3).

Time Management Log

Name: _____

Date: _____

Position: _____

Task	Hour 1	Hour 2	Hour 3	Hour 4	Hour 5	Hour 6	Hour 7	Hour 8	Hour 9	Hour 10	Total Units of Service
Screening											
Direct care											
Indirect care											
Support services											
Nonproductive											
										Total:	

DAILY STATISTICS

Unit Census

	Total
# high-complexity patients	
# moderate-complexity patients	
# noncompromised patients	

Tasks Due Today

	Total Due and Done	Total Due and Not Done
High-complexity assessments		
Moderate-complexity assessments		
Noncompromised assessments		
High-complexity reassessments		
Moderate-complexity reassessments		
Noncompromised reassessments		

Instructions: For each hour of the day, record the time spent performing each task by entering a "1" in each small box (unit of service) for each 15-minute increment. In the Daily Statistics section, use the Unit Census to record the daily number of patients on the unit. Use Tasks Due Today to document initial assessments and reassessments that should have been done according to the standards of practice. Use the column for Total Due and Not Done to document essential patient care left at the end of the day that should have been done according to the standards of practice.

Figure 6.7 Daily Time Management Log

Ambulatory Care (Outpatient MNT) Management

The need for nutrition education and consultation in ambulatory care is expanding. Lengths of stay in acute care have become shorter, and patients are discharged in a sicker state and may have been unable to listen and learn in the hospital. Additionally, the increased incidence of chronic disease in an aging population and growing public interest contribute to the demand for ambulatory nutrition services. Disease state management (protocols of care) is an approach that contributes to cost control and quality care. Protocols provide for evidence-based, cost-effective, and equitable care; define MNT in concrete terms; increase the effectiveness of care by promoting consistency; and are compatible with current trends in health care financing (3).

The appropriate size of the staff depends on the number of enrollees, clients, and/or members (covered lives); the type of facility; and patient education requirements. In free-standing clinics, the recommended ratio of nutrition professionals to enrollees or members is expressed as 1 FTE to a certain number of enrollees/members (eg, 1 FTE to 15,000 members). The exact ratio varies considerably, depending on factors such as specific disease states treated at the clinic, the percentage of members with those diseases, the percentage of members anticipated to receive nutrition counseling services, and the service delivery method. Specialty clinics (eg, clinics for cystic fibrosis, organ transplant, radiation oncology, or high-risk pregnancy) have traditionally had higher staffing ratios of RDs to patients than family medicine clinics. A ratio of new/initial assessment versus reassessment/follow-up will also have an impact on the hours available for nutrition counseling (3).

Staffing needs are determined by the following key elements:

- Percentage of time allocated for initial contact (billable time)
- Percentage of time allocated for reassessment (billable time)
- Percentage of time allocated for chart reviews, documentation, and communication back to referring provider
- Percentage of time spent in program planning and development, education materials, patient care conferences, meetings, education days, vacation, and sick days
- Percentage (or number) of no shows and cancellations
- Time for scheduled classes and time allotted for preparation
- Time for returning phone calls
- Use of electronic or telehealth services and group classes versus individual face-to-face counseling

Ideally, no more than 60% to 65% of the day should be allocated for direct patient contact and follow-up billable time, with the remaining time 35% to 40% of the day set aside for chart reviews, documentation, communication, returning phone calls, patient conferences, and other commitments. If a greater percentage of time is dedicated to initial or follow-up consults, other tasks/work may not be accomplished within an 8-hour work day. If approximately 60% of time is allocated for direct patient contact and follow-up, and 40% is dedicated to activities that do not involve face-to-face contact, FTE per day might include the following:

- 4.8 hours (60% × 8 hours) in direct patient care (eg, approximately two new consults [2.0 hours] plus six follow-up consults [3.0 hours] per day)
- 2.5 hours in chart review/documentation
- 0.2 hour for returning phone calls and patient conferences

The total number of hours worked in this example is 7.5. (Note that if more time is dedicated to initial or follow-up consults, the RD may not accomplish all work within an 8-hour work day.) Over the course of a year, this full-time workload could equal to 1,200 to 1,500 billable encounters with patients. These numbers assume the work year has 260 days (with adjustments for cancellations/no shows, vacation, sick days, holidays, and education days) and do not include services provided without billing (3).

Outpatient productivity assessment and staffing analysis continue to be linked with fee-for-service reimbursement, as most outpatient MNT visits are reimbursed at either a set rate per 15-minute increment, a percentage of the charges, or the cash price if the service is not reimbursable. As innovations in ambulatory care and payment programs such as accountable care organizations (ACOs), shared medical visits, and bundled payments (where health care providers receive a single payment for all care provided, both inpatient and outpatient, during an episode of illness) are piloted and gain popularity, outpatient reimbursement methods could be altered significantly (8). It is important for the CNM to keep abreast with the current evolution in health care reimbursement and how developments may affect how outpatient MNT programs are staffed.

For reimbursement from the Centers for Medicare & Medicaid Services, the following Current Procedural Terminology Codes (CPTs) have been assigned to MNT for diabetes mellitus and chronic kidney disease:

- 97802: Individual face-to-face initial assessment and intervention, recorded in 15-minute increments
- 97803: Individual face-to-face reassessment and intervention, recorded in 15-minute increments
- 97804: Group (2 or more individuals) MNT in 30-minute increments

Outpatient RDs should have knowledge of the billing and reimbursement practices for their primary payers and how best to meet the needs of the patients in this regard. As the complexity or acuity of the patient increases, the time it will take for initial assessment, establishment of nutrition diagnosis (or diagnoses), and reassessment also increases. Care for patients with language barriers and literacy challenges may take more time than anticipated, even if their nutrition care needs are less complex. It is imperative that hospital administrators and financial officers understand the total time needed for quality care of ambulatory patients. The following are examples of time recommendations for each level of complexity that can be encountered in the ambulatory setting (9):

- **Initial assessment and intervention—low-complexity** (ie, counseling with patient with one diagnosis, limited data to be reviewed, and low risk of nutrition-related complications):

  ◊ Preservice time: 10 minutes
  ◊ Intraservice time: 30 to 45 minutes (face to face)
  ◊ Postservice time: 15 minutes

- **Initial assessment and intervention—moderate complexity** (ie, counseling with patient with one or more medical diagnosis and co-morbidities, with moderately complex data to be reviewed, and a risk of nutrition-related complications):

  ◊ Preservice time: 15 minutes
  ◊ Intraservice time: 45 to 60 minutes (face to face)
  ◊ Postservice time: 20 minutes

- **Initial assessment and intervention—high complexity** (ie, counseling with patient with one or more medical diagnosis and co-morbidities of a highly complex nature, with highly complex data to be reviewed, and a high risk of nutrition-related complications):

  ◊ Preservice time: 20 minutes
  ◊ Intraservice time: 60 to 75 minutes (face to face)
  ◊ Postservice time: 20 minutes

Productivity Studies

The same type of productivity study used in acute care can be done in the ambulatory setting. Figure 6.8 (page 134) can be used as a productivity form, utilizing 15-minute increments in the chart review, assessment, education, and documenting squares. This study can be done quarterly to quantify which type of diseases/conditions involve nutrition consults and the average time dedicated to the assessment, education, and documentation of these patients. It will demonstrate the average patients per day per dietitian, data that will be helpful in the budget process. No-shows can be part of the data collected by adding another column indicating the no-show and the anticipated number of RVUs. This data will indicate the percentage rate of no-shows and how much potential revenue is lost (3).

Time Management

While it is important to track and understand how much time your staff is spending in chart review, consult preparation, and documentation, these are not billable

Ambulatory Care Productivity Log

Date: _____

Dietitian: _____

Patient Name	Diagnosis	Nutrition Diagnosis	New	Return	Chart Review (minutes)	Assess Patient (minutes)	Educate (minutes)	Document (minutes)

Figure 6.8 Sample Outpatient Productivity Form

activities, and they are therefore typically perceived to be of less value. Hospital administrators and financial officers typically want to see revenues, costs, and number of consults/visits. They may look at the billed charges as well as what is actually collected/reimbursed, so it is important to understand costs compared to actual revenue received.

If you determine the amount of time spent in preservice and postservice activities is excessive, some of the following improvement activities may help improve efficiency (3,9):

- Provide RDs with laptops and train staff on ways to review patient data and document assessment and care activities during face-to-face consults.
- Develop standardized paper or electronic forms to simplify medical record documentation and physician communication.
- Utilize support staff for appointment scheduling, reminder calls, prepopulation of some fields in paper or electronic forms, and billing.
- Develop spreadsheets to capture patient outcome data and have support staff complete data entry.

Outpatient RD productivity can be enhanced by maximizing the amount of time spent in billable face-to-face care. As there is no standard benchmark, the time spent in face-to-face care varies substantially from facility to facility. The CNM needs to consider the following when determining the goal for his or her department:

- Facility-specific benchmarks for other services, such as outpatient physical or speech therapy
- Payer mix and average reimbursement per initial and follow-up consults
- The no-show rate—if high, consider double-booking (eg, if the no-show rate is 25%, overbook by 25%)
- Other required, nonpatient care activities, such as participation in health fairs, marketing, and community presentations
- Availability and skill set of support staff
- Availability of technology
- Efficiency of office space
- Budget targets
- RD job satisfaction (when the percentage of time spent in direct patient care is too high, this may negatively affect RD satisfaction and increase staff turnover)

Figure 6.9 (page 136) demonstrates a format to track where time may be spent. All time needs to be accounted for to accurately assess staff productivity.

Daily Time Management Log

Name: _____   Position: _____
Date: _____

Instructions: For each hour of your shift, track the time you spend in the tasks listed by marking one box for each 15-minute increment of time. For no-shows, mark the estimated time you would have spent on the task.

Task	Hour 1	Hour 2	Hour 3	Hour 4	Hour 5	Hour 6	Hour 7	Hour 8	Hour 9	Hour 10	Total units of service
Chart review											
Assessment											
Intervention											
Documentation											
Program development											
Classes											
No-shows (estimated RVUs)											
Communications											
Phone calls											
Wait time											
Support services											
Outcome tracking											
											Totals:

Figure 6.9 Daily Clinic Time Management Form

Summary

As methods of delivery and payment for MNT continue to evolve, it is more important than ever to track and justify clinical nutrition staffing. Determining patient acuity is a key component in evaluating clinical staffing. As acuity rises, demand for clinical nutrition resources may rise proportionately. However, very little research has been conducted to verify this premise.

Selection of essential staff is vital to achieving the goals and objectives of the mission statement of the facility. It is important to develop clinical measures of staffing effectiveness that demonstrate patients' nutritional needs are being met in an evidence-based and cost-effective manner. A productivity study along with the identification of the population at risk will help determine the number and type of clinical staff needed to provide optimal nutrition care. It is imperative to evaluate staffing levels and requirements using productivity reports and time management studies in both the inpatient and ambulatory settings.

Time management studies should be done yearly in both the inpatient and ambulatory care settings. Productivity and staffing statistics, as well as any improvement in patient outcomes, need to be shared with hospital administration. This information may be used to justify the current staffing or the need for increased staffing. It is imperative that the administration comprehends the value that nutrition care provides.

References

1. The Joint Commission. *Benchmarking in Health Care.* 2nd ed. Oak Brook, IL: Joint Commission Resources; 2012.
2. What Is Benchmarking? Benchnet: The Benchmarketing Exchange website. www.benchnet.com/wib/htm. Accessed January 7, 2014.
3. Grant A, DeHoog S. *Nutrition: Assessment, Support, and Management.* 5th ed. Seattle, WA: Grant and DeHoog; 1999:44-54, 70–83.
4. Measuring and evaluating staffing effectiveness. In: Biesemeier CK. *Achieving Excellence: Clinical Staffing for Today and Tomorrow.* Chicago, IL: American Dietetic Association; 2004:85–117.
5. Simmons ML. Patient acuity staffing study. *Future Dimensions Clin Nutr Manage.* 1997;16(4):1–4,6.
6. Johnson SE, Newton WP. Resource-based relative value limits: a primer for academic family physicians. *Fam Med.* 2002;34(3):172–176.
7. Escott-Stump S. Nutritional acuity ranking study by diagnosis/condition. *Future Dimensions Clin Nutr Manage.* 1997;16(2):1–6.
8. Boyce B. Paradigm shift in health care reimbursement: a look at ACOs and bundled service payments. *J Acad Nutr Diet.* 2012 112(7):974–979.
9. DeHoog S. *Guidelines for Establishing Times for Ambulatory Care.* Seattle, WA: University of Washington Medical Center.

Strategic Planning

Marsha K. Schofield, MS, RD, LD

Introduction

Consider the following two scenarios:

Scenario 1: Mary is clinical nutrition manager (CNM) for a 300-bed local community hospital. She has been in this position for 3 years and feels like she spends most of her time putting out fires: rearranging staffing to cover maternity leaves, responding to demands from her director to increase patient satisfaction scores, trying to figure out whether a staff member might be available to speak to a community group on nutrition, and doing last-minute preparations for Joint Commission surveys. Every year when it is time to prepare her annual budget, she just quickly takes last year's budget and adjusts it for inflation.

Scenario 2: Susan is CNM for a regional home infusion company. After 7 years in the position, she has expanded the staff from three to five registered dietitians (RDs) with specialty credentials. She has expanded contracts with health care systems in the region and has achieved a 100% referral rate for nutrition consults for all patients receiving home infusion services. These successes are partially attributed to the fact that her staff is actively engaged in collecting outcomes data on all their clients. Eighty percent of Susan's time is spent overseeing implementation and regular evaluation of her unit's strategic plan. While Susan often faces unanticipated requests and demands from the company's administration, she feels comfortable using the strategic plan to guide her responses and courses of action.

Why is Mary enmeshed in solving daily crises whereas Susan can focus on the future? Is Mary just a less-experienced manager than Susan? Do Mary's challenges stem from the size and/or type of facility in which she practices? Would their stories change if Mary's and Susan's roles were reversed?

The key distinguishing feature between Mary's and Susan's stories is the presence or absence of strategic planning. No matter the size of the facility, the type of practice setting, or the years of experience in the role, a CNM's success depends on his or her ability to plan strategically. The importance of strategic planning skills is highlighted in a 2008 study conducted by the Center for Creative

Leadership (1). In a survey of 2,200 leaders from 15 organizations in three countries, strategic planning was identified as one of seven critical leadership skills; however, the same survey identified it as one of the top four weakest competencies for today's leaders. CNMs must develop strong strategic planning skills to meet future leadership requirements.

Whether you are an experienced CNM or new to the role, reading this chapter will give you a framework for understanding what strategic planning is, why it is important, and how to do it. The following information applies to CNMs working in all types and sizes of organizations.

What Is Strategic Planning?

Evashwick and Evashwick define strategic planning as "the process for assessing a changing environment to create a vision of the future, determining how the organization fits into the anticipated environment based on its institutional mission, strengths and weaknesses, and then setting in motion a plan of action to position the organization accordingly" (2). It is a process that enables an organization or unit within an organization to chart where it is going over the next 3 to 5 years, how it is going to get there, and how to know if it got there. Simply put, strategic planning is an attempt to shape the future.

Businesses have used strategic planning since the late 1940s and early 1950s. The concept first took hold in the health care industry in the 1970s, and has become more prominent as the industry has adopted more of a business mindset (3). The importance of strategic planning in health care is evidenced by its inclusion in the Baldrige National Quality Program's Health Care Criteria for Performance Excellence (4).

Strategic planning prepares you to move into the broader world of strategic management. Creating a plan is not enough. You must also implement and manage it to ensure that the intended results are achieved. The world continues to change during implementation. Therefore, you will inevitably face difficulties and need to adjust strategies along the way (5).

Why Do Strategic Planning?

"To be in hell is to drift; to be in heaven is to steer."
— George Bernard Shaw

Strategic planning, when it is done well, allows you to steer and have control over your future. Strategic plans enable you to do the following:

- Create organizational focus.
- Motivate the workforce.
- Build stakeholder support.
- Identify how to allocate resources.

- Set priorities.
- Make short-term decisions based on long-term implications.
- Be proactive, not reactive.
- Make your organization competitive.

A strategic plan helps you shape your entity into the organization you want it to become. According to Barksdale and Lund, "if done correctly, the strategic plan should be a document that motivates employees to achieve the plan's stated goals and tactics" (6). And, as Collins points out in his landmark book, *Good to Great* (7), there are three pieces to becoming a great company:

- Disciplined people
- Disciplined thought
- Disciplined action

Strategic planning is one method for achieving the latter two pieces.

Organizations can benefit from both the actual plan and the planning process itself. While the plan provides a roadmap to success, the planning process can help unite the organization, facilitate communication, and forge bonds among stakeholders. In addition, people learn through the process how to think strategically and make strategic decisions on a continuing basis.

You may have previous experience with strategic planning that resulted in a beautiful document that then collected dust on the shelf. This often happens when leaders expect the production of a plan to be the final outcome of strategic planning. In reality, the outcome of strategic planning should be the achievement of objectives and realization of a vision.

How to Do Strategic Planning

Step 1: Choosing the Process

When reviewing books, articles, and websites about leadership, you can find many models for strategic planning. Most are similar in nature. Your choice of models is not as important as due diligence to the process and implementation, so don't agonize over which one to pick. Recognize that both simple and complex models can result in both good and bad strategic plans.

If your organization already does strategic planning, it makes sense to use the model adopted by the leadership and look to experienced colleagues within your organization for mentoring. If your organization does not do strategic planning, select a model that makes sense to you. Choose a process that you understand; that is appropriate and feasible in terms of sophistication, complexity, and organizational culture; and that supports the types of outcomes that you and your organization desire. If you are embarking on your first attempt at strategic planning, a simple model may be best. Your planning efforts can evolve into a more sophisticated process as your experience and expertise grow. Remember the KISS ("Keep it simple, Stupid") principle.

Step 2: Planning to Plan

The best-executed strategic planning processes involve careful planning up front. Ideally, all strategic decisions, operational plans, and budgets should be completed by the time the fiscal year starts. Some key considerations in planning are discussed in the following sections.

What Are the Desired Outcomes of the Strategic Planning Effort?

While the desired outcomes of strategic planning may seem obvious to you, it is important for everyone to understand what you are trying to achieve. Ask yourself how you would complete the following statement: *Develop a strategic plan for the next 3 years that will . . . .* The following are some possible desired outcomes:

- Position clinical nutrition services as a source of revenue for the organization.
- Gain respect from physicians and/or the administration.
- Establish department employees as vital collaborators or leaders within the organization.
- Improve awareness within the organization of the value and offerings of the clinical nutrition services department.

Who Should Be Included in Strategic Planning?

When considering who to include in developing the strategic plan, ask yourself two questions:

- *Whose support will you need to ensure adoption and execution of the plan?* In other words, who are the stakeholders? The first group to consider is department staff. Inclusion of staff in the process helps to build their buy-in and commitment to the plan. The next group to consider is organizational leadership (within your department and outside).
- *Whose perspectives will be valuable to include and/or will enhance the quality of the plan?* One pitfall you want to avoid is "group think." While we often feel more comfortable in a conflict-free situation, your planning group should include individuals who can challenge traditional thinking and/or play devil's advocate as well as people who hold traditional views. Consider including individuals from outside your department and organization (such as administrators, other health care professionals, and patients/customers). Obtain as many different perspectives in the planning process as possible.

How Many People Should Be Included in the Planning Committee?

As is true for any committee work, the size of the planning group often affects its effectiveness. When you choose the number of people for your committee, keep in mind the first question we asked: What are the desired outcomes? You may also need to think about budget considerations when creating the planning committee. An optimal size for the strategic planning committee is 5 to 10 people.

Who Do You Want to Facilitate the Process?

A good facilitator will help ensure that the traditional and nontraditional thinkers on your committee work together in a constructive manner. Consider whether an internal facilitator (someone from within your organization) or an external one is most advantageous for your situation (see Table 7.1) (8). Ideally, you should not facilitate the process yourself because your staff may feel inhibited about openly sharing their ideas and challenging your thinking if you direct the committee proceedings. You want everyone in the process to have an equal voice and don't want to do anything that hampers open discussion and creative thinking. Using a facilitator also frees you up to participate in the planning process.

How Will You Implement the Process?

Working with your facilitator, map out an action plan and timeline for your strategic planning process. Your approach and timeline will depend on several factors:

* Whether you are revising an existing plan or creating one for the first time
* The complexity of the department or organization
* Your previous experience doing strategic planning

Table 7.1 Choosing an Internal or External Facilitator

	Advantages	Disadvantages
Internal facilitator	• Familiar with the organization, the people, and the issues • May inspire a higher level of comfort in discussions of sensitive issues • Less expensive than hiring an external facilitator	• May lack objectivity • May lack ability to realign the group if discussion digresses or implodes • May have limited time to keep the process on course
External facilitator	• May have a broad wealth of experience working with other organizations • Able to work with the group throughout the planning process and preparation of the final plan • Perceived as being objective	• Limited knowledge of the group and its specific issues • More expensive than using an internal facilitator

Source: Adapted with permission from reference 8: *Strategic Planning: The Roadmap to Success. A Guide for Affiliates and Dietetic Practice Groups*. Chicago, IL: American Dietetic Association; 2006.

- Whether necessary data are readily available
- The availability of committee members to participate and complete assignments

A strategic plan can take anywhere from 3 months to 1 year to completely develop. At a minimum, expect development to take 3 to 6 months. If you try to create and implement a plan too quickly, you risk sacrificing quality. If you stretch out the development process over too long a period of time, interest and momentum may wane. You may also fall prey to "paralysis of analysis."

When setting the timeline, consider whether you want to do everything via face-to-face meetings or complete some pieces outside of the meetings (eg, via technology). Will you expect participants to do any "homework" in advance of meetings? Will you expect participants to complete assignments between meetings? Understand that individuals involved in the strategic planning process will need to take time away from their daily responsibilities to participate in meetings and other activities.

Plan at least one face-to-face meeting that lasts 1 to 2 days. Pick a location away from the worksite so the group is free of distractions. If committee members carry pagers, arrange for other staff to take their pages so they are not interrupted. You may have appropriate meeting space within your facility or you may need or want to find an off-site location. Off-site meetings do not need to be expensive. Many community agencies, churches, and public libraries offer free meeting space. For both face-to-face and virtual meetings (including e-mail exchanges), consider adopting a set of ground rules agreed upon by the group. See Box 7.1 for a sample set of ground rules.

One effective approach to the planning process is to divide it into three phases: premeeting, meeting, and postmeeting. See Figure 7.1 (pages 144–145) for an example of such a staged strategic planning process.

Box 7.1 Sample Ground Rules for Strategic Planning

- Start and stop sessions on time.
- Prepare for and actively participate in discussions.
- Stay focused on the topic at hand.
- Exhibit courage when called to make tough decisions.
- Prioritize what is best for the organization when deliberating.
- Declare any conflicts of interest.
- Ask for clarification if needed.
- Respect different points of view.
- Listen when others are speaking; avoid side conversations.
- Encourage others to provide their perspectives.
- Respect time limits—they are necessary to achieve what the organization needs to accomplish.
- Stay open to new ideas.
- If you commit to a task, follow through according to the agreed-upon timeline.

Nutrition Department 6-Month Planning Process

Phase 1: Premeeting (complete over 3 months)

Action	Desired Outcome	Person(s) Responsible	Deadline
1.0 Conduct orientation session.	Participants will understand basic strategic planning concepts; goals of the project; the process to be used; and expectations of participants.	Facilitator, CNM, participants	
2.0 Conduct environmental analysis. 2.1 External trends: Provide list of trends culled from research and ask group (electronically) to rate their relevance. 2.2 Internal trends: Conduct a SWOT analysis electronically.	Identify top 10 trends affecting the clinical nutrition unit. Provide a clear snapshot of unit's current position.	Facilitator, CNM, participants	
3.0 Identify, collect, and review relevant data and documents.	Strategic planning participants will become familiar with this information to prepare them to fully participate in strategic planning meeting.	Facilitator, CNM, participants	

Figure 7.1 Sample Strategic Planning Process

Phase 2: Face-to-Face Meeting (1 day)

Time	Session	Session Outcome
30 minutes	**1.0** Introduction	Review purpose, plan, desired outcomes, and ground rules.
30 minutes	**2.0** Ice-breaker activity	Stimulate creative thinking.
1 hour	**3.0** Results of environmental analysis	Confirm top 10 trends affecting the clinical nutrition unit. Approve or modify results of SWOT analysis.
30 minutes	**4.0** Vision statement and mission statement	Approve or modify unit's vision statement and mission statement.
1 hour	**5.0** Strategic goals	Develop three strategic goals for the unit in alignment with those of the organization.
	Lunch	
2 hours	**6.0** Objectives and tactics for each strategic goal *(Conduct first as small-group activity, then have entire group review and rank options.)*	Identify potential objectives and tactics *(what* and *how)* for each strategic goal set under item 5.0.
1 hour	**7.0** Measurement system *(Conduct first as small-group activity, then have entire group review and rank options.)*	Identify potential performance measures for each objective.
30 minutes	**8.0** Summary and next steps	Review accomplishments of meeting. Determine future assignments.
	9.0 Adjourn	

Phase 3: Postmeeting (complete over 3 months)

Action	Desired Outcome	Person(s) Responsible	Deadline
1.0 Compile summary of meeting outcomes and distribute to participants for review.	Approve or modify draft.	Facilitator, participants	
2.0 Develop executive summary and final strategic plan document.	Final documents are ready for distribution.	Facilitator, CNM	
3.0 Finalize and launch communications plan.	Strategic plan is communicated to key stakeholders.	CNM	
4.0 Implement plan.	Clinical Nutrition Unit begins to operate under new strategic plan.	CNM	

How Will You Orient the Strategic Planning Team?

The individuals you invite to participate in the strategic planning process may or may not have experience in strategic planning. Even if they are an experienced group of individuals, they will gain from basic orientation that covers your goals for the process, describes the process, introduces participants, and sets expectations for participants. If members of the team have never done strategic planning before, you will need to expand the orientation to include an introduction to some basic concepts. The orientation can be provided in written communications (such as e-mail), a conference call, a webinar, or a face-to-face meeting—choose the communication method that is suited to the needs of your particular group.

Step 3: Identifying Your Mission, Vision, and Values

Before you can map out your future, you need to understand what the organization is, why it exists, and its desired future. This information is typically expressed through a mission statement, a vision statement, and a stated set of values. These statements may already exist for your department and/or the entire organization.

The mission and vision serve as guides in resource-allocation decisions. They should also provide a screen for evaluating opportunities and proposals and a guide for making decisions. Therefore, as the first step in the strategic planning process, affirm or modify existing mission and vision statements, or create new statements if none exist. When the organization as a whole has a mission and a vision, you may decide to adopt the statements for your department's use or personalize the language to fit your needs.

The mission statement answers the question, "Why do we exist?" It describes what the organization does and for whom. A good mission statement is brief (generally one sentence) and to the point. For example, the mission of a clinical nutrition department might be: "Enhance the health and quality of life of our patients through individualized, evidence-based nutrition care." Generally speaking, mission statements are not time-limited; therefore, you probably will not need to significantly change one that already exists.

The vision statement describes the organization's desired future (no more than 10 years out). It should describe how the organization will look when the strategy has been achieved. It is an aspiration, and as such it should be motivational. The vision is your destination, and the strategic plan is your road map to get there. One approach to creating a vision statement is to ask the group: "Imagine we are 5 years into the future and your most desirable organization has been created. How would you describe what the organization looks like?" One possible answer could be: "Our clinical nutrition services department will be the provider of choice for pediatric nutrition services in the region." If a vision statement already exists for your department, you will likely need to update it as you develop the strategic plan. If one exists for the entire organization, you will want to adapt it to fit your specific department.

Values statements define the organizational culture. They identify traits, behaviors, and qualities that should be displayed through decisions and actions. Values statements are only meaningful if they are translated into organizational activities and policies. In other words, the organization needs to "walk the talk," making its values readily evident to outsiders through behaviors and actions. If the overall organization has values statements, you should not change them for your department. After all, your department culture should blend in with the larger culture. If the organization does not have values statements, you should develop them for your department to communicate to your staff and others the behaviors that are considered important as you conduct your business.

Step 4: Environmental Analysis

The next step in strategic planning involves understanding the internal and external environments and how they might affect your ability to achieve your desired future. This step initiates what is commonly referred to as a SWOT (strengths, weaknesses, opportunities, and threats) analysis. A SWOT analysis is designed to help the group identify and understand the department's current state so you can determine what actions will be needed to take the department to its desired future. The analysis should form the basis for developing your goals and strategies. Be candid and realistic in your SWOT analysis. There is nothing to be gained by putting blinders on.

The external environment is defined as the industry or segment in which the organization competes, its competitors, its markets, and other relevant environmental trends and changes. You need to understand how the relevant environment is changing and might change in the future. When analyzing the external environment, consider four important forces as they relate to the health care industry (9):

- Social forces—eg, the aging population
- Economic forces—eg, a downturn in the economy
- Political forces—eg, health care reform
- Technological innovations—eg, electronic care processes, such as e-prescribing and telehealth

Many sources of information help you analyze the external environment. For example, the Academy of Nutrition and Dietetics conducts and publishes an environmental scan on a regular basis (10), and the Institute for Alternative Futures (11) develops future scenarios for health care. Professional and industry journals and other publications may also provide useful information, and your organization may conduct market research that would aid your analysis. Last, you can gather your own data by conducting personal interviews with key industry leaders within and outside your organization.

Your analysis of the internal environment should examine the following items:

- Financial performance and condition
- Organizational/departmental capabilities, including facilities, technologies, staff competencies, and processes
- Competitive strengths
- Organizational culture

- Management and leadership capabilities
- Strengths and weaknesses—that is, resources or capabilities that help the organization accomplish its mission *and* deficiencies in resources and capabilities that hinder the organization's ability to accomplish its mission
- Opportunities and threats—that is, forces and events in the external environment that create new markets or need for services or might limit or interfere with the organization's efforts to accomplish its mission

A strong internal analysis will draw from both quantitative and qualitative data. Some possible sources of information include accreditation surveys, patient satisfaction surveys, employee satisfaction surveys, performance improvement data, financial reports (including billing and revenue data), benchmarking data, staffing patterns, productivity data, patient acuity data, personal interviews (eg, feedback from physicians, other health professionals, and leadership staff), focus groups (eg, feedback from clients), and data from organization-wide strategic planning efforts. Asking others within your organization for input during this stage of the process may showcase your leadership skills to key decision makers and set the stage for needed support when it comes time to ask for resources and execute your strategic plan.

As you do your internal assessment, try to not get bogged down in analyzing the past. Don't make historical performance a point of major focus; instead, look at the past just enough to learn for the future (3). Also keep in mind that the effectiveness of your strategic plan depends on the quality, and not necessarily the quantity, of the data used to build tactics. Before you spend too much time collecting data that you don't need, ask yourself why you need the information and how you will use it.

The following questions about internal and external environments can help guide your SWOT analysis:

- What are the expectations of your patients/clients and stakeholders?
- What are the current and future requirements and opportunities of the health care market?
- What are the opportunities for innovation?
- What are your unit's core competencies?
- How does your unit's performance compare to that of your competitors and similar organizations?
- What innovations or changes might affect your health care services and how you operate? For example, how is technology likely to affect future operations?
- What are your workforce development and hiring needs?
- What are the potential financial, societal, ethical, regulatory, technological, and security risks and opportunities?
- What is the current state of the local, national, or global economy? What economic trends seem likely in the future?
- What changes are taking place in your parent organization?

Step 5: Establishing Goals

Now that the planning group has developed a clear picture of the current environment, the state of affairs, and the desired future, it should formulate goals. Goals define in a broad sense what you want to achieve. They are global statements for the duration of the plan that identify important endpoints that fulfill the strategic vision.

There is no magic number of goals. A group that is new to strategic planning should focus on a small number of key goals (1-3). Barring some major, unanticipated change in the environment, goals generally remain stable over the life of the plan. The following are examples of goals:

- Position clinical nutrition services for inclusion in a health system's new accountable care organization. (Fill in the name of the specific system.)
- Use technology to enhance the efficiency and cost-effectiveness of clinical nutrition services.

Step 6: Establishing Objectives/Strategies

"A goal without a plan is just a wish."

—Antoine de Saint-Exupery

How are you going to achieve the goals? Objectives (or strategies) break goals into specific activities that need to be completed to help you reach your goals. They are your game plan. Objectives should answer the questions "What" and "How." The results of your SWOT analysis should drive development of the objectives.

One technique for developing objectives is the TOWS matrix (see Figure 7.2). This tool integrates the SWOT analysis to come up with objectives that take advantage of strengths and opportunities, minimize or downplay weaknesses, and counter threats (12). S-O strategies allow you to pursue opportunities that capitalize on the department's strengths. W-O strategies are ways to overcome the department's weaknesses and pursue opportunities. S-T strategies are ways that the department can use its strengths to minimize its vulnerability to external threats. Last, W-T strategies prevent the department's weaknesses from making it susceptible to external threats. Keep in mind that you do not need to develop objectives to fit all four quadrants. Rather, use the matrix as a guide for brainstorming.

	Strengths	Weaknesses
Opportunities	S–O strategies	W–O strategies
Threats	S–T strategies	W–T strategies

Figure 7.2 TOWS Matrix

Since every organization has resource limitations, you will need to prioritize your objectives and determine which ones deliver the biggest bang for the buck. Typical priorities include the following (6):

- Revenue generation
- Competitive advantage
- Customer satisfaction
- Public perception/reputation
- Safety
- Regulatory compliance
- Labor availability
- Employee satisfaction
- Leading edge in marketplace
- Technological development
- Resource availability
- Operational efficiencies

Your objectives should match your priorities and align with your vision. Keep in mind that your objectives should not be set in stone and may need to be refined over time. Some examples of objectives are as follows:

- Improve continuity of care through implementation of electronic health records (EHRs).
- Increase outpatient revenue for nutrition services through expanded marketing efforts.
- Build staff expertise in pediatric weight management.

Step 7: Establishing Tactics

Tactics are the specific steps or short-term activities needed to meet the objectives. Tactics should answer the question, "Who is going to do what when?"

Tactics should be the most flexible part of the plan. Based on new information, changes in the internal or external environment, or the outcomes achieved, tactics may be added, abandoned, or revised. You will gain nothing by blindly clinging to tactics that do not support objectives. As you define your tactics, be sure to specify the resources needed to complete the activity. Figure 7.3 provides a sample form to help your group develop tactics for each objective (8). The following are examples of tactics related to the objectives listed previously for step 6:

- By end of first quarter, the nutrition informaticist to work with software vendor to map out EHR implementation timeline.
- CNM to meet with marketing department by June 1 to design marketing brochure.
- Sally Smith, RD, to attend March Commission on Dietetic Registration Certificate of Training in Childhood and Adolescent Weight Management workshop.

Tactics Plan

Goal: _____

Objective: _____

Instructions: Use this form as a template to develop a plan of action for each objective. Keep copies handy to bring to meetings for review and to update regularly. You may decide to develop new or revised action plans over time. This worksheet can be used in the development of tactics and to review progress of each tactic throughout the program year. This worksheet can also be used as a tool to update and modify tactics for annual program planning.

Tactics/Action Steps *What Will Be Done?*	Resources *Funding/Time/ People/Materials*	Responsibilities *Who Will Do It?*	Timeline *By When (Day/Month)*	Progress
1.				
2.				
3.				
4.				
5.				
6.				
7.				
8.				
9.				
10.				

Figure 7.3 Tactics Planning Worksheet. Source: Adapted with permission from reference 8: *Strategic Planning: The Roadmap to Success. A Guide for Affiliates and Dietetic Practice Groups.* Chicago, IL: American Dietetic Association; 2006.

Before finalizing the objective and tactics, it is a good idea to "test" them against some agreed-upon criteria, such as the following:

- Do the objective and tactics help us fulfill our mission?
- Is this tactic related to our goals and objectives?
- Do we have or can we obtain the resources to meet our objective?
- Is the strategy measurable and are its results meaningful to the organization?

Step 8: Measuring Success

The final component of the strategic plan is the measurement system. You need to know whether your strategy is working and whether you are achieving your goals. Define indicators that will be monitored to measure progress. Good performance measures focus employees' attention on the factors that matter most to success. The indicators should focus on outcomes (accomplishments), not processes (the work that was done). In other words, the measurement system should not simply evaluate whether a tactic was completed; it must also tell you whether the tactic achieved the desired goal. For example, if the goal is to use technology to enhance the efficiency and cost-effectiveness of clinical nutrition services, "use of technology" is a tactic and "efficiency and cost-effectiveness" are outcomes. In this situation, you could use a combination of productivity data, quality measures, and financial data (expenses) as indicators. The measurement system should define the indicators, target values, how the information will be collected, who will collect it, and how often the indicators will be evaluated. Figure 7.4 provides a template for your measurement system.

Step 9: Communicating the Plan

Your strategic plan can be a strong marketing tool for your organization. It can let internal and external stakeholders know who you are and what you are striving to achieve. As such, a strategic plan can be used to build commitment, support, and potentially even funding for your efforts. It also can help you achieve recognition and respect. But it cannot do any of these things if it is not shared.

Before you can share the plan, it needs to be captured in writing. The final strategic plan document should include the following items:

- Executive summary of the plan (rationale for preparation of the plan; background on process used; major findings; major recommendations)
- Mission, vision, and values
- Outcomes, goals, and objectives
- Tactics and resources
- Commitment/authorization from upper management

The communication plan should not be an afterthought. Instead, start developing it at the beginning of the strategic planning process, taking care to define what types of information are going to be shared, the audience(s) for this information, and the means and timing of communications. The communications plan should

Strategic Plan Measurement System				
Goal:				
Indicator	Target Value	Data Collection		Frequency
		Who?	How?	

Goal:				
Indicator	Target Value	Data Collection		Frequency
		Who?	How?	

Figure 7.4 Measurement System Worksheet

span the life of the strategic plan. In addition to announcing the launch of the plan, share your progress and results when you reach milestones or key points in time. At a minimum, you should communicate results annually. Tailor what you share and how you share it to the target audience. Put yourself in their shoes and ask, "What's in it for me (WIIFM)?" For each piece of the plan, develop a few key talking points that you and your staff can use when communicating with stakeholders. See Figure 7.5 for a worksheet you can use to develop your communication plan (8).

Step 10: Monitoring the Plan

Your strategic plan will go nowhere if you fail to develop a monitoring plan that defines both scheduled and unscheduled times for evaluating progress and making "course corrections" (ie, change tactics). As you create your monitoring schedule, consider your measurement indicators and how frequently that information will be available for review. For example, if most of the information is reported on a quarterly basis, there is no point in monitoring the plan on a monthly basis.

Scheduled review should occur at least once a year and include a limited update about the environmental assessment, modification of goals, new or revised objectives and tactics, and assessment of progress. For the annual review, ask the team the following questions:

- What are we trying to achieve?
- Are the objectives still relevant given the current environment?
- Do we need to add or delete any objectives?
- What is needed to successfully execute the plan?

Keep in mind that a strategy could be working even if the objectives have not been met. Consider the following possibilities:

- Was the strategy appropriate but poorly executed?
- Did we underestimate how long the strategy would take?
- Were our objectives too ambitious or otherwise unreasonable?

During the strategic planning process, the team should identify triggers for revisiting the plan at times other than the scheduled reviews. Triggers are events or results that, if they occur, lead you and your team to discuss whether "course corrections" are indicated. For example, an organizational merger or a change in the facility's software might trigger a review. An additional approach to consider is contingency planning, where the team anticipates what could change in the future and proactively identifies ways to address such a change.

Communication Plan

Directions: Use the provided template to create a communication plan that answers the following questions:

- With whom do you want to communicate?
- Why do you want to communicate?
- What do you want to communicate?
- How do you want to communicate?
- When do you want to communicate?
- Who will be responsible for the communication?

Stakeholders for Communication (Identify groups and individuals who need communication updates)	Objectives to Be Communicated (What you plan to accomplish with the communication)	Content of Communication (General types of information)	Method of Communication (Oral presentations, written reports or communiqués, electronic communiqués, etc)	Timeline (Frequency of communication)	Responsibility for Communication (Identify person or group)

Figure 7.5 Communication Plan Worksheet. Source: Adapted with permission from reference 8: Strategic Planning: *The Roadmap to Success. A Guide for Affiliates and Dietetic Practice Groups.* Chicago, IL: American Dietetic Association; 2006.

Implementing the Plan

"Vision without execution is hallucination."

—THOMAS EDISON

The strategic planning process does not end once the plan is written. In fact, the work has just begun. The best plan is worthless if it is not executed (13). Your job now is to inspire and lead your team towards realization of the defined future.

The best way to ensure that the plan does not collect dust on a shelf is to integrate it directly into department operations. The strategic plan should drive all aspects of department management, forming the basis of an ongoing cycle of implementation, assessment, refinement, implementation, reassessment, and so on. The department's infrastructure needs to be aligned with the plan in terms of staffing and daily operations. For example, measurement indicators should be part of your performance improvement system. Include periodic monitoring of the strategic plan as a standard agenda item for staff meetings. Require staff to set goals related to the strategic plan as part of their annual performance reviews (and do so for yourself—hold yourself accountable for implementation of the plan). Use the strategic plan on an annual basis to design the department budget. Overall, the strategic plan should provide a framework for daily decision making. Also remember to celebrate achieving specific milestones along the way; such commemorations help keep staff engaged in the plan and motivated. Figure 7.6 provides a sample tool that you can use to monitor progress.

Tips for Success

As you embark on strategic planning for your department, there are several key things you can do to increase the likelihood of success in achieving your vision. Some of these ideas have already been mentioned, but they bear repeating:

- *Devote adequate time to the process.* A good strategic plan is not developed overnight. The carpenter's adage "Measure twice and cut once" also applies to strategic planning. You want to make sure you take the time to both plan the process and conduct it. Doing so will enhance the quality of the end product.
- *Be sure to involve the right people in the process.* It is important to include key constituencies so they will "buy into" and support the strategic plan. Consider asking constituents for their input through interviews, surveys, and/or focus groups. Involve your staff early in the process so they become committed to the plan. By doing so, you can help them think strategically and place their specific roles in a broader context. In addition, involvement in strategic planning helps staff develop important decision-making skills.
- *Coordinate strategic planning with financial planning.* Time the strategic planning process so the plan is written prior to the start of the budget development cycle. In that way, the budget can be built based on the priorities and needs set forth in the strategic plan. In subsequent years, plan to complete an annual

Annual Progress Report for Strategic Plan

Goal: _____

Objectives	Tactics for Current Year	Responsible Party or Parties	Resources Needed (Funding, Time, People, Materials/Equipment)	Status	Outcome/Completion Date

Figure 7.6 Strategic Plan Monitoring Tool

review and update the strategic plan prior to submitting your annual budget request. (See Chapter 2 for more information on the budgeting process.)

- *Develop consensus about the organization's internal and external environment.* The environmental analysis drives development of the entire strategic plan. If the parties involved in planning do not agree on the analysis, the final plan will lack the necessary focus and direction.

- *Don't fall prey to "paralysis of analysis."* While understanding the past is important, do not spend too much time analyzing historical data at the expense of thinking about the future. People sometimes overfocus on data analysis because thinking creatively about the future takes them out of their comfort zone. A skilled facilitator can help the group avoid this common pitfall.

- *Don't be afraid to confront the critical issues.* While it may be difficult to do so, the planning team must identify and face the critical issues in order to create an effective plan. You will never be able to reach your vision if you pretend certain environmental issues (internal or external) do not exist or if you omit key tactics necessary for success from the plan.

- *Don't assume the objectives will take care of themselves.* Just as a garden will not grow without tending, your goals will not be achieved without conscious action. To keep the momentum going, identify a champion for each goal. Designate times to periodically review your progress (eg, annually or quarterly).

- *Exercise discipline with flexibility.* On the one hand, you need to be prepared to stick with a plan for as long as several years before you can tell whether your strategy has been successful. On the other hand, staying locked into your plan can do more harm than good if you miss the need for a critical course correction. As your plan progresses, keep an eye open for emergent strategies and be prepared to make adjustments and respond creatively to unexpected events.

Parting Thoughts

While you may consider strategic planning a daunting task, it needn't be so. The time invested up front will pay dividends later when you realize that you are spending less time in crisis-management mode and more time building on the successes achieved by an engaged and high-performing team. CNMs who have never done strategic planning may want to begin with a simple version of the process to get their feet wet; as you build experience with the concept, you can advance to a more sophisticated planning process.

Your decision to do strategic planning should not depend on whether your department or organization has a strategic plan, or on the size of your department or organization. While strategic planning is often a top-down process, beginning with top leadership in an organization and cascading down to the department level, it does not need to happen that way. In the spirit of "managing up," a clinical nutrition unit can take the lead in developing a process and strategic plan that serves as a model for the rest of the department and organization.

Finally, make strategic planning an ongoing process similar to performance improvement. Create a culture of strategic thinking where you and your staff are continually analyzing the environment, evaluating progress, and revising tactics as needed to achieve your vision. Figure 7.7 illustrates the cyclical nature of strategic management.

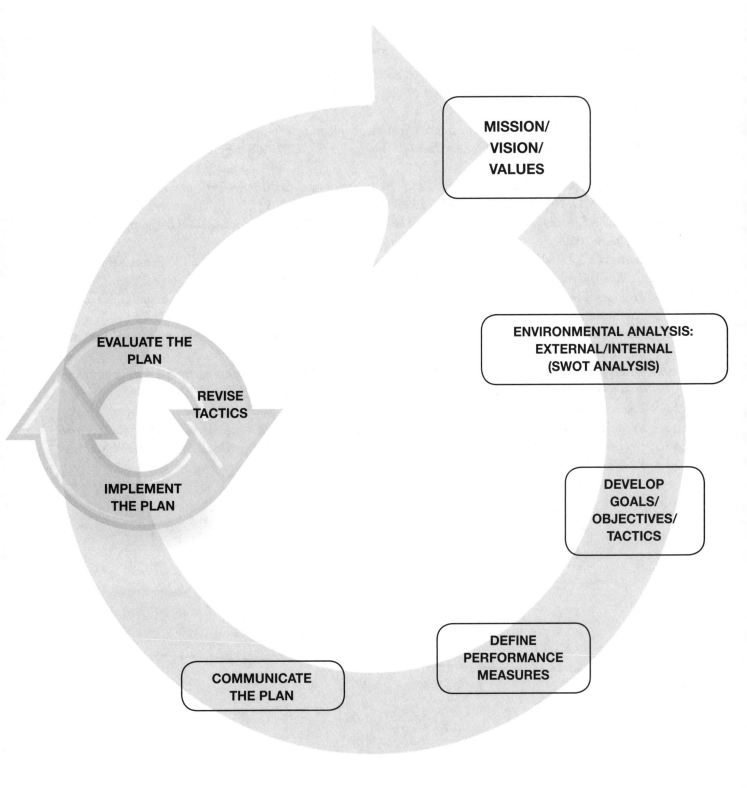

MISSION/
VISION/
VALUES

ENVIRONMENTAL ANALYSIS:
EXTERNAL/INTERNAL
(SWOT ANALYSIS)

EVALUATE THE
PLAN

REVISE
TACTICS

IMPLEMENT
THE PLAN

DEVELOP
GOALS/
OBJECTIVES/
TACTICS

DEFINE
PERFORMANCE
MEASURES

COMMUNICATE
THE PLAN

Figure 7.7 Strategic Planning Cycle

References

1. Leslie J. *The Leadership Gap: What You Need, and Don't Have, When It Comes To Leadership Talent.* Center for Creative Leadership. 2009. www.ccl.org/leadership/pdf/research/leadershipGap.pdf. Accessed July 25, 2013.

2. Evashwick C, Evashwick W. The fine art of strategic planning. *Provider.* 1988;14(4):4–6.

3. Zuckerman A. *Healthcare Strategic Planning: Approaches for the 21st Century.* Chicago, IL: Health Administration Press; 1998.

4. Baldridge National Quality Program. *2011-2012 Health Care Criteria for Performance Excellence.* Gaithersburg, MD: National Institute of Standards and Technology; 2011.

5. Abraham S. *Strategic Planning: A Practical Guide for Competitive Success.* Mason, OH: Thompson South-Western; 2006.

6. Barksdale S, Lund T. *10 Steps to Successful Strategic Planning.* Alexandria, VA: ASTD Press; 2006.

7. Collins J. *Good to Great.* New York, NY: HarperCollins; 2001.

8. *Strategic Planning: The Roadmap to Success. A Guide for Affiliates and Dietetic Practice Groups.* Chicago, IL: American Dietetic Association; 2006.

9. Harrison J, St. John C. *Foundations in Strategic Management.* Mason, OH: Thompson South-Western; 2008.

10. Jarrett J, Mahaffie J. The profession of dietetics at a critical juncture: a report on the 2006 environmental scan for the American Dietetic Association. *J Am Diet Assoc.* 2007;107(7 Suppl):S39-S57.

11. Institute for Alternative Futures. www.altfutures.com. Accessed July 25, 2013.

12. Weihrich H. The TOWS matrix: a tool for situational analysis. *Long Range Planning.* 1982;15(2):54–66.

13. Bossidy L, Charan R, Burck C. *Execution: The Discipline of Getting Things Done.* New York, NY: Crown Business; 2002.

Emerging Trends and Innovations in Clinical Nutrition Management

Sherri L. Jones, MS, MBA, RD, LDN, FAND

Introduction

In today's dynamic and competitive health care environment, clinical nutrition managers (CNMs) need to stay on top of trends in the health care industry and find innovative ways to reinvent what they and their staff do. As Judith C. Rodriquez, PhD, RD, LDN, FADA (2010–2011 American Dietetic Association president) has emphasized, innovation helps RDs "keep up with the times or, better yet, lead them" (1). This chapter covers the topic of health care trends and innovation from a CNM's perspective. It reviews methods that CNMs can use to find information on current or emerging trends and innovations. The trend of cultural competency is highlighted because it is of increasing relevance as the US population becomes more diverse and because the Joint Commission (TJC) has revised its cultural competency standards. The Institute of Medicine's aims for health care improvement (see Chapter 5) provide the framework for the examples of innovative initiatives that are shared in this chapter. The chapter concludes with a brief discussion on adopting innovation.

Finding Information about Trends and Innovations

If there is an emerging trend affecting health care, the leadership team at your facility is likely aware of it. Therefore, to learn about general health care trends, stay engaged in the facility or organization in which you work. Your leadership team probably conducts meetings on a routine basis to discuss the organization's past performance, current expectations, and upcoming issues. Try to attend such meetings, and also join interdisciplinary committees within your organization. These committees typically discuss new initiatives that the organization has chosen or been mandated to implement. Examples of such committees include Quality, Compliance, Safety, and Patient Satisfaction. The key is to get involved, stay connected, and keep your eyes and ears open at your organization.

Becoming a member of professional organizations, such as the Academy of Nutrition and Dietetics, is another good way to stay connected with the trends and learn about innovations in nutrition care. The Academy has many resources to keep members informed about current trends in dietetics, including environmental scans, mega issues, and dietetic practice groups (DPGs).

Environmental (Future) Scans

Many industries perform environmental scans (also known as future scans) to determine what trends will shape their industry and to help them develop strategies for the future. The Academy conducts such a scan for the dietetics profession on a regular cycle (approximately every 5 years). Its most recent future scan was conducted in 2010, with the results published in the March 2012 issue of the *Journal of the Academy of Nutrition and Dietetics* (2). The Dietetics Workforce Demand Study Task Force commissioned the scan, which involved a 1-day workshop with 14 thought leaders representing a diversity of perspectives, as well as a wide-ranging literature review. After analysis and prioritization, the thought leaders organized the trends and issues shaping the dietetics profession into 10 change drivers (see Table 8.1) (2). However, as the *Journal* article (2) points out, the industry trends that were identified in the most recent scan may not be the same as trends at a future date. Therefore, all CNMs should be proactive and stay abreast of current literature and information on industry trends.

Mega Issues

Other Academy resources about trends affecting the dietetics profession include the "Mega Issues" list and corresponding "Backgrounders" available on the Academy website (3). Mega issues are of particular interest to the leadership of the Academy because they are issues of strategic importance that typically affect several goals or outcomes. For this reason, the Academy's House of Delegates (HOD) meets to discuss the mega issues, and delegates seek member input on the issues. Some recent mega issues include participating in health care reform to support the future role of RDs; incorporation of an evidence-based approach in all areas of dietetics practice; and positioning management as a key skill of advanced practice. To see a complete list of the mega issues affecting the profession and learn how to suggest future mega issues for HOD consideration, Academy members can refer to the Academy website (www.eatright.org).

Table 8.1 Environmental/Future Scan: Change Drivers and Trends

Change Driver	Trend Summary
Aging population	Aging of the US population will usher in widespread changes in US communities and workforce and health care systems.
Population and workforce diversity	The dietetics profession needs to develop cross-cultural skills and knowledge of other cultures to grow in a more diverse country.
Workforce education	A more diverse student population seeks flexibility, convenience, and affordability in education to prepare for and maintain employability.
Interdisciplinary teaming	Interdisciplinary teams will drive innovation and solve problems in all kinds of arenas where nutrition matters.
Generalist vs specialist careers	Dietetics practitioners can thrive as adaptable generalists if they cultivate an interdisciplinary perspective and leadership qualities that employers value.
Technology transformations	Technologies will empower customers, clients, and patients to manage their own diet.
Personalized nutrition	New personal health testing and monitoring technologies will create opportunities for dietetics practitioners.
Food industry priorities	The food industry will respond to public priorities to transform the current food supply chain into a more healthful, safer, and more sustainable system.
Health care reform	Dietetics practitioners are valued members of coordinated care teams and deliver consistent nutrition therapies to people with chronic diseases.
Population risk factors	Widespread chronic disease, obesity, and socioeconomic challenges make nutrition initiatives and life-course interventions a public priority.

Source: Data are from reference 2.

Dietetic Practice Groups

The Academy has a variety of DPGs related to specific practice areas or shared interests, such as research, food and culinary, and diabetes care and education. The Clinical Nutrition Management DPG is made up of Academy members who have worked in, are currently working in, or are interested in clinical nutrition management. Its member benefits include full access to the CNM website (www.cnmdpg. org) and resources, quarterly newsletters, an annual educational symposium, and a member e-mail listserv (4). Often, trends or issues are discovered through review of the listserv messages and dialogue. CNM members pose questions and seek advice from other CNMs through this forum, which can be of particular value when you are dealing with unfamiliar trends.

Cultural Competency

Cultural competency is becoming more important for RDs because, as noted in the Academy's 2010 future scan (see Table 8.1 on page 163), population and workforce diversity are driving change in dietetics (2), and cultural competency helps RDs successfully work with diverse teams and patients. Furthermore, cultural competency has become a regulatory compliance issue. TJC's January 2010 release of revised standards for patient-centered communication (5) includes standard PC.02.01.21, which states, "The hospital effectively communicates with patients when providing care, treatment, and services." The standard was developed as part of TJC's project to advance effective communication, cultural competence, and patient- and family-centered care. Compliance with the standard, as evaluated by TJC surveyors, began January 1, 2011. (See Chapter 3 for additional information on compliance.)

To assist hospitals with compliance of this standard, TJC created *Advancing Effective Communication, Cultural Competence, and Patient- and Family-Centered Care: A Roadmap for Hospitals* (6). This resource is a comprehensive guide for interpretation of the standard and it provides implementation suggestions. Cultural diversity is an important issue for all types of health care organizations, regardless of whether they are accredited by TJC. Therefore, this resource from TJC is relevant in *all* health care settings. Chapter 6 of TJC's publication covers the topic of organization readiness for those in leadership roles and includes recommended issues to address as well as specific practice examples. This chapter may be especially valuable for CNMs who are responsible for ensuring that nutrition/dietetics staff are prepared to deliver care in a culturally competent way. Box 8.1 presents some strategies that CNMs can use to promote and ensure the cultural competence of staff (6).

Box 8.1   Strategies to Promote Cultural Competency

- Create a diverse workforce by targeting recruitment to consider diverse and bilingual candidates.
- Ensure that staff are aware of relevant policies, programs, and services for appropriate patient-to-provider communication and cultural competence.
- Include cultural competency expectations as a part of new-hire orientation.
- Provide staff training opportunities throughout the year.
- Incorporate cultural competency into staff's annual performance expectations.
- In-service staff on how to access language services (including non-English and sign language) and appropriately work with interpreters.
- Make sure that staff document the use of language services in the medical record.
- Obtain or create nutrition education materials in non-English versions to meet the language needs of the most common non-English speaking patient populations.

(continues)

Box 8.1 *(continued)*

- Investigate the procedure to have nutrition education materials translated into Braille and in-service staff on the procedure.
- Create nutrition education materials written at a 5th grade reading level or lower.
- Obtain or create non-written nutrition education materials, such as videos or pictograms.
- Train staff on the use of the "teach back" method and ensure its use when providing nutrition education to patients.
- Encourage staff to ask open-ended questions when conducting a patient history or patient visit.
- Provide resources to staff about religious or cultural food practices.
- Encourage staff to discuss the challenges and barriers to providing care to patients with unique or different needs.

Source: Data are from reference 6.

The Academy offers additional resources and tools that CNMs can review to understand cultural competency, including the May 2010 supplement to the *Journal of the American Dietetic Association,* titled "Culturally Competent Dietetics: Increasing Awareness, Improving Care" (7), which collects several relevant articles from previous issues of the journal. The article by Stein (8) is of particular interest because it describes several models of cultural competency created and used to guide practice (see Table 8.2 on page 166).

CNMs should think of ways to incorporate cultural competency into staff development and training programs, new-hire orientation, and annual competency validation. Dietetics staff need to practice proper communication with patients, as TJC standard PC.02.01.21 states, and they also need to understand the cultural or religious food practices that particular patient populations may follow. One resource that can help is the Academy's Nutrition Care Manual, which contains reference information on the cultural food practices of various groups, including African Americans, Asian Indians, peoples of the Caribbean/Trinidad and Tobago, Chinese, Ecuadorians, Filipinos, Hispanics, Jews, Koreans, Mormons, Muslims, and Native Americans (Alaska Native, Apache and Navajo, Hopi, Ojibwe, Pima, Sioux, and Tohono O'odham) (9).

Notable Innovations

The Institute of Medicine (IOM) report *Crossing the Quality Chasm: A New Health System For the 21ˢᵗ Century* (10) opens with the following statement: "The US health care delivery system does not provide consistent, high-quality medical care to all people." Unfortunately, this rather bold statement is true. (See Chapter 5 for more information on this report.) As health care providers, we need to find ways to

Table 8.2 Models of Cultural Competency

Model	Description
ETHNIC model	Communication between health care provider and patient focusing on Explanation, Treatment, Healers, Negotiation, Intervention, Collaboration
LEARN model	Guidelines for circumventing communication barriers by the following: Listen, Explain, Acknowledge, Recommend, Negotiate
BATHE model	Incorporates the following tenets of patient concern and provider communication: Background, Affect, Trouble, Handling, Empathy
GREET model	Specifically focuses on immigrant populations and how the patient comprehends the information by considering the following: Generation, Reason, Extended family, Ethnic behavior, Time living in the United States
Purnell model	Derived from multiple theories and includes a schematic circle depicting an outer rim, 3 inner layers, and 12 cultural domains
Explanatory models approach	A six-step mini-ethnography that encourages practitioners to set their knowledge alongside the patient's viewpoint
Campinha-Bacote model	A framework for incorporating cultural competence into the health care encounter through a five-step process focusing on awareness, knowledge, skill, encounter, and desire

Source: Reprinted with permission from reference 8: Stein K. Moving cultural competency from abstract to act. *J Am Diet Assoc.* 2010;110(5 suppl 1):S21–S27.

improve the care we deliver. For this reason, the Academy added innovation as one of the values in its strategic plan for the dietetics profession (see Table 8.3). With innovation, the Academy intends to embrace change with creativity and strategic thinking (11).

What innovations should the health care industry focus on? As described in greater detail in Chapter 5, the IOM report (10) recommends that all parties involved in health care "adopt a shared vision of six aims for improvement" built around the core needs of health care. The aims are safe, timely, effective, efficient, equitable, and patient-centered care. These may seem basic, but they can become complex when applied to the delivery of care to "people by people." As we all know, no two people are the same. Therefore, patient care must be individualized even as the processes or systems that create the framework for care delivery are standardized and consistent.

The remainder of the chapter briefly presents a few examples of innovations that are of interest to CNMs. For more details about these specific innovations, refer to the sources cited for each topic. For information on launching revenue-generating innovations in your facility, refer to Chapter 10. For information on planning research projects, refer to Chapter 11.

Table 8.3 Academy of Nutrition and Dietetics Strategic Plan Values

Value	Description
Customer focus	Meet the needs and exceed the expectations of all customers
Integrity	Act ethically with accountability for life-long learning and commitment to excellence
Innovation	Embrace change with creativity and strategic thinking
Social responsibility	Make decisions with consideration for inclusivity as well as environmental, economic, and social implications

Source: Data are from reference 11.

Patient-Centered Medical Homes

The term "medical home" has been around since the 1960s, when the American Academy of Pediatrics used it to refer to a central location for archiving a child's medical records (12). Over time, the medical home concept has evolved into the patient-centered medical home (PCMH) model, which has been adopted by organizations such as the American Academy of Family Physicians and the American College of Physicians for care of both pediatric and adult patients. The PCMH model provides a comprehensive care program that facilitates partnerships between personal (primary care) physicians and patients and their families. In this model, each patient has a personal physician who coordinates his or her care, refers the patient to other health care providers as necessary, and manages the central depository of the patient's medical information and care plan.

Currently, several PCMH models are in place across the United States. They typically start as demonstration or pilot projects to determine whether they provide better patient outcomes and decreased costs. Some benefits of PCMH have been identified, such as improved quality of care, increased focus on prevention, and early management of health problems (13). Can you see where nutrition fits into this model? If personal physicians refer their PCMH patients to RDs early in their care, the patients may benefit from nutrition care that could improve outcomes. For example, when a patient's body mass index is increasing steadily, a referral to the RD could help that patient get his or her weight under control before related health conditions develop. Or, if a patient has a strong family history of heart disease, an RD referral for education on heart-healthy eating practices could help prevent cardiovascular conditions from developing. The Academy advocates for the participation of RDs in PCMHs. The Academy website states that "registered dietitians can be an integral part of the team that provides patient-centered care to individuals through the medical home," and the Academy Medical Home Workgroup asserts that "since medical home tenets include disease prevention and management of comorbidities, RD participation is essential to improve patient health outcomes and reduce cost" (14).

NutritionDay

NutritionDay is among the most significant and well-known initiatives across the world to focus on the problem of malnutrition in health care. Launched in 2005 in Europe and 2009 in the United States, NutritionDay is an annual event to collect and share outcomes data to identify the prevalence of malnutrition among patients in health care facilities. The mission of the US NutritionDay nonprofit organization is to improve patient safety and quality of care by raising awareness and increasing knowledge about disease-related malnutrition (15). To support this mission, RDs are encouraged to participate in NutritionDay efforts to collect data about the nutritional status of patients in their facilities. It is anticipated that the data obtained from NutritionDay in the United States will help support and justify improvements within health care facilities.

To participate, US facilities must pre-register at www.nutritionDayUS.org. The website provides detailed information on the process and includes tips for pre- and postevent preparations as well as the necessary forms and tools. RDs who want to participate should seek approval from their facility's Institutional Review Board (IRB) before taking part in this research project. A minimum of 20 patients are needed to participate, but it is not necessary to collect data for all patients in a facility. Obviously, the more patients that are included, the more inclusive the data will be. Eligible patients must be at least 18 years of age. Data can be collected from patients in intensive care units (ICUs) as well as from non-ICU patients and residents of skilled nursing homes.

Participating facilities collect data on NutritionDay, which takes place every year on the first Thursday in November. After data are collected, they are submitted online via the NutritionDayUS website. Compliance with privacy rules of the Health Insurance Portability and Accountability Act (HIPAA) is maintained by coding the raw data to make the information anonymous. Statisticians at Austria's Medical University of Vienna analyze the data to determine the relationship between patient condition and nutrient intake, and the findings will be used to raise awareness about the prevalence of health care malnutrition and about malnutrition's impact on costs, length of stay, patient complications, and readmissions.

Participating CNMs can advance the profession of dietetics by contributing to aggregate data findings *and* acquire valuable comparative information about their own organization's performance. Individual facilities receive a detailed report showing their data benchmarked against data from similar facilities. By participating annually, facilities can monitor their results over time and identify the effect of nutrition care practices. This year-to-year analysis may be especially beneficial when evaluating whether implementing process improvements leads to improved patient outcomes. For more information on this program, visit www.nutritionDayUS.org.

Telehealth

Due to innovations in communications technology, many patients no longer need to be seen in-person to interact with a health care provider; instead, their health care needs can be addressed with telehealth, which the Academy defines as "the use of electronic information and telecommunications technologies to support long-distance clinical health care, patient and professional health-related education, public health, and health administration" (16). As the Academy elaborates, telehealth:

> Includes both the use of interactive, specialized equipment, for such purposes as health promotion, disease prevention, diagnosis, consultation, and/or therapy, and noninteractive (or passive) communications, over means such as the Internet, e-mail, or fax lines, for communication of broad-based nutrition information that does not involve personalized nutrition recommendations or interventions (16).

This type of health care can be particularly beneficial for patients living in rural locations who find traveling to see a provider inconvenient or difficult, due to a lack of transportation, physical and/or medical disabilities, financial hardships, or other factors. Telehealth fits with the push toward patient-centered care, which emphasizes the needs and preferences of patients over the convenience of the provider (see Box 8.2 for a case example).

Box 8.2 Case Example of Telehealth: The Author's Experience

As the clinical nutrition manager responsible for the oversight of the University of Pittsburgh Medical Center (UPMC) Cancer Center's nutrition program, I was faced with the challenge of providing dietitian nutrition services to eight rural satellite hospital–based clinics with limited staff resources as well as the main urban cancer center. There were two full-time registered dietitians (RDs) providing nutrition services to the main urban cancer center and they had a very heavy existing caseload. These RDs could not possibly visit the eight rural centers in addition to their daily coverage at the urban center.

Because the rural satellite centers fell under the same regulatory license as the main urban center, we needed to follow the same policies and procedures at all sites to ensure compliance, particularly for nutrition screening and assessment. Although staff at the rural centers performed nutrition screenings, these clinics did not have an available RD to assess patients found to be at nutritional risk. To comply with policy and fulfill the need for dietitian services at the rural centers, we developed and implemented a telehealth approach.

Using the new approach, staff at the rural clinics referred patients identified to be at nutritional risk through the existing screening process to the two RDs in the main urban center. The RDs then contacted the patients by telephone and remotely conducted nutrition assessments and counseled patients as needed. To ensure that the telehealth program ran smoothly, we developed a detailed process flowchart that clearly identified the personnel responsible for each step in a patient's nutrition care (from screening to intervention and follow-up). The steps in the process were as follows:

(continues)

Box 8.2 *(continued)*

Step I: Nutritional Risk Screening

1. Nursing or medical assistant will use the comprehensive intake/assessment form and complete the Nutrition Screening section for all satellite clinic patients.
2. If the patient's response is "yes" to *any* of the questions, the patient has triggered positive for nutritional risk.
3. If the medical assistant conducts the screening, he or she must contact the nurse if the patient triggers for nutritional risk.

Step II: Communication to Nutrition Services (Satellite Clinic Nurse to Urban Clinic Dietitian)

1. The nurse will scan components of the medical record of any patients who trigger positive for nutritional risk.
2. The following information from the patient's medical record will be scanned all at once:

    (a) Most recent history and physical (H&P) that is currently available;
    (b) Medication reconciliation list;
    (c) Most recent laboratory results;
    (d) Copy of the Nutrition Section of the intake/assessment form;
    (e) Patient demographic information—specifically patient contact information.

3. All relevant patient information will be scanned together and sent as one document to the Nutrition Service email account.
4. The nurse will follow-up immediately by calling to the urban center dietitian to inform him or her of the consult and provide any further details.

Step III: Nutrition Referral and Work Handoff

1. The dietitian receiving the call will record any relevant details provided verbally by the nurse.
2. The patient referral will be triaged to the dietitian with lesser work volume or who is most available to contact the patient.
3. The dietitian given the referral will access the email service account to retrieve/review the patient's medical record information.

Step IV: Nutrition Intervention

1. The dietitian will call the patient *within two business/week days* of receipt of the referral.
2. Three attempts will be made to call the patient. (After the third unsuccessful attempt to speak with the patient, a chart note will be documented and sent back to the clinic indicating that three attempts were made to contact the patient without success).

(continues)

Box 8.2 *(continued)*

3. Once the dietitian speaks with the patient, a nutrition consultation will occur over the telephone. The nutrition consultation should include obtaining subjective assessment data, evaluating the patient's nutrition status and needs, developing a nutrition care plan and patient nutrition goals, and educating the patient and/or providing nutrition recommendations as needed.

4. The dietitian will provide the patient with a follow-up phone number in case the patient has any nutrition-related questions later.

5. A nutrition assessment note will be documented using the current nutrition assessment forms.

Step V: Communication to the Satellite Hospital-Based Clinic
(Urban Clinic Dietitian to Satellite Clinic Nurse)

1. The dietitian will fax a copy of the nutrition assessment form to the Hospital-Based Clinic.

2. A special fax cover sheet will be completed to highlight any recommendations or necessary follow-up.

3. The fax will be addressed to the designated "point person" as determined by the clinic.

Step VI: Satellite Clinic Follow-up

1. The nurse "point person" will review the fax cover sheet and note any follow-up recommendations.

2. The nurse will forward any recommendations indicated for the physician.

3. The nurse will follow through with any recommendations indicated for the nurse.

4. The nurse will file the nutrition assessment in the appropriate patient's clinic medical record.

Adequate communication is an important aspect of a successful telehealth program. Thus, a communication cover sheet was developed to easily identify and communicate the RD's follow-up recommendations to both the physician and the nurse caring for the patient. The RD's nutrition assessment is sent via fax to be placed in the patient's paper chart, since the outpatient medical record documentation is not yet electronic. The cover sheet communicates the follow-up needs of the nutrition care plan in a more effective and succinct manner. For example, it includes checklists for making recommendations for physician orders/referrals (eg, order appetite stimulant, consult speech therapy, consider feeding tube placement/tube feeding) and nursing care (eg, encourage small, frequent meals; encourage consumption of high-calorie/high-protein foods; suggest nutrition supplements).

CNMs should note that "telehealth" is the general term used for every type of electronic information exchange or telecommunication, regardless of whether it is interactive or passive. In contrast, "telepractice" specifically involves an interactive exchange between the health care provider and the recipient (patient). This distinction is important as it relates to the Centers for Medicare & Medicaid Services (CMS) reimbursement policies. RDs who are Medicare providers can be reimbursed for medical nutrition therapy (MNT) telehealth services as long as they comply with specific terms and regulations, some of which pose increased risks and considerations (16,17). For example, CMS telehealth regulations require that telehealth services be provided via a telecommunications system with interactive audio and interactive video. The services also must be provided in "real time" to be covered, and the RD must be licensed in the state in which his or her office or facility is located as well as in the state where the patient resides. In addition, the Medicare patient must receive the teleservices while located at an originating site that qualifies as a rural Health Professional Shortage Area or a county outside of a Metropolitan Statistical Area (18). For more information about CMS telehealth regulations, visit the CMS website (19); Academy members can also find guidelines and resources on the Academy website (20).

Despite the various restrictions on and potential pitfalls of MNT telehealth coverage, RDs at facilities such as Memorial Sloan-Kettering Cancer Center in New York (21), the VA Hospital in Hines, Illinois (22), and the Evanston Northwestern Medical Group in Evanston, Illinois (22) are providing telehealth services with positive outcomes. The two Illinois facilities compared patient satisfaction with telehealth nutrition counseling to traditional face-to-face methods of nutrition counseling and found that 99.6% of patients were satisfied with the traditional method and 94.3% were satisfied with telehealth counseling (22). This difference was not statistically significant, and it was therefore determined that telehealth nutrition counseling effectively satisfies patients.

Malnutrition Recognition

In recent years, clinical nutrition managers at facilities across the United States have been involved in innovative efforts to achieve greater recognition of malnutrition in acute care and improve reimbursement for nutrition-related services. Since 1983, the Medicare payment system for acute care hospitals has been based on diagnosis-related groups (DRGs), where hospitals are paid a set dollar amount based on the patient's assigned International Classification of Diseases (ICD-CM) diagnoses rather than on the patient's length of stay or actual resources used. Initially, this reimbursement format may have discouraged hospitals from coding malnutrition as a comorbidity—the coding process was cumbersome, and overall reimbursement in many facilities was not significantly affected by recognizing malnutrition. However, selected examples from the 1990s suggested the substantial financial impact that malnutrition recognition could have. According to Funk and Ayton, "effective identification of malnutrition leading to enhanced reimbursement strengthens the leadership potential of hospital dietitians and improves hospital revenues" (23). Examples of success stories include a malnutrition recognition program implemented at Saint Mary of Nazareth Hospital Center in Chicago. In this quality management study, Sweeney shared that her malnutrition recognition program revenue exceeded program costs and secured an RD coordinator position salary (24).

In 2007, revisions to CMS Hospital Prospective Payment Systems included replacing the existing DRGs with new severity-adjusted DRGs, called the Medicare Severity DRGs (MS-DRGs) (25). With this severity adjustment, CMS basically determined which diagnoses or comorbidities are associated with more severely ill patients and typically use more of the hospital's resources. CMS then financially weighted the diagnoses based on the comorbidity severity levels, reimbursing hospitals more for higher severity MS-DRG ICD-9-CM codes and less for lower severity MS-DRG ICD-9-CM codes.

This CMS Medicare Severity payment structure change has had a notable impact on reimbursement. Several malnutrition-related diagnoses/comorbidities have been identified by CMS as contributing to severity of illness, thus making coding for malnutrition a more cost-effective process. Hamilton et al implemented a malnutrition DRG coding process at Carondelet Health in Kansas City, and in 2009-2010, the health system received $79,567 in malnutrition reimbursement as well as recognition of the value of the RD from physicians and senior management (26). At Decatur General Hospital in Alabama, Cobb et al found that RD-driven reimbursement through the malnutrition recognition program resulted in an average of $30,000 in reimbursement per month for a community-based hospital (27).

RDs are obligated to identify malnutrition in hospitalized patients and implement the appropriate nutrition plan of care to help resolve it, even if malnutrition recognition provides no financial benefit. However, it is worth recognizing that the identification of malnutrition can affect the financial payments that your hospital receives from CMS or other health care insurance providers. In addition to enhanced reimbursement from diagnosis coding, effective and timely identification of malnutrition may assist your facility's Medicare reimbursement by impacting the risk-adjusted mortality rate. The risk adjustment method for mortality rate is used by CMS to account for the impact of individual risk factors such as age, severity of illness, and other medical problems (such as malnutrition) that can put some patients at greater risk of death than others. It conceptually allows for a comparison of a particular hospital's performance given its case mix to an average hospital's performance with the same case mix. Thus, a lower ratio indicates lower-than-expected mortality or better quality, and a higher ratio indicates higher-than-expected mortality or worse quality (28). It is very important to work with your hospital's case management and coding department as well as medical providers to identify how proper identification and documentation of malnutrition in the health record can affect overall severity of illness adjustment and possibly risk-adjusted mortality rate.

As mentioned previously, the Medicare Severity CMS payment system includes several malnutrition-related comorbidity ICD-CM codes that, when identified and coded, can provide enhanced reimbursement to hospitals. In the ICD-9 code set, major complication/comorbidity (MCC) codes (which are reimbursed at the highest rate) include 260.0 Kwashiorkor, 261.0 Marasmus, and 262.0 Severe Pro-Cal Malnutrition. Complication/comorbidity (CC) codes reimbursed at a lesser rate include 263.8 Other Pro-Cal Malnutrition, 263.9 Unspecified Pro-Cal

Malnutrition, 799.4 Cachexia, 263.0 Malnutrition of Moderate Degree, and 263.1 Malnutrition of Mild Degree. The ICD-9 codes with the lowest rates of reimbursement are known as non-complication/comorbidity (non-CC) codes. It should be noted that prior to October 1, 2012, Moderate and Mild malnutrition codes (263.0 and 263.1, respectively) were non-CC codes and provided minimal to no reimbursement. CMS subsequently recognized the impact malnutrition has on patient's utilization of hospital resources and potential patient outcomes and therefore moved these codes higher in the reimbursement rate structure. When ICD-10-CM codes are adopted and implemented in the United States (at the time this book went to press, the scheduled deadline was October 1, 2014) (29), facilities will need to use revised code numbers and corresponding malnutrition-related terms. For a crosswalk of the ICD-9-CM and ICD-10-CM codes for malnutrition, refer to the Academy's Nutrition Care Manual (9) or visit the CMS website (29).

Malnutrition recognition and coding programs can clearly benefit the health care institution and potentially improve the value of the RD. However, it is no simple feat to develop, implement, and effectively manage a malnutrition recognition program. Such an innovation takes research, planning, time, and collaboration to achieve success, and one implemented improperly or with poorly defined criteria for malnutrition can put the facility at risk for fines from CMS. Refer to Figure 8.1 for a sample malnutrition recognition program checklist. The checklist is arranged in a recommended order of steps. However, it is not imperative that the steps be followed in the precise order listed.

As you can see from the checklist, there are many steps and issues to consider. An important issue to note is that a malnutrition DRG recognition program cannot work if only RDs are involved. There are two other key players required in the process: the physician and the medical record coder. In general, the process flow consists of several steps as follows:

1. The RD identifies a patient who meets the established criteria that qualify a patient for the corresponding malnutrition comorbidity ICD-CM code and communicates this information to the physician in the medical record (see Figure 8.2 on page 176).
2. The physician must agree with the recommended malnutrition comorbidity and, in turn, document the DRG comorbidity in his or her physician progress notes and/or sign off on the RD documentation.
3. Once the patient is discharged, the medical record coder reviews the patient's medical record for documentation of DRG comorbidities and determines the proper ICD-CM codes to submit to the insurance provider.
4. If proper documentation by the physician is lacking, despite documentation by the RD, the medical record coder must contact the physician to alert him or her to the issue and request additional documentation. (The medical record coder cannot code a particular ICD-CM without physician agreement as indicated by proper physician documentation in the official patient medical record.) Mainstream use of electronic health records provides excellent potential for automating the process through use of automated triggers and queries and expediting communication between players.

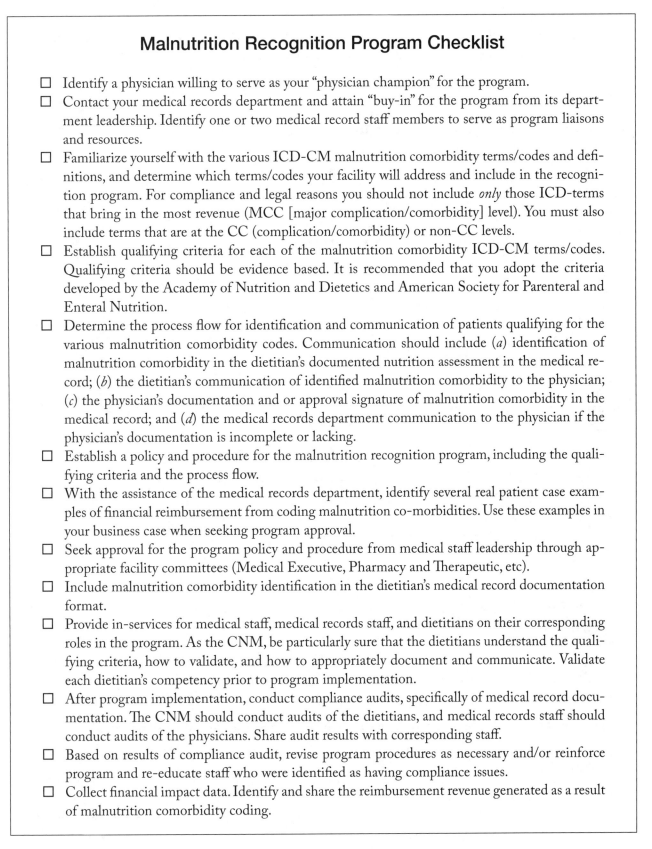

Malnutrition Recognition Program Checklist

☐ Identify a physician willing to serve as your "physician champion" for the program.

☐ Contact your medical records department and attain "buy-in" for the program from its department leadership. Identify one or two medical record staff members to serve as program liaisons and resources.

☐ Familiarize yourself with the various ICD-CM malnutrition comorbidity terms/codes and definitions, and determine which terms/codes your facility will address and include in the recognition program. For compliance and legal reasons you should not include *only* those ICD-terms that bring in the most revenue (MCC [major complication/comorbidity] level). You must also include terms that are at the CC (complication/comorbidity) or non-CC levels.

☐ Establish qualifying criteria for each of the malnutrition comorbidity ICD-CM terms/codes. Qualifying criteria should be evidence based. It is recommended that you adopt the criteria developed by the Academy of Nutrition and Dietetics and American Society for Parenteral and Enteral Nutrition.

☐ Determine the process flow for identification and communication of patients qualifying for the various malnutrition comorbidity codes. Communication should include (*a*) identification of malnutrition comorbidity in the dietitian's documented nutrition assessment in the medical record; (*b*) the dietitian's communication of identified malnutrition comorbidity to the physician; (*c*) the physician's documentation and or approval signature of malnutrition comorbidity in the medical record; and (*d*) the medical records department communication to the physician if the physician's documentation is incomplete or lacking.

☐ Establish a policy and procedure for the malnutrition recognition program, including the qualifying criteria and the process flow.

☐ With the assistance of the medical records department, identify several real patient case examples of financial reimbursement from coding malnutrition co-morbidities. Use these examples in your business case when seeking program approval.

☐ Seek approval for the program policy and procedure from medical staff leadership through appropriate facility committees (Medical Executive, Pharmacy and Therapeutic, etc).

☐ Include malnutrition comorbidity identification in the dietitian's medical record documentation format.

☐ Provide in-services for medical staff, medical records staff, and dietitians on their corresponding roles in the program. As the CNM, be particularly sure that the dietitians understand the qualifying criteria, how to validate, and how to appropriately document and communicate. Validate each dietitian's competency prior to program implementation.

☐ After program implementation, conduct compliance audits, specifically of medical record documentation. The CNM should conduct audits of the dietitians, and medical records staff should conduct audits of the physicians. Share audit results with corresponding staff.

☐ Based on results of compliance audit, revise program procedures as necessary and/or reinforce program and re-educate staff who were identified as having compliance issues.

☐ Collect financial impact data. Identify and share the reimbursement revenue generated as a result of malnutrition comorbidity coding.

Figure 8.1 Steps to Implementing an Inpatient Malnutrition Recognition Program

Your patient has been seen by the Nutrition Service. Please review the findings and complete the documentation below. For additional information, please see complete consult in medical record.

Dietitian Name/Signature: _____

Date: _____   **Pager:** _____

Clinical Indicators of Nutrition Comorbidity:

☐ % Weight loss: _____   ☐ BMI: _____
☐ Poor intake: _____ % est. needs   ☐ Loss of subcutaneous fat: moderate/severe
☐ Fluid accumulation: moderate/severe ☐ Reduced grip strength
☐ Muscle loss: moderate/severe   ☐ Other: _____

Nutrition-Related Comorbidities (ICD-9 Terminology)

☐ Kwashiorkor   ☐ Cachexia
☐ Marasmus   ☐ Underweight (BMI <19)
☐ Severe Protein Calorie Malnutrition   ☐ Overweight
☐ Moderate Malnutrition   ☐ Obesity, unspecified
☐ Mild Malnutrition   ☐ Morbid Obesity (BMI ≥40)
☐ Other Protein Calorie Malnutrition   ☐ Other: _____
☐ Unspecified Protein Calorie Malnutrition

Recommended Interventions:
Food/Nutrient Delivery:

☐ Change diet to: _____
☐ Start/change TF of/to: _____
☐ Recommend MVI with minerals
☐ Assist with feeding
☐ Other: _____

Coordination of Care:

☐ Speech Pathology consult   ☐ Nutrition Support Service consult
☐ Other: _____

Monitoring & Evaluation:

☐ Weight: ☐ Now   ☐ Daily
☐ Albumin   ☐ Prealbumin
☐ Other: _____

Physicians: Please indicate your review and assessment of these findings, then sign below.

☐ I have reviewed and agree with the nutrition comorbidity AND all treatment recommendations.
☐ I ONLY agree with comorbidity, NOT treatment recommendations.
☐ I DO NOT agree; instead, my findings and recommendations are:

_____
_____

Physician/CRN/PA name: _____   **Signature:** _____
Date/Time: _____   **Pager:** _____

Figure 8.2 Sample Malnutrition Recognition Communication Form

In addition to the key players, another important aspect of a malnutrition DRG recognition program is the development of criteria for each of the malnutrition-related ICD-CM coding terms. The criteria should be agreed upon and approved by the medical team in order to promote compliance through consistent identification, treatment, and documentation of all identified cases of malnutrition (26). There are no standard criteria identified in the International Classification of Diseases Manual. Therefore, facilities must determine their own criteria to qualify a patient for a particular malnutrition-related ICD-CM code. Guidelines published in the May 2012 *Journal of the Academy of Nutrition and Dietetics* represent a consensus statement of the Academy of Nutrition and Dietetics (the Academy) and the American Society for Parenteral and Enteral Nutrition (A.S.P.E.N). The Academy and A.S.P.E.N. both advocate for provider use of a standardized set of diagnostic characteristics to identify and document adult malnutrition (30).

Patient-Controlled Liberalized Diet Program (PCLDP)

The Patient-Controlled Liberalized Diet Program (PCLDP) exemplifies how CNMs and RDs at a particular facility can identify an area for innovation and test and implement their improvement project. The program was developed as part of Transforming Care at the Bedside (TCAB), which was launched in 2003 by the Institute for Health Care Improvement and the Robert Wood Johnson Foundation to transform patient care in medical/surgical units through the development of innovative models of care at the bedside that focus on the work of frontline staff and direct care processes (31).

The framework for TCAB was built around the IOM aims for improvement in health care (discussed in Chapter 5) and organized into four themes: Safety and Reliability, Care Team Vitality, Patient-Centeredness, and Increased Value (31). The University of Pittsburgh Medical Center (UPMC) Shadyside was one of three initial hospitals to serve as prototypes for the TCAB initiative. UPMC developed the PCLDP as a patient-centered pilot program following a "deep dive" session in which the frontline staff (including dietitians, dietetic technicians, and foodservice workers) came together in focus groups to identify types of problems that they directly experienced or had learned about from patients. After the problems were identified, the team brainstormed potential solutions.

Participants at UPMC identified food as an ongoing patient and family satisfaction issue (32). Patients frequently complained about the quality of the food and reiterated the popular belief that hospital food is substandard. In addition, patients on therapeutic diets did not always understand the specific guidelines of their prescribed diet, and therefore did not understand why they could not receive exactly what they selected from the patient menu. It seemed that patients who could benefit from diet education were not always identified because they typically received diet education only if an RD was already involved in their care, or if a physician ordered an RD consult for diet education.

So, a question was posed at UPMC: "What if we allow patients to eat as they do at home and do away with therapeutic diets?" Unsurprisingly, this concept was met with considerable backlash from the staff RDs, including this author. How could we do this? The proposed change would harm the patients and make nutrition therapy seem less important. However, the administration insisted that we explore this approach and develop an innovative program to support the notion of "patients eating as they would at home." Our journey began. We conducted a literature search to see whether any programs to liberalize diets in an acute care setting already existed, and no research on the topic was found. Liberalization of diets was a somewhat common practice in the long-term care setting but not in acute care.

The CNM and clinical dietitians decided that diets would be liberalized in a sense, although patients would still need their appropriate therapeutic diet ordered by the physician in order to comply with TJC and CMS regulations. The clinical nutrition staff reviewed diet orders and determined which diet orders would be "liberalized" as a part of the program and which diet orders would be exempt from liberalization for patient safety purposes. The clinical nutrition staff also analyzed their workflow and determined that if a patient was ordered a diet that could be liberalized, his or her selected menu would not be edited or altered by staff in any way. Instead, the patient's menu selections would be monitored for several days, and a member of the clinical nutrition staff would visit and offer diet education if the patient's selections were noncompliant with the therapeutic diet guidelines. The patient would then choose whether to receive education and change his or her eating habits.

In short, the PCLDP put patients in control of their food selections and resulting meal service. The goal of the PCLDP was "to improve the nutritional status and satisfaction among patients during their hospital stay by empowering them to make menu selections and providing individualized nutrition education. Bringing patients into the dietary decision-making process gets to the heart of patient-centered care delivery" (32).

Rapid turn-around with small tests of change is an aspect of the TCAB model. Therefore, the PCLDP was initiated in one medical nursing unit and then the results were analyzed. After the first 6 months, meal consumption increased by 25%; patient satisfaction with meal service increased by 58%; compliance with appropriate food selections increased by 7%; diet education opportunities increased by 36%; and the number of calls to the kitchen for second trays decreased by 18% (32). Also, inclusion in the PCLDP did not result in any negative patient clinical incidents. Refer to Table 8.4 for a summary of the PCLDP planning process.

Implementing Innovations

As you consider innovations for your organization, remember that every environment is different and what works for one facility may not necessarily work for another. CNMs need to clearly understand the environment in which they manage. Implementing change is not easy, even if you are implementing a program that has already been developed elsewhere.

Most innovations are going to affect your staff and the work they do. Some people deal with change better than others, and their adjustment speed varies. As a manager, you will need to anticipate the potential for change to be disruptive and

Table 8.4 Patient Controlled Liberalized Diet Program Planning

Task	Time Needed	Owner(s)
Develop steering committee	1 week	
Identify mission/issues to be addressed	3 days	Steering committee
Collect baseline data	2 weeks	Full staff
Gain administrative/physician approval	1 week	Steering committee
Write policy	3 days	Steering committee
Present to staff (clinical, food services, etc)	1 day	Steering committee
Formulate program design for facility	2 weeks	Multidisciplinary committee
Adjust to clinical changes	2 weeks	Clinical staff
Redesign menu	4 weeks	Multidisciplinary committee/food services
Collect baseline data	2 weeks	Full staff
Develop education materials PRN	1 week	Clinical manager/staff
Develop documentation guidelines	1 week	Clinical manager/staff
Develop timeline roll-out plan	2 days	Steering committee
Develop staff scripts	3 days	Clinical/food services manager
Food service/trayline education	1 week	Food services manager
Nursing/physician communication	1 week	Steering committee
Adjust diet manual	1 week	Clinical manager/staff
Unit trial	1 month	Full staff
Second unit trial	2 weeks	Full staff
Housewide implementation	Months	Full staff

be prepared to resolve problems. Furthermore, as a CNM you need to evaluate the change initiative itself to forecast whether it would be of benefit. There is no sense in implementing change if does not promote an improvement. Even if it is clear that improvements could be achieved, you will need to consider factors such as the availability of resources, whether the proposed timeframe is realistic, your other priorities, and the degree of support you can expect for the initiative.

That is a lot to think about and evaluate. One resource that may help you is *Will It Work Here? A Decisionmaker's Guide to Adopting Innovations* (33), from the Agency for Healthcare Research and Quality (AHRQ). The guide is organized by sections that follow a logical step-by-step decision-making process. It promotes

Table 8.5 Things to Consider When Deciding to Implement an Innovation

Considerations	Questions to Ask
Is the innovation the right fit?	What is the scope of the innovation and how does it work? Is there enough evidence that the innovation worked when it was implemented elsewhere? Will the innovation address our problems and help achieve our goals? Can the innovation be adapted to be compatible for our environment?
Should we implement the innovation here?	What benefits will the innovation generate? Will these benefits be visible to the staff who implement it, the leaders who support it, and ultimately the patients/families in our care? What resources will be needed and are there costs associated with the innovation? Do we need to prepare a business case to justify the innovation? Are there risks involved with the innovation? Do the benefits outweigh the risks?
Can we implement the innovation here?	Have we been successful with change initiatives in the past? Is the staff open to change? How will they react to this particular innovation? Do we need expertise or could we identify a change champion on the staff? What process or workforce changes will we need and are they possible?
How will we implement the innovation here?	How will we evaluate the impact? What measures will we use? What will the timeline be? On what scale will we implement the change? Should we pilot it on a small scale first? Will we be able to sustain the change?

Source: Adapted from Exhibit 1 of Brach C, Lenfestey N, Roussel A, Amoozegar J, Sorensen A. *Will It Work Here? A Decisionmaker's Guide to Adopting Innovations.* Prepared by RTI International under Contract No. 233-02-0090. Agency for Healthcare Research and Quality (AHRQ) Publication No. 08-0051. Rockville, MD: AHRQ; 2008.

evidence-based decision making and helps readers evaluate whether an innovation would be a good fit for their health care organization. Table 8.5 outlines the four sections of the guide and notes some of the questions that should be asked to make an informed decision about adopting an innovation (33).

Summary

The health care industry is ever–changing, and the field of dietetics offers endless opportunities for growth. As a CNM, you need to be aware of the trends that could affect clinical nutrition practice and continually reinvent the nutrition services you manage. As stated in the March 2012 *Journal of the Academy of Nutrition and Dietetics* "Future Scan" article, "The most valuable outcome of future scanning . . . is not scoring the likely impact of different trends and issues; it is *anticipating* the future challenges and opportunities that arise from these changes" (2).

Never simply accept the status quo. Instead, find ways to reinvent and improve the programs and processes that you oversee. Look for ways to implement innovations, especially if they promote the IOM's six aims for health care improvement and are well suited to your particular environment. We conclude with this challenge to you: Be a visionary leader by practice, and not merely a manager by title. Become a clinical nutrition leader.

References

1. Rodriguez J. ADA value: innovation. *J Am Diet Assoc.* 2010;110(9):1279.

2. Rhea M, Bettles C. Future changes driving dietetics workforce supply and demand: Future Scan 2012–2022. *J Acad Nutr Diet.* 2012;112(3 suppl 1):S10–S24.

3. Academy of Nutrition and Dietetics. Mega Issues and Backgrounders. www.eatright.org/hodmegaissues. Accessed December 2, 2013.

4. Clinical Nutrition Management Dietetic Practice Group website. www.cnmdpg.org. Accessed December 2, 2013.

5. The Joint Commission. *2010 Comprehensive Accreditation Manual for Hospitals.* Oakbrook Terrace, IL: Joint Commission Resources; 2010.

6. The Joint Commission. *Advancing Effective Communication, Cultural Competence, and Patient- and Family-Centered Care: A Roadmap for Hospitals.* Oakbrook Terrace, IL: The Joint Commission; 2010.

7. Culturally competent dietetics: increasing awareness, improving care. *J Am Diet Assoc.* 2010;110 (5 suppl 1):S7–S67.

8. Stein K. Moving cultural competency from abstract to act. *J Am Diet Assoc.* 2010;110(5 suppl 1):S21–S27.

9. Academy of Nutrition and Dietetics. Nutrition Care Manual. www.nutritioncaremanual.org. Accessed September 12, 2013.

10. Institute of Medicine, Committee on Quality of Health Care in America: *Crossing the Quality Chasm: A New Health System for the 21st Century.* Washington, DC: National Academy Press; 2001.

11. Academy of Nutrition and Dietetics. Values, Goals, and Strategies of the Academy's Strategic Plan. www.eatright.org/About/Content.aspx?id=8266. Accessed September 12, 2013.

12. Patient-Centered Primary Care Collaborative. Joint Principles of the Patient Centered Medical Home. February 2007. www.pcpcc.net/content/joint-principles-patient-centered-medical-home. Accessed December 2, 2013.

13. American Dietetic Association. Case for Change to the PCMH Model. www.eatright.org/Health Professionals/content.aspx?id=7059. Accessed December 2, 2013.

14. American Dietetic Association. RDs in the Medical Home Model of Care. www.eatright.org /HealthProfessionals/content.aspx?id=7057. Accessed December 2, 2013.

15. About nutritionDayUS. www.nutritiondayus.org/index.php?option=com_content&view=article&id=5 &Itemid=6. Accessed December 2, 2013.

16. Busey JC, Michael P. Telehealth: opportunities and pitfalls. J Am Diet Assoc. 2008;108(8):1296–1301.

17. Hager M. Centers for Medicare and Medicaid Services telehealth coverage of MNT: what ADA members need to know. *J Am Diet Assoc.* 2006;106(4):513–516.

18. Centers for Medicare & Medicaid Services. Telehealth Services. Rural Health Fact Sheet Series. ICN 901705. February 2012. www.cms.gov/Outreach-and-Education/Medicare-Learning-Network-MLN /MLNProducts/downloads/TelehealthSrvcsfctsht.pdf. Accessed December 2, 2013.

19. Centers for Medicare & Medicaid Services. Telehealth. http://cms.gov/telehealth. Accessed December 2, 2013.

20. Academy of Nutrition and Dietetics. Telehealth. www.eatright.org/Members/content.aspx?id=7341. Accessed December 2, 2013.

21. Isaacs-Jordan B, McLymont V, Lambrou K, Pennella M, Sandone M. Implementing telehealth outpatient nutrition consults: Memorial Sloan-Kettering Cancer Center's experience. *J Am Diet Assoc.* 2001;111(9 suppl. 2):A22.

22. Foley S, Sprengelmeyer K, Strohmaier D, Berard N, Ambrose K. Satisfaction with telehealth for nutrition counseling. *J Am Diet Assoc.* 2008;108(9 suppl):A59.

23. Funk K, Ayton C. Improving malnutrition documentation enhances reimbursement. *J Am Diet Assoc.* 1995;95(4):468–475.

24. Sweeney KC. The malnutrition initiative: results of a program enhancing dietitian impact on revenue generation. *J Am Diet Assoc.* 1999;99(9 supplement):A130.

25. Centers for Medicare & Medicaid Services, 42 CFR Parts 409, 410, 412, 413, 414, 424, 485, 489, and 505[CMS-1488-F; CMS-1287-F; CMS-1320-F; and CMS-1325-IFC4] RINs 0938-AO12; 0938-AO03; 0938-AN93; and 0938-AN58. Medicare Program; Changes to the Hospital Inpatient Prospective Payment Systems and Fiscal Year 2007 Rates. August, 18, 2006. www.cms.gov/AcuteInpatientPPS/downloads/cms1488f.pdf. Accessed December 2, 2013.

26. Hamilton M, Bullard S, Fugett K, Health J, Jackson T, Jakobe D. Increasing the value of the RD through malnutrition DRG coding. *J Am Diet Assoc.* 2010;110(9 suppl):A83.

27. Cobb B, Harkin E, Click A, Watson L. Customizing malnutrition documentation accelerates hospital revenue and RD value. *J Am Diet Assoc.* 2011;111(9 suppl):A77.

28. National Quality Measures Clearing House. Agency for Healthcare Research and Quality. www.qualitymeasures.ahrq.gov/content.aspx?id=35573. Accessed November 15, 2013.

29. Centers for Medicare & Medicaid Services. ICD10: Official CMS Industry Resources for the ICD10 Transition. www.cms.gov/Medicare/Coding/ICD10. Accessed December 2, 2013.

30. White J, Guenter P, Jensen G, et al. Consensus statement of the Academy of Nutrition and Dietetics/American Society for Parenteral and Enteral Nutrition: characteristics recommended for the identification and documentation of adult malnutrition (undernutrition). *J Acad Nutr Diet.* 2012;112(5):730–738.

31. Rutherford P, Lee B, Greiner A. Transforming Care at the Bedside. IHI Innovation Series White Paper. Boston: Institute for Healthcare Improvement; 2004. www.IHI.org.

32. Smith J, Greenhouse P. Transforming Care at the Bedside: Patient-controlled liberalized diet. *J Interprofessional Care.* 2007;21(2):179-188.

33. Brach C, Lenfestey N, Roussel A, Amoozegar J, Sorensen A. *Will It Work Here? A Decisionmaker's Guide to Adopting Innovations.* Agency for Healthcare Research and Quality (AHRQ) Publication No. 08-0051. Rockville, MD: AHRQ; 2008.

## 9

Nutrition Informatics

Pamela Charney, PhD, RD, CHTS-CP

Introduction

This chapter addresses the important question of how clinical nutrition managers (CNMs) can ensure that their staff understand and use health care informatics and health care information technology (IT) to provide appropriate and effective nutrition care for their patients. It provides an overview of the field of health informatics, explains why informatics is of increasing relevance to CNMs today, describes some of the technologies that every registered dietitian (RD) should understand, and gives an overall picture of the informatics-related competencies required for success in nutrition care today.

In health care today, information resources are computer-based more often than not. Therefore, this chapter will focus on computer and technology-based resources, including electronic health records (EHRs). However, a couple of caveats should be noted. First, information resources predate the "technology age" (many of us recall the days when the National Library of Medicine sent hard copies of *Index Medicus*, the forerunner of PubMed, to medical libraries every month!). Second, informatics is *not* merely a synonym for IT or EHRs.

What Is Health Care Informatics?

In his "Fundamental Theorem of Informatics," Charles Friedman describes "what informatics is and what it is not" (1). He posits that informatics is a tool clinicians can use to improve practice and "a person working in partnership with an information resource is 'better' than that same person unassisted" (1). Notably, this theorem does not equate informatics with technology alone. Instead, it focuses on two components: technology and the people who use it. When either side of the equation is ignored, mistakes are bound to happen. People can use technology incorrectly, but there is also ample evidence that technology can fail to meet the needs of clinicians in practice (2–6). In sum, health informatics is the discipline that focuses on using information to optimize patient care and health outcomes.

According to the American Medical Informatics Association (AMIA), health care informatics is focused on all aspects of "understanding and promoting the effective organization, analysis, management, and use of information in health care" (7). The health care informatician can be described as someone who creates and supports information resources that augment clinician reasoning (1). Health informatics tools assist clinicians in using information to ensure that care provided is of the highest quality. Health care informatics are involved in management of complex databases needed for research; integration of knowledge sources in health care; evaluation of clinical systems; and ensuring seamless communication among providers, patients, and other stakeholders. It is vital that CNMs understand and use health informatics tools to ensure that the dietetics practitioners they manage have the skills needed to thrive in an environment that is increasingly dependent on technology.

Informatics, Patient Safety, and Meaningful Use

Patient safety is one of the leading issues driving the health informatics movement. Have you ever had trouble reading a health care provider's handwriting in a paper-based medical record? Have you ever found mistakes made when patient data, such as height or weight, are written on a nutrition assessment form? Do clinicians sometimes forget to order vital components of a multi-part feeding protocol? Do food-medication interactions ever occur when an unconscious patient is transferred between facilities because information regarding medication orders is unavailable? Each of these scenarios can be defined as a preventable medical error, and the appropriate use of health care IT could help avert such mistakes.

A preventable medical error occurs when a clinician inadvertently omits some component of care or makes a mistake in implementing care. It has been estimated that 180,000 people die every year in the United States as a result of preventable errors (the equivalent of three jumbo jet crashes every two days) (8). Unsurprisingly, these statistics have led to an outcry for improvements in the way health care is delivered in the United States, and many people and organizations have advocated for technological solutions. For example, the Institute of Medicine (IOM) report *Crossing the Quality Chasm* (2001) concluded that preventable medical errors were a major problem in the US health care system and suggested that improved use of IT, including implementation of EHRs in all care settings, could help decrease the incidence of medical errors and improve patient safety (9). See Table 9.1 for information about some of the other groups and agencies involved in health technology and the roles they play (10–12).

Meaningful Use of Electronic Health Records

Although many health care facilities have used health care IT tools for decades, implementation of the EHR in all US health care settings has become a national priority in recent years. In 2009 President Barack Obama signed the American Recovery

Table 9.1 Partners in Technology Implementation in Health Care

Organization/Institution	What They Do
Office of the National Coordinator for Health Information Technology (ONCHIT)	• Major goal is to support development of interoperable health record system by 2014. • Provides guidance to other governmental agencies; coordinates all federal health information technology (HIT) activities. • Oversees federal 5-year HIT strategic plan.
American Health Information Community (AHIC)	• Made recommendations to ONCHIT regarding enablers and barriers to use of HIT. • Completed work in 2008.
National eHealth Collaborative (NeHC)	• Working toward secure, nationwide health information network. • Public-private group representing organizations driving adoption of health information technology.
Health Information Technology Standards Panel (HITSP)	• Public-private partnership working toward acceptable standards to support widespread adoption of health information technology.

Source: Data are from references 10, 11, and 12.

and Reinvestment Act (ARRA). Part of this landmark legislation is the Health Information Technology for Economic and Clinical Health Act (HITECH), which provides significant funds to spur the implementation and use of technology in health care. One component of the legislation gives incentives for health care providers and organizations that demonstrate they are "meaningfully using" EHRs and penalizes those that do not meet meaningful use (MU) criteria (13,14). In July 2010 final rules were released that described separate sets of criteria that providers and health care organizations have to meet in order to qualify for financial incentives based on their MU of an EHR.

To demonstrate MU, health care providers and facilities must show that they are using "interoperable" computer systems (ie, systems that have the ability to safely and accurately share information). As you can imagine, making sure that systems are interoperable is a huge task. In addition to making sure that systems can "talk" to each other, someone has to develop a method to transfer the vast amount of patient care information that is found in paper records to an electronic format. Also, as information is moved into an electronic format, it is necessary to determine how to make the information available only to those individuals who are authorized. Finally, in order to study health outcomes informatics, professionals with skills in data extraction and analysis are needed to retrieve the information to generate reports.

Meaningful Use and Nutrition Care

At this time, RDs are not identified in HITECH as providers who must demonstrate MU. However, when RDs are included, those in ambulatory settings or in private practice will be required to purchase, install, and use certified EHRs that can share information with all referring health care providers. Also, RDs working in clinical settings will be included under the facility's requirements for demonstration of MU.

Requirements for MU are designed to support the following five national health outcome goals (15):

- Improving the quality, safety, and efficiency of health care while reducing health disparities
- Engaging patients and their families in their health care
- Improving care coordination
- Improving population and public health
- Ensuring adequate privacy and security for personal health records

Each of these goals has implications for nutrition care. See Table 9.2 for some actions that RDs can take to support optimal national health outcomes (15,16).

Table 9.2 Five National Health Outcome Goals and the Role of the Registered Dietitian (RD)

Health Outcome Goal	Suggested RD Role
Improving the quality, safety, and efficiency of health care while reducing health disparities	Work with community leaders to identify "food deserts" that may impact nutritional health.
Engaging patients and their families in their health care	Use health information technology (HIT) to ensure that patients/clients have ready access to information about diet and nutrition. Develop nutrition sections of personal health records.
Improving care coordination	Lead or participate as a member of a multidisciplinary medical home team.
Improving population and public health	Develop, implement, and evaluate community nutrition programs.
Ensuring adequate privacy and security for personal health records	Take steps to ensure that patient/client information is protected. Share only information that is needed to accomplish safe patient care.

Source: Data are from references 15 and 16.

What Education, Training, and Skills Are Needed to Work in Nutrition Informatics?

As this chapter has emphasized, RDs must become comfortable with and skilled in technology to succeed in the current health care environment. In this endeavor, RDs are not alone. Kirshbaum studied the attitudes and perceptions of professional staff at two large hospitals in the United Kingdom and found that while 40% of the staff had completed some form of computer training, 55% felt that the EHR would be too complex for them to use (17).

But what sort of education and training leads to success in health or nutrition informatics? This question is subject to ongoing debate. In the past, it was possible to obtain positions in informatics or IT departments without formal training in the field, but these opportunities are rare now unless you have extensive on-the-job experience. Today, most positions require advanced training in the form of baccalaureate or graduate degrees in health or biomedical informatics.

In 2013 the Commission on Accreditation for Dietetics Education (now known as Accreditation Council for Education in Nutrition and Dietetics) adopted a new set of standards for dietetics education (18). Information technology is included in the standards, but the concept is vaguely defined, giving educators great leeway in incorporation of technology in dietetics education. Unfortunately, educators who have not been exposed to emerging technology may not fully understand the full range of tools available for nutrition care and may not require that dietetics students master technology beyond the use of word processing, spreadsheet, and presentation software. Therefore, CNMs cannot assume that RDs who have completed training in the past few years have all the skills they need to function in today's technology-dependent health care setting. Instead, CNMs must evaluate the varied IT skills of staff and be ready to provide training as needed.

As RDs debate how nutrition informatics will affect the dietetics profession, it can be instructive to look at developments in related health care fields. Medical and nursing professional organizations are beginning to develop basic competency sets for physicians and nurses working in clinical practice along with advanced competencies for those specializing in health informatics.

Lessons from Medical Informatics

In 2008 AMIA's board of directors approved core content and training program requirements for physicians in clinical informatics. These requirements allow for the establishment of formal training programs for physicians at the Fellow level, or those who have completed medical education and residency training. Proposed components of the core content are divided into four major categories: informatics fundamentals, clinical decision making and care process improvement, health information systems and leadership, and change management (19). AMIA's application for approval by the American Board of Medical Specialties (ABMS) for formal establishment of clinical informatics as a medical subspecialty has been approved. Work is now underway to determine the educational resources needed for training programs in medical informatics (20). Box 9.1 on page 188 provides a broad overview of the knowledge required by physicians who plan to specialize in clinical informatics (20).

Box 9.1 Knowledge and Skill Categories for Physicians Practicing in Clinical Informatics

- Medical knowledge
- The field of informatics
- The health care environment, including the flow of data through health care systems and business practices
- How information systems and processes enhance or compromise the decision-making and actions of health care team members
- Re-engineering health care processes
- Fundamental information system concepts:

    ◊ System life cycle
    ◊ Evolving capabilities of information technology and health care
    ◊ Technical and nontechnical issues surrounding system implementation

- Impact of clinical information systems on users:

    ◊ How to support users
    ◊ How to promote clinician adoption of systems

- Evaluation of clinical information systems
- Leadership in organizational change

Source: Data are from reference 20.

Lessons from Nursing Informatics

Nurses make up approximately half of the health care workforce and are major users of health informatics tools in all care settings. As health care becomes increasingly dependent on technology to accomplish many patient care tasks, the need for basic knowledge and skill in nursing informatics has become evident. In 2007, Bond (21) described nursing as a profession that lacked sufficient technology skills and divided nurses into three groups based on their attitudes toward IT: engagers (those who have experience using computers in work settings as well as using computers to research evidence-based care resources), the worried willing (those who would use computers if they felt they had the skills needed to effectively do so), and resisters (those who did not want to use computers and felt that computers interfered with effective care).

Interestingly, neither age nor experience necessarily correlates with competency in information technology in the nursing profession. Although it is often assumed that older health professionals are less likely to possess computer skills, a survey of Australian nurses found that computer use and skills were not associated with either age or length of nursing career (22).

In the same survey, more than 92% of respondents reported that computer skills were essential for nursing practice. Only 2.9% stated that they avoided using computers whenever they could (22).

Aware that educational programs may not be providing student nurses with the skills needed to thrive in a care environment that is heavily dependent on informatics, the TIGER (Technology Informatics Guiding Educational Reform) Collaborative was charged with developing solutions (23). Informatics skills are now being incorporated into entry-level nursing education (24), and the computer skills and informatics competencies proposed for undergraduate nursing programs may help CNMs assess the learning needs of current staff as well as new hires. These competencies include the following (25):

- Understand computer basics (file and folder management, basic troubleshooting)
- Understand and meet information needs to support individual professional practice as well as patients' information needs
- Be able to work in an environment that relies heavily on information and technology

Developments in nursing informatics at more advanced levels could also provide models for nutrition informatics. Nurses can now achieve certification in informatics from several organizations (26,27), and professional nursing organizations are developing competencies for nurses who specialize in informatics practice (28,29). Furthermore, there are several accredited graduate level programs in nursing informatics. Of particular interest to CNMs and RDs, some of these programs, such as the Clinical Informatics and Patient Centered Technology program at the University of Washington (30), do not require nursing experience for entry.

Electronic Health Record Systems: What They Are and What They Do

As noted earlier in this chapter, EHRs are only one component of the field of biomedical and health informatics. However, for many CNMs and the staff they manage, EHRs are the primary technology encountered in the workplace. CNMs must understand the capabilities of the EHR to ensure that information needed by dietetics practitioners and other providers is timely, accurate, and readily available.

The electronic health record is not simply a computerized replacement for the paper medical record. While early versions of the EHR included only transcribed versions of patient encounters and had limited functionality for data sharing or editing, such "flat" files are rapidly becoming a thing of the past. Current technology has expanded the scope of the EHR from a simple repository of clinical encounters for use in one setting to an interactive database containing information that can be accessed and utilized by clinicians in a variety of care settings. The ultimate goal in implementation of the EHR is to provide individuals with a repository of their personal health information that is accessible to authorized users regardless of the setting.

EHR systems vary depending on facility needs and budget. Older "legacy" systems may provide limited interoperability (information sharing between different departments or systems) whereas new systems purchased or licensed from commercial vendors might offer seamless interface between departments and facilities. System interface is an important concept for dietetics practitioners to understand as interoperability directly affects the efficiency and accuracy of clinical nutrition operations. For example, if a facility's foodservice department is using a commercial program to manage menus and inventory that is not interoperable with the EHR system, there will be no automated way for diet orders entered in the EHR to be correctly transmitted to Food and Nutrition Services.

Although the concept of an interface between systems might seem simple at first glance, health care providers must overcome major hurdles to ensure that data are shared safely. Until recently, standards for data transmission were not available, and as a result systems might not be able to reliably send data to other systems. Current initiatives are focusing on developing data standards that will be used by all vendors that sell clinical information systems. However, even when all users agree on a data standard, clinicians will likely continue to encounter roadblocks to information sharing that need to be overcome. Therefore, CNMs must be wary when told that systems are "completely interoperable." In order to ensure that information is appropriately transmitted, CNMs need to work closely with the IT department and EHR vendor to define each type of information being sent.

To envision what is meant by standards for transmission/communication of data, it can be helpful to think about other standards that have become part of daily life. When you purchase an electrical appliance, you do not need to determine how electrical current will be supplied to the appliance. There is a standard that specifies which type of electrical outlet will be used in home construction and which type of plug will be used to connect appliances to electricity sources. At this time, there is no accepted data transmission standard comparable to the one used for electricity. However, the organization HL-7, which stands for "health level 7" (the application level in standards), is developing and promoting communication standards for use in exchanging information in health care. It is hoped that universal use of these standards will facilitate smooth sharing of information within and outside of health care organizations (31). The following sections briefly describe some of the ways CNMs and their staff are involved in information sharing and the use of technology to transmit data.

Food and Nutrition Management Software Systems and the EHR

CNMs may be expected to take the lead in managing food and nutrition management software (FNMS) for a health care facility. A variety of FNMS systems are available to manage food production and management, clinical nutrition functions, or both. These systems are typically a small component of a facility's software needs. Therefore, the CNM must articulate departmental needs and capabilities during the early phases of any major facility software purchase or upgrade. When evaluating FNMS systems, the following issues should be considered:

- Who will be responsible for database maintenance?
- Can the FNMS system interface with the facility's EHR?
- Can the system manage patient allergies and preferences?
- Can the software be customized to meet user needs?

Components of an Electronic Health Record

In addition to focusing on the interoperability of FNMS systems and EHR systems, CNMs should understand more generally how EHR systems can differ in capabilities, both so they can use the facility's system correctly and so they can effectively explain the differences among systems to their staff. Newly hired staff might have experience in facilities using different systems with differing capabilities, or their formal education about EHRs may have been limited in scope. The successful CNM will help RDs on staff understand that solutions that work in one care setting might not work in others due to differences in vendor contracts, system capabilities, and organizational behaviors.

Several vendors offer EHR products. Most of these systems provide a graphic user interface (GUI) with icons and buttons used to navigate through the system. This interface is sometimes referred to as the "front end" and will vary depending on facility needs and vendor design. All EHR systems also have a huge database of consolidated information regarding every patient's demographic profile, health insurance coverage, clinical data, and providers (ie, the "back end").

Health care professionals responsible for evaluating EHR products can become overwhelmed with the complexity of systems offered. Vendors might offer products focused on one particular function in health care (eg, admissions, discharges, and transfers [ADT] software; pharmacy software; or laboratory software) or products that purport to meet the needs of an entire facility or system. Federal standards provide guidance regarding which core functions must be included in the EHR system to meet MU requirements (13). Among them are the following (this list is not exhaustive) (32):

- Structured clinical documentation, which enables all providers to document the care provided in the system
- Computerized provider order entry (CPOE), which allows authorized providers to enter patient care orders directly into the system
- Documentation of patient demographics
- Retrieval of laboratory, procedure, and test reports
- Access to all provider clinical notes, past and present
- Clinical decision support systems (CDSS): alerts, reminders, and clinical practice guidelines
- Medication management and tracking
- Clinical flow sheets (vital signs, input/output records, etc)
- Problem list documentation

Clinical Documentation

The transition from documenting patient care in a paper medical record to entering patient information into an EHR is incredibly complex. Although health care providers spend a good deal of time documenting patient care, some evidence indicates that much of this documentation is not read by others (33). Thus, EHR documentation tools should ideally be designed to ensure that information documented by all providers is easily accessible to others. Information contained in the EHR must be accessible for several uses, including:

- Billing
- Regulatory compliance
- Medicolegal action
- Quality assurance
- Teaching
- Communication

CNMs must be aware of all of these potential uses of information when developing documentation formats and screens for nutrition care.

One decision that must be made regarding documentation concerns the type of data (structured vs unstructured) that can be entered into the EHR. Structured data entry allows discrete segments of information (such as patient demographics, medical diagnoses, and laboratory and test results) to be saved and reused based on a predetermined format that defines where information is placed in a database. This type of data entry is often accomplished through use of drop-down lists, menus of radio buttons, and other choice-limiting features, and it supports the extraction of information from the EHR.

Unstructured (free-text) data refers to information that does not have special formatting applied to it to allow for searching or retrieval. A narrative description of a patient care encounter is an example of unstructured/free-text data. Natural language processing (NLP) is the area of clinical informatics that focuses on finding relevant information in free-text data. To illustrate the challenges involved in NLP, consider the word "lead." It might be present in an EHR in reference to an electrocardiogram lead, the heavy metal lead, or a lead role assumed by providers. NLP software must be able to properly evaluate each of these uses. Current technology does not allow efficient or accurate searching of free-text data in most EHR systems.

Clinicians often prefer the rich narrative capabilities of free-text documentation whereas database managers and administrators prefer the ability to analyze and reuse information entered as structured data. Therefore, interface designers must carefully determine what information should absolutely be entered as structured data and what can be entered as free text. CNMs should develop documentation formats that use both free-text and structured data entry as appropriate to the needs of clinicians and the facility (34). Structured data that can be used by the CNM to justify staffing and to gain knowledge needed to improve care processes include the following:

- Measures of patient acuity (see Chapter 6)
- Nutrition diagnoses

- Nutrition interventions
- Monitoring and evaluation of patient response to nutrition interventions

Use of structured data is facilitated by incorporation of standardized terminologies into the EHR. The Academy of Nutrition and Dietetics has developed the International Dietetics and Nutrition Terminology (IDNT) to provide a mechanism to define and capture aspects of dietetics practice in standardized terms (35). CNMs should require that nutrition care staff use IDNT terms to describe the work of dietetics in the steps of the Nutrition Care Process (nutrition assessment, nutrition diagnosis, nutrition intervention, and nutrition monitoring and evaluation). When the IDNT is used, CNMs can evaluate timeliness and effectiveness of nutrition care provided.

Computerized Provider Order Entry

Implementation of CPOE has been a major thrust of the patient safety movement. Use of electronic systems for order entry ensures that orders are timely, correct, and legible. CPOE systems allow order entry by all providers who have order-writing authority, including those RDs who are authorized by facility bylaws and licensure/ scope of practice. While not without controversy, CPOE has been shown to be cost-effective and to prevent medication errors (36). For example, compared with a manual system, a CPOE system for parenteral nutrition (PN) orders in a pediatric hospital led to fewer errors in ordering and calculating PN solutions (37).

Development of orders and order sets for use in CPOE is extremely complex, and lack of attention to provider needs during development of CPOE systems may be a contributing factor to less-than-ideal rates of implementation. Poorly designed systems can also lead to increased time required for order entry, errors in data entry, and frustration with and rejection of systems. Therefore, to improve acceptance, use, and efficacy of CPOE systems, providers must be involved in all steps in their development and implementation.

Implementation of CPOE can lead to dramatic changes in workflow for all involved (38). System developers must be aware of the human factors aspects of CPOE implementation and take steps to ensure a smooth transition from paper to electronic order entry. When order sets are developed, they must include all necessary components of the order and be designed to minimize "click time" for the providers who are ordering diets or medications. During the development process, CNMs must carefully evaluate how diets and nutrition-related orders are entered in paper systems and translate this process to ensure that the CPOE system is easy to use. For example, if the CPOE system forces the user to enter 10 different items before a complex diet can be ordered, providers will find the system to be less efficient than the previous practice of simply writing the desired order.

Clinical Decision Support Systems

Clinical decision support systems (CDSS) provide clinicians with guidelines, reminders, and alerts. Depending on the knowledge base associated with the system, information provided may range from simple reminders for appointments, preventive care, and follow-up to diagnostic decision support. Advanced CDSS systems scan for patient characteristics that match information stored in the knowledge base (39) and provide sophisticated decision tools to aid clinicians in the diagnostic and therapeutic process. For example, a CDSS focused on nutrition support would identify patients who are receiving enteral nutrition (EN) or PN. The system would then provide clinicians caring for the patient with guidance in selecting feeding routes, formulas, and monitoring information. Providers who are initiating EN or PN would then be asked whether a nutrition support consult is needed. To encourage referrals to the nutrition support teams, the CDSS system could make it easier for the provider to request the consult than to not request the consult.

Coding and Terminology

Standardized terminologies are now part of EHR databases, but they were used by health care providers long before the advent of electronic systems. Most CNMs are familiar with the International Classification of Diseases (ICD) terminology, which has its modern origins in the 19th century, when it was used to facilitate reporting of mortality statistics (40). Currently, health care providers in the United States use ICD clinical modifications (ICD-CM) to code medical diagnoses for billing purposes. At press time, transition from the 9th edition (ICD-9-CM) to the 10th edition (ICD-10-CM) was scheduled to finish by October 2014. Because the terminology was not originally intended to be used as a vehicle for billing, ICD-9-CM has been criticized for several reasons (41,42). In many cases, multiple ICD-9-CM codes could be used to identify a medical problem. Additionally, ICD-9-CM codes were often assigned before complete information was available, resulting in coding errors (43). Attempts to better identify and study some medical conditions have resulted in the development of coding algorithms that can be used to improve accuracy in documenting diagnostic data (44).

Other terminologies used in health care include Current Procedural Terminology (CPT); Systematized Nomenclature of Medicine Clinical Terms (SNOMED CT); Logical Observation, Identifiers, Names and Codes (LOINC); and the North American Nursing Diagnosis Association (NANDA) terminologies. As mentioned earlier, IDNT can be used specifically for standardized terms in nutrition care.

Support for Evidence-Based Practice

Evidence-based practice (EBP) in health care demands that the clinician use the best published scientific evidence, combined with clinical experience and judgment, to provide high-quality patient care (45). EBP has been touted as a major mechanism to improve the safety and quality of health care (46,47). EHRs have the ability to provide clinicians with quick access to a wealth of information to support EBP. However, EBP resources are not always used at the point of care. Reasons for not using such resources include their lack of applicability, difficulty accessing the information, and lack of awareness (48,49). RDs should ensure that EBP tools used in practice are accurate, up to date, and user-friendly. Resources available for RDs include the Academy of Nutrition and Dietetics Evidence Analysis Library, the Cochrane Library, and the ACP Journal Club. While these tools provide a readily available source of information that has presumably been reviewed and analyzed by experts in the field, they do not relieve the RD from learning skills needed to find and analyze information.

Privacy and Security

Use of technology in health care ensures that patient information is private and secure. When Congress enacted the Health Insurance Portability and Accountability Act (HIPAA) in 1996, the original intent was to prevent abuse of information related to health insurance and ensure that individuals had access to insurance coverage when changing jobs (50). Administrative simplifications to HIPAA added more protection for patients regarding the electronic sharing of personal information (51). HIPAA regulations can be complex and confusing; RDs are urged to contact compliance specialists to ensure that appropriate information about patients and clients is shared only with those who have a need to know (52).

Other Technologies: Social Networks, Smart Phones, and Collaborative Workspaces

No discussion of technology in health care is complete unless it addresses emerging (and sometimes already entrenched!) trends in social networking, smart phone use, and electronic communication tools such as wikis, blogs, and online collaboration software. It would be impossible to provide a detailed description of all of these tools, particularly since they are constantly changing and evolving. Instead, the following sections briefly describe some newer technologies that allow the rapid sharing of information. Dietetics practitioners should become familiar with technology tools and use critical thinking to determine which appropriately support application of the NCP.

Social Networking

The term "social networking" was coined to describe web-based tools (although social networking can occur in person!) that allow individuals to connect with others in a common space. It is a good idea to follow trends in social networking among clients and other health care professionals because the tools may rapidly change as new technologies are developed (see Table 9.3 on pages 196–197). For example, from its beginning in 2004, Facebook has been one of the fastest growing and most popular social networking websites. It now has more than 500 million users worldwide. As with other social networking sites, Facebook users create a profile including personal interests, hobbies, location, and other information and communicate with others in the network by posting messages, links, and images (in this sense, the site functions like a virtual bulletin board). It is also possible to create groups and special interest pages for organizations, topics, or products. Although social networking can be fun and/or help build your professional contacts, CNMs must be sure that they and their staff understand privacy concerns and how to appropriately represent themselves, their employers, and the dietetics profession. Refer to your employer's social media policy before engaging in any social network.

Table 9.3 Selected Social Networking Sites for Business and for Fun

Name (URL)	Description
Social networks	
Cafemom (www.cafemom.com)	• Targeted to mothers. • Users can join groups. • Users can post photos, polls, and journals and play games. • Users can send messages to each other. • Users can set security levels.
Caring Bridge (www.caringbridge.org)	• Targeted to people who have a serious illness. • Functions mainly as a blog; used to share information with others. • User can post updates, others can read updates and send messages. • Individual accounts are not accessed by search engines; visitors must be invited.
Facebook (www.facebook.com)	• More than 500 million users. • Initially focused on college students, now widely used. • Users set security levels. • Users create profiles, including interests, contact information, and photos (unlimited photo posting). • Can join groups and "like" pages. • Users intact through "wall," "poke," photos, and status updates.
LinkedIn (www.linkedin.com)	• Business-oriented social networking. • Users invite others to become connections. • Users can follow companies, post resumes, provide recommendations for each other.
My Space (www.myspace.com)	• Users can customize background on profile page. • Users can send messages and join groups. • New users receive recommendations based on previous search history. • Users set security levels.
Social bookmarking	
Delicious (www.delicious.com)	• Users store and share bookmarks. • Users tag bookmarks with index terms they choose. • All bookmarks are public but users can mark as private. • Public aspect of sharing bookmarks is main feature.
Stumble Upon (www.stumbleupon.com)	• Users discover and rate random websites. • Users click "stumble" on site's toolbar and are presented with websites based on previous ratings. • Stumble Thru allows users to stumble within a site, such as YouTube.

(continues)

Table 9.3 *(continued)*

Name (URL)	Description
Photo sharing	
Flickr (www.flickr.com)	• Users can post and share photos and videos. • Free and paid accounts. • Users set security levels. • Users can create web albums.
Picasa (www.picasa.google.com)	• Users can post and share photos. • Users can tag photos, use facial recognition features. • Users can create web albums.
Microblogging	
Twitter (www.twitter.com)	• Users post 140 character updates (tweets). • Tweets posted on user's home page (public). • Users can "follow" each other.

Smart Phones

Smart phones (eg, iPhone and Blackberry) are cell phones that do much more than simply send and receive telephone calls. They have Internet connectivity and offer a wealth of tools such as calendars, calculators, cameras, contact management databases, and thousands of applications related to health care and nutrition (as well as other topics).

Smart phones are small and easily carried at work and can provide a multitude of tools to facilitate patient care. However, the advantages of smart phones must be weighed against the potential risks associated with their use. Because these devices are small, they can easily be lost or stolen, which can put protected health information at risk. CNMs who are contemplating use of or are already using these handy tools must be careful to ensure that any patient/client information is stored in an employer-approved, password-protected manner. Policies that provide clear guidance on proper security measures along with penalties for improper use of these powerful tools must be developed and explained to staff. It would be advisable to check with security experts at the workplace to ensure that protected health information is kept safe and secure. Furthermore, when selecting apps to use for reference, communication, and productivity, care must be taken to choose tools that are reliable, accurate, and compliant with standards and regulations.

It is also helpful for CNMs and other health care providers to understand how patients are using apps to manage their health care. An emerging area of research involves using smart phones as tools to facilitate adherence to complex medical regimens (53,54). In addition, patients are using their smart phones to track calories and exercise, find recipes, make shopping lists, and look for information on health, nutrition, and well-being.

Collaborative Workspaces

The user-generated encyclopedia Wikipedia (from the Hawaiian word for "quick") was the first successful collaborative workspace. It and other collaborative workspaces allow users to directly edit materials online, eliminating the need to download and share document files.

Wikipedia allows users to register for free accounts, which permit them to add content. Because Wikipedia users are not required to log in or register to edit content, concerns have been raised regarding the accuracy of the encyclopedia's articles. (Wikipedia does have some rules regarding content entry, but they are mainly focused on preventing misinformation in biographies of living people.) Nevertheless, health-related content on Wikipedia seems to meet an acceptable level of accuracy (55,56).

In dietetics, collaborative workspaces are becoming more popular because they allow users to create and edit pages while keeping a record of edits made. RDs might use a collaborative workspace to create educational materials, coordinate meeting schedules and agendas, or maintain shared information in a central repository. A number of collaborative workspace tools, including pbworks and wikispaces, are available. Both pbworks (http://pbworks.com) and wikispaces (www.wikispaces.com) offer basic collaborative tools for free as well as several levels of paid support. In addition, RDs may have access to employer-provided spaces, such as eRoom or network drives assigned to specified groups.

Summary

The past few decades have seen tremendous changes in the way health care professionals do their work, and the next few years will see even more changes as EHRs and other technology systems are implemented in all health care settings. Dietetics practitioners must therefore possess a strong framework to evaluate, implement, and use technology to support practice in all health care settings.

Health and nutrition informatics experts will be leaders in the efforts to develop and implement tools designed to improve patient care. Health informatics aims to turn information into knowledge and uses technology to support this objective. When used appropriately, technology helps the user and does not replace the critical thinking skills implicit in the NCP. More and more dietetics professionals are getting on the technology bandwagon and seeking tools that will support positive changes in how we work. However, unintended consequences can occur when the wrong technology is selected. It is therefore crucial that dietetics practitioners use the NCP to support decision-making when identifying and using technology in the workplace.

References

1. Friedman CP. A "fundamental theorem" of biomedical informatics. *J Am Med Inform Assoc.* 2009;16(2):169–170.

2. Ash JS, Sittig DF, Poon EG, Guappone K, Campbell E, Dykstra RH. The extent and importance of unintended consequences related to computerized provider order entry. *J Am Med Inform Assoc.* 2007;14(4):415–423.

3. Baron RJ, Fabens EL, Schiffman M, Wolf E. Electronic health records: just around the corner? Or over the cliff? *Ann Intern Med.* 2005;143(3):222–226.

4. Fieschi M, Dufour JC, Staccini P, Gouvernet J, Bouhaddou O. Medical decision support systems: old dilemmas and new paradigms? *Meth Inform Med.* 2003;42(3):190-198.

5. Ford EW, Menachemi N, Peterson LT, Huerta TR. Resistance is futile: but is it slowing the pace of EHR adoption nonetheless? *J Am Med Inform Assoc.* 2009;16(3):274–281.

6. Harrison MI, Koppel R, Bar-Lev S. Unintended consequences of information technologies in health care: an interactive sociotechical analysis. *J Am Med Inform Assoc.* 2007;14:542–549.

7. American Medical Informatics Association. www.amia.org. Accessed October 1, 2007.

8. Leape LL. Error in medicine. *JAMA.* 1994;272(23):1851–1857.

9. Committee on Quality of Healthcare in America, Institute of Medicine. *Crossing the Quality Chasm: A New Health System for the 21st Century.* Washington, DC: National Academy Press; 2001.

10. National eHealth Collaborative. www.nationalehealth.org. Accessed December 1, 2011.

11. Health Information Technology. http://healthit.hhs.gov. Accessed December 1, 2009.

12. HITSP: Enabling Healthcare Interoperability. www.hitsp.org. Accessed November 30, 2011.

13. US Department of Health and Human Services. The Office of the National Coordinator for Health Information Technology. 2011. http://healthit.hhs.gov/portal/server.pt/community/healthit_hhs_gov __home/1204. Accessed July 15, 2011.

14. Blumenthal D. Launching HITECH. *N Engl J Med.* 2010;362(5):382–385.

15. Halamka JD. Making the most of meaningful use. *Health Aff.* 2010;29(4):596–600.

16. Darmon N, Drewnowski A. Does social class predict diet quality? *Am J Clin Nutr.* 2008;87:1107–1117.

17. Kirshbaum MN. Are we ready for the Electronic Patient Record? Attitudes and perceptions of staff from two NHS trust hospitals. *Health informatics J.* 2004;10(4):265–276.

18. Commission on Accreditation for Dietetics Education. 2008 Eligibility Requirements and Accreditation Standards. www.eatright.org/cps/rde/xchg/ada/hs.xsl/CADE_17877_ENU_HTML.htm. Accessed September 1, 2008.

19. Gardner RM, Overhage JM, Steen EB, et al. Core content for the subspecialty of clinical informatics. *J Am Med Inform Assoc.* 2009;16(2):153–157.

20. Detmer DE, Lumpkin JR, Williamson JJ. Defining the medical subspecialty of clinical informatics. *J Am Med Inform Assoc.* 2009;16(2):167–168.

21. Bond CS. Nurses' requirements for information technology: a challenge for educators. *Int J Nurs Studies.* 2007;44(7):1075–1078.

22. Eley R, Soar J, Buikstra E, Fallon T, Hegney D. Attitudes of Australian nurses to information technology in the workplace. *CIN: Computers, Informatics, Nursing.* 2009;27(2):114–121.

23. TIGER Initiative. TIGER Initiative: an update. 2009. www.tigersummit.com. Accessed May 27, 2009.

24. National League for Nursing. Informatics in the nursing curriculum: a national survey of nursing informatics requirements in nursing curricula. *Nurs Educ Perspectives.* 2008;29(5):312–321.

25. Bond CS, Procter PM. Prescription for nursing informatics in pre-registration nurse education. *Health informatics J.* 2009;15(1):55–64.

26. Bakken S, Stone PW, Larson EL. A nursing informatics research agenda for 2008-2018: contextual influences and key components. *Nurs Outlook.* 2008;56(5):206–214.

27. American Nursing Informatics Association. Certification in Nursing Informatics. www.ania.org /Education.htm. Accessed May 25, 2009.

28. Hart MD. Informatics competency and development within the US nursing population workforce: a systematic literature review. *CIN: Computers, Informatics, Nursing.* 2008;26(6):320–329.

29. Staggers N, Gassert CA, Curran C. A Delphi study to determine informatics competencies for nurses at four levels of practice. *Nurs Res.* 2002;51(6):383–390.

30. Clinical Informatics and Patient Centered Technology Program. School of Nursing. University of Washington. http://nursing.uw.edu/academic-services/degree-programs/cipct/cipct-curriculum.html. Accessed December 20, 2013.

31. Health Level 7. www.hl7.org. Accessed December 10, 2011.

32. Hoyt RE, Sutton M, Yoshihashi A. *Medical Informatics: Practical Guide for the Healthcare Professional.* Pensacola, FL: University of West Florida; 2008.

33. Hripcsak G, Vawdrey DK, Fred MR, Bostwick SB. Use of electronic clinical documentation: time spent and team interactions. *J Am Med Informatics Assoc.* 2011;18(2):112–117.

34. Rosenbloom ST, Denny JC, Xu H, Lorenzi N, Stead WW, Johnson KB. Data from clinical notes: a perspective on the tension between structure and flexible documentation. *J Am Med Informatics Assoc.* 2011;18(2):181–186.

35. Academy of Nutrition and Dietetics. *International Dietetics and Nutrition Terminology (IDNT) Reference Manual: Standardized Language for the Nutrition Care Process.* 4th ed. Chicago, IL: Academy of Nutrition and Dietetics; 2013.

36. Teich JM, Glaser JP, Beckley RF, et al. The Brigham integrated computing system (BCIS): Advanced clinical systems in an academic hospital environment. *Int J Med Informatics.* 1999;54:197–208.

37. Lehmann CU, Conner KG, Cox JM. Preventing provider errors: online total parenteral nutrition calculator. *Pediatrics.* 2004;113(4):748–753.

38. Maslove DM, Rizk N, Lowe HJ. Computerized physician order entry in the critical care environment: a review of current literature. *J Intensive Care Med.* 2011;26(3):165–171.

39. Andersen JA, Willson P. Clinical decision support systems in nursing: synthesis of the science for evidence-based practice. *CIN: Computers, Informatics, Nursing.* 2008;26(3):151–158.

40. Duisterhout JS, de Vries PF, Flier FJ, van der Maas AAF, McCray AT. Coding and classification. In: van Bemmel JH, Musen MA, eds. *Handbook of Medical Informatics.* Bohn, Germany: Springer; 1997:81–98.

41. Cimino JJ. Review paper: coding systems in health care. *Methods Inform Med.* 1996;35:273–284.

42. McCarthy EP, Iezzoni LI, Davis RB, et al. Does clinical evidence support ICD-9-CM diagnosis coding of complications? *Med Care.* 2000;38(8):868–876.

43. O'Malley KJ, Cook KF, Price MD, Wildes KR, Hurdle JF, Ashton CM. Measuring diagnoses: ICD Code accuracy. *Health Serv Res* 2005;40(5 pt 2):1620–1639.

44. Ginde A, Blanc P, Lieberman R, Camargo C. Validation of ICD-9-CM coding algorithm for improved identification of hypoglycemia visits. *BMC Endocr Disord.* 2008;8(4).

45. Sackett DL, Straus SE, Richardson WS, Rosenberg W, Haynes RB, eds. *Evidence-Based Medicine: How to Practice and Teach EBM.* 2nd ed. Edinburgh, UK: Churchill Livingstone; 2001.

46. Green LA, Seifert CM. Translation of research into practice: why we can't "just do it." *JABFM.* 2005;18:541–545.

47. Miser WF. An introduction to evidence-based medicine. *Prim Care Clin Office Pract.* 2006;33:811–829.

48. Liang L. The gap between evidence and care. *Health Aff.* 2007;26(2):W119–W121.

49. Stewart W, Shah N, Seina M, Paulus R, Walker J. Bridging the inferential gap: the electronic health record and clinical evidence. *Health Aff.* 2007;26(2):W181–W191.

50. Centers for Medicare & Medicaid Services. HIPAA: General Information. www.cms.hhs.gov /hipaaGenInfo. Accessed November 30, 2009.

51. Chung K, Chung D, Joo Y. Overview of administrative simplification provisions of HIPAA. *J Med Systems.* 2006;30(1):51–55.

52. Choi Y. Challenges associated with privacy in health care industry: implementation of HIPAA and the security rules. *J Med Syst.* 2006;30(1):57–64.

53. Carroll A, Marrero D, Downs S. The HealthPia GlucoPack Diabetes Phone: A usability study. *Diab Tech Ther.* 2007;9(2):158–164.

54. Marshall A, Medvedev O, Antonov A. Use of a smartphone for improved self-management of pulmonary rehabilitation. *Int J Telemed Applic.* 2008:753064.

55. Haigh C. Wikipedia as an evidence source for nursing and healthcare students. *Nurse Educ Today.* 2011;31(2):135–139 (ePub ahead of print Jun 19 2010).

56. Younger P. Using wikis as an online health information resource. *Nurs Standard.* 2010;24(36):49–56.

## 10

Revenue Generation, Marketing, and Business Plans

Julie A. Grim, MPH, RD, LD

Introduction

In health care, the clinical nutrition department has traditionally been considered a cost center, not a revenue generator, and little attention has been paid to outpatient services and expansion of billable activities. However, as the health care climate evolves, facilities are seeking innovative ways to generate revenue. As prevention becomes more of a focus in health care, the potential to generate revenue from governmental and private payer reimbursement for medical nutrition therapy (MNT) expands. Registered dietitians (RDs) in private practice have been quick to jump on these opportunities, but many of the revenue-generating activities are also applicable to the hospital setting. This chapter provides tools to identify, implement, and evaluate various revenue-generating opportunities; practical tips for developing an effective business plan to sell your concept; and a sample business plan.

Identifying Opportunities

To expand nutrition-related revenue, you must first assess how the following factors affect your current market and opportunities:

- The market/climate within your own institution
- Your competition
- The skill set of your team

Your goal in this assessment is to identify what services you are currently providing, what services are available from your competition, and how your services compare with those offered by competitors. The comparison helps you define your opportunities and explore how to take advantage of them. For example, how do your prices compare to those of your competitors when you both offer similar services? If your competition offers services that your facility does not provide, could you add those services, perhaps at lower prices? Can you offer any superior or unique services? It is important to think broadly and not limit yourself to the traditional services that RDs provided in the past.

Market/Climate Within Your Institution

As you look for revenue-generating opportunities in your facility, begin by identifying the interests and needs of the key stakeholders in your market, your physicians. Given the power of their referrals, they will have a strong impact on the success or failure of your services. The factors to evaluate include the following:

- Do physicians typically refer patients to multidisciplinary providers for services such as MNT, care coordination, and medication management, or does their office staff handle these activities?
- If physicians send patients to RDs for MNT, do they refer their patients to the hospital RDs for services, or do they make referrals to RDs in private practice? If physicians are not using the services of the clinical nutrition department, it is critical that you find out why.
- Are your physicians employed by the facility or in private practice?
- Are their offices near the facility or far away?
- Are disease-specific outpatient clinics already associated with your facility, and can your department coordinate services with them?
- Who are the physician leaders and what are their referral patterns? Look for physicians with formal leadership positions as well as those who lead informally by reputation or political power. What process do these leaders use to refer patients to other providers?

If you do not know your physicians well enough to answer these questions, determine who can answer them and enlist their help. For example, the physician's office manager, the individual in charge of referrals, or someone in your outpatient registration department can likely assist with many of your questions.

In addition to learning about your physician market, factors to assess include the following:

- How are referrals ordered? For example, is there a universal outpatient order sheet or an online method of requesting services, or are referrals handled by telephone?
- If your department provides outpatient MNT services, are your physicians aware that these services are available?
- Do you routinely meet with physicians when they join the facility or participate in their orientation to make them aware of your services?
- What types of data are you collecting to demonstrate the effectiveness of your services? Diagnosis-specific outcomes data are considered the gold standard, but testimonials can also be persuasive.

- How do you communicate your outcomes to your physician base?
- Do staff in the physician offices understand insurance coverage for MNT? If they do not, the Academy of Nutrition and Dietetics *MNT Works Toolkit* (1) is a great resource.

In addition to evaluating your physician population, you should also analyze the following characteristics of your hospital environment that will affect how you effectively target your services:

- What are the high-volume diagnoses with nutritional implications?
- What is the age range of patients served? For example, if the patient population is young, you might focus on maternal and pediatric nutrition services instead of MNT for chronic diseases associated with an aging population.
- What is the general demographic profile of the patient population? For example, you might gather information about patients' access to transportation, the ratio of working individuals to retirees, and the percentages of military and nonmilitary patients. Such data can help you figure out the types of insurance coverage that your population may have and evaluate their ability to keep multiple face-to-face appointments.
- Which employers have large numbers of employees in the local area? What insurance plans do these employees have? This information can assist you in determining the potential for worksite wellness programs and tell you whether the employers' insurance plans cover MNT.
- What is your facility's payer mix? In other words, what percentage of the patients at your facility are covered by Medicare? Medicaid? Private insurance? How many self-pay for health care? This information should be available from your admissions or finance department.
- What percentage of your services is currently being reimbursed? Hospitals are reluctant to invest time and resources in services with poor reimbursement rates unless there is convincing evidence that individuals will pay out of pocket or that the specific service will substantially affect other financial metrics, such as emergency department visits or readmissions within 30 days. In addition, physicians are reluctant to give referrals for services if they think insurance will not cover those services. Note: As various reforms, such as medical homes and new payment models, change the health care landscape, options for referrals and reimbursement will continue to evolve.
- Does your hospital have a minimum threshold for precertification? For example, some institutions will not accept insurance assignment for amounts below a minimum dollar amount; any charge less than that amount must be paid in full in cash. The positive aspect of this type of policy is you know you will collect 100% of the fee. On the negative side, a minimum threshold could discourage patients from using your services, particularly when the economy is bad. In other words, such a threshold makes your revenue opportunities more vulnerable to changes in the economy.

- Do the insurance plan options that your facility provides for its own employees cover MNT? For what diagnoses? Are your physicians aware of these aspects of the employer plan?
- Do you work for a not-for-profit facility? If you do, can you identify possible sources of revenue from your facility's community health needs survey (which the Internal Revenue Service now requires for tax-exempt facilities)?
- How does your facility use midlevel providers? Nurse practitioners, physicians' assistants, and other midlevel providers are often collaborative and prevention-focused. Even though they cannot order MNT independently, they can provide access to your physicians.
- What is the employee base at your facility (total number, ages, and ratio of men to women)?
- What staff from other departments can help you? For example, some health care institutions employ physicians' liaisons (typically as part of the marketing department) to reach out to physicians within the community, with the aim of increasing referrals to the hospital. They visit with physician groups and provide literature on services. In addition to staff in the marketing department, you may find "allies" in billing and finance, case management, and quality management.

Assessment of Competition

The second component of your assessment of revenue-generating opportunities involves analyzing your competition. Who else in your community is delivering nutrition programs? Your potential competition could be the outpatient departments of other hospitals; RDs in private practice; weight management programs and businesses, such as Weight Watchers, Jenny Craig, and Nutrisystem; or even online weight management programs such as eDiets.com. Once you have identified your competitors, you need to find out what specific services they provide, what their fees are, and how their services and fees compare with your offerings.

Assessment of Current Staff Skill Set

As you look for ways to increase revenues, you also need to identify what unique skills you and your team have that will enable you to effectively fulfill unmet needs in your market. These skills can be viewed in two categories: credentials and competencies:

- Do you or your staff have any credentials that may be either required by or attractive to your target market, such as weight management certification, Board Certified Specialist in Pediatrics, coaching certification, or culinary school diplomas?
- Does your team have any special competencies or skills that you could use to generate revenue, such as motivational interviewing, public speaking, self-

management training, media outreach, preceptorship, cooking demonstrations, marketing, advanced practice clinical skills, teaching, or writing?

Potential Service Offerings

Once you have done a basic market assessment and evaluated the skill set of your team, you are ready to consider what types of services you would like to offer. For example, suppose you determine that your patient population is predominately on Medicare and you identify a large nephrology group that provides inpatient services at your facility and has offices in the local area. Based on this assessment of the market and recognizing that Medicare covers MNT for kidney disease, you may plan to focus your efforts on increasing revenue from nutrition services for patients with stage 3 renal disease. Note: More information on Medicare coverage, Current Procedural Terminology (CPT) codes used for MNT, and the Medicare billing process is available from the Academy of Nutrition and Dietetics website (2).

As you consider potential product or service lines, it is essential to stay abreast of current trends in food and nutrition. Many resources about current and emerging trends are available, including electronic newsletters, blogs, web forums, and RSS feeds (frequently updated links to syndicated online content) on various nutrition topics. The following are some recent and potential future trends (3,4):

- Canning and other types of food preservation as healthful and economical options for home cooks
- Budget-friendly cooking ideas for men
- The importance of family dinners
- Fresh, sustainable, and local foods (eg, rooftop gardens, community gardens, school gardens, locally grown foods, small farms, and hospital-based farmers markets)
- Chefs and healthier meals in schools
- Meatless Mondays and eating less meat
- Greater regulation and transparency regarding nutrition information (eg, food labeling laws; nutrition information in restaurants; and sales restrictions or taxes on soft drinks, snack foods, and other "empty calorie" foods)
- Social media/food apps, including apps for grocery store coupons, recipes, and restaurant discounts and reservations
- Vegan and gluten-free foods
- Vitamin D supplementation
- Childhood obesity intervention
- Grass-fed meats, cage-free eggs, raw (unpasteurized) milk
- Fair-trade products such as coffee
- Bariatric surgery
- Heart-healthy fats and their uses

With the burgeoning interest in health and wellness, there is tremendous potential to expand your services. Potential business lines to explore to generate revenue for your institution can be divided into two categories: traditional and non-traditional. Examples of traditional services include the following:

- Individual MNT
- Group weight-management classes
- Diabetes self-management training
- Cookbooks
- Worksite wellness
- Presentations to community and corporate groups
- Bariatric education

Nontraditional services that you could offer might include the following:

- Telephone- or computer-based counseling
- Restaurant consultation
- Cooking demonstrations
- Health coaching by a licensed wellness coach
- Web-based training
- Video demonstrations
- Advanced practice training
- Grocery store consulting
- Consultations about food codes and regulations related to locally grown foods, gardening, farmers markets, or direct purchase from farmers
- Chef-RD partnerships
- Training for RD extenders (non-RDs who provide basic nutrition education, such as community health workers and dietetic technicians, registered)
- Consultations or menu development for day care facilities or social service organizations, such as the Salvation Army
- Nutrient analyses for local restaurants
- Sales of collaterals, such as spices, cookbooks, or small wares
- Apps for smartphones and tablets
- Healthy take-home meals
- Partnerships with culinary schools to teach nutrition topics

Business Plan Development

Once you have done the assessment described in the preceding sections of this chapter and identified possible ways to expand your services or perhaps deliver a totally new service, such as cooking classes or advanced practice training, you are ready for the next step, the business plan. Facilities usually require such plans for all proposals for new services, especially if the initiative will require funding for staff, computers, and so on.

Even if it is not required to justify the facility's investment, a business plan is an essential tool in making your business a success. Make sure the plan you create is specific, not vague. Your goal is to demonstrate how your business will solve a real problem or fill an actual need (5,6). See the Appendix to this chapter (pages 223–228) for a sample business plan for a start-up outpatient nutrition counseling program.

Creating a business plan is not as difficult as you might think. There is a multitude of print, online, and software resources to assist you in this process, and you can find advisers at Small Business Development Centers (SBDCs) (7) and business schools. In sum, a successful business plan does the following (5,8):

- Presents a well-conceived idea
- Contains clear and concise writing
- Has a clear and logical structure
- Illustrates management's ability to make the business a success
- Communicates a practical approach
- Assigns tasks to people or departments and sets milestones and deadlines for tracking implementation
- Shows profitability

In most cases, the sole audience for your business plan will be the administration at your health care institution, as funding for your plan will come from the institution in the form of allocated dollars in your budget. However, grant funding may be another option to consider, particularly if you work for a not-for-profit institution. Be aware, though, that grant writing is not for the faint of heart! Grant applications are often cumbersome and targeted to specific objectives. Check with your institution to determine whether someone with expertise and proven success in grant writing can help you identify appropriate grants and write winning proposals (9). The requirements of the grant proposal may not be exactly the same as the business plan described here, but many of the same elements will be needed.

Sections of the Business Plan

There are many models for business plans, some of which are much more extensive and detailed than others. For the purposes of this chapter, our model will contain the following sections:

- Executive summary
- Market analysis
- Company/department description
- Organization and management
- Marketing and sales management
- Service or product line
- Strategy and implementation
- Financial analysis

Section 1: Executive Summary

The executive summary—a succinct overview of the entire plan along with a history of your programs and services— is the first and most important section of your business plan. This section describes why you think your business ideas will succeed and tells the hospital leadership where you want to take your department. It is the first part of the business plan that your administrators will see, and it will either grab their interest and make them want to keep reading or make them want to put the plan down and forget about it. Typical content in the executive summary includes the following (5,6):

- Your mission statement
- Business start date or projected start date
- Names of your management team and functions they perform
- Number of employees on your team
- Description of facilities
- Products manufactured or services rendered
- Summary of business growth, including financial or market highlights
- Summary of future growth plans

The executive summary should be brief (one to two pages), with the details for each of these sections reserved for the body of your business plan. Although it appears first, write the executive summary last, after you have worked out all the details of your plan and are in the best position to effectively summarize it (5,6).

Section 2: Market Analysis

The market analysis section illustrates your knowledge about the particular services or products that your business will provide. It should also present general highlights and conclusions about any marketing research data you have collected. Imagine, for example, that your goal is to expand services in the areas of fee-based continuing education and advanced practice training. Given this objective, the information you provide in this section could include the following:

- A summary of the type of advanced practice and continuing education programs RDs typically attend
- The market outlook for this type of training—ie, the size of your target market, which might be RDs in your service area or, if you plan to offer web-based training, a national audience
- Evaluations of the proposed training from RDs who have previewed your draft educational programs
- The amount of time required to prepare your training programs for implementation
- A summary about the competition—who else provides this type of training; what they charge; and why your offerings are superior

- Information about why this type of education is particularly timely—eg, note relevant changes in health care regulations, evidenced-based guidelines, or reimbursement methods

You may find that the data you collected for your original exploratory analysis is sufficient to write the market analysis section, or you may need to expand your information base. Make sure your competitive analysis has been thorough. It should identify your competitors by product line or service as well as by market segment; assess their strengths and weaknesses; evaluate how important your target market is to your competitors; and point out any barriers that may hinder you as you are entering the market (6). Figure 10.1 is a sample survey tool that can be used to obtain basic information on competitors in your area for outpatient MNT services. The survey could be completed via telephone or electronic communication. (Note that results from the survey and any other specific details of your marketing research studies can be included in an appendix to your business plan, rather than in the marketing analysis section.)

As part of the market analysis, you also need to define the levels of your pricing; your gross margin levels; and any institutional discount structures that apply to your business, such as volume/bulk discounts or prompt payment discounts. If relevant to your plan, gather information about how your primary payers reimburse for services, as this data can help you determine the length of billable time allowed for initial and follow-up appointments for outpatient MNT. Also, if your facility offers a discount for outpatients who pay in cash, be sure to consider how that discount could affect your targets.

The following are other components to include in the market analysis:

- Resources for finding information related to your target market
- Media you will use to reach your target audience
- The purchasing cycle of your potential customers (eg, January tends to be the busiest month for weight management programs, and December tends to be the slowest; August through November may be very busy months because patients who have met their insurance deductibles will request appointments before the end of the year.)
- Trends and potential changes that may impact your primary target market
- Notable characteristics of your secondary markets (ie, customers other than those to whom a product was originally offered, such as hospital employees or visitors who buy cookbooks designed and priced for patients)

The final area that you should evaluate as you complete your market analysis is regulatory issues. Be sure to capture data about current customer or governmental regulatory requirements as well as any potential changes in the future. For example, your plan might need to address how new regulations related to meaningful use will likely affect your services.

If your business plan involves any sort of initiative to generate revenues from reimbursement, be sure to discuss the idea with your finance department before you submit your plan to administrators. Many hospital financial officers are reluctant to charge for a service for which the Centers for Medicare & Medicaid Services

Competitor Analysis Survey

	Hospital A	Hospital B	The New You Weight Loss Center	Private Practice RD 1	Private Practice RD 2
1. What type of counseling do you provide?					
2. How long are the sessions?					
3. Charge per session					
4. What does insurance reimburse?					
5. Do you file insurance?					
6. Availability of group classes					
7. Availability of special services: phone, follow-up email, journals, etc					
8. Measures of success (patient outcomes such as average pounds lost, improvement in cholesterol or hemoglobin A1C levels, etc)					

Figure 10.1 Information on Competitors for Business Plan

(CMS) have not provided clear rules regarding reimbursement. For example, your facility might be reluctant to approve a plan for web-based or telephone consultations because current US regulations regarding telepractice reimbursement tend to be vague or in the early stages of development. If your telehealth plan targets private payers, recognize that few insurance policies have specific clauses about reimbursement for webcam-based telepractice; be prepared to contact payers to determine their specific telepractice policies (10).

You should also determine whether regulations related to the Health Insurance Portability and Accountability Act (HIPAA) are relevant to your plan and be prepared to ensure compliance. For example, if you plan to offer a service that is not usually reimbursed, such as health coaching sessions, you will need a process to ensure that Medicare patients are notified that this service is not reimbursed by Medicare. Discuss with your finance or billing department if an advanced beneficiary notice should be provided to patients for this service. The Academy's MNT Provider newsletter is a great resource to keep you abreast of Medicare coverage changes (11).

Section 3: Company/Department Description

The company or department description section outlines your management structure, other services you provide, how long you have provided specific services, and other general information about operations. A brief description of the start-up plan for your new revenue-generating opportunity should also be provided here.

Section 4: Organization and Management

The organization and management section should include a broad picture of how all the different parts of your business fit together, such as your department's organizational structure and the qualifications and roles of you and your team. The length of this section will vary with the size and complexity of your department or company.

Section 5: Marketing and Sales Management

The marketing and sales management section describes your market penetration strategy, strategies for growing your business, and communications strategies, as well as the methods you will use to evaluate the effectiveness of your marketing plan. When determining what tools to use to reach potential customers, marketing experts recommend a combination of the following promotions: advertising, public relations, personal selling, social media, and printed materials (such as brochures, catalogs, and flyers). In your plan you may want to include sample copies of your actual or proposed marketing brochures and flyers, or screen shots from your website (5).

Potential methods of marketing your services inside your institution include the following:

- Partnering with your facility's wellness program
- Describing your services at relevant physician section meetings, such as gastroenterology, family practice, or internal medicine, or at key department meetings, such as care coordination/case management

- Direct marketing to physician's offices and physician's office managers
- Creating a universal referral form that inpatient physicians can use or building automatic referral language into discharge protocols in your electronic health record
- Offering "lunch and learns" to hospital employees
- Promoting services via the hospital e-mail system, facility intranet, or hospital newsletters
- Including a brochure or other material describing your services in inpatient discharge packets
- Becoming a credentialed provider for MNT

Potential methods of marketing your services outside the walls of your institution include the following:

- Joining the local Chamber of Commerce and attending its functions
- Networking with RDs who do not provide competitive services at events hosted by local organizations, such as district dietetic associations, so they can be a referral source for you
- Performing community service and networking through service-oriented organizations, such as a local branch of Rotary International (www.rotary.org) or Kiwanis (www.kiwanis.org)
- Connecting with women in a spectrum of professional areas through organizations for women in business
- Joining a local Toastmasters club (www.toastmasters.org)
- Networking with local personal trainers
- Volunteering at community events with a health component, such as local races for runners, walkers, or bikers
- Sending e-newsletters on health and wellness to interested customers
- Writing for or advertising in relevant dietetic practice group (DPG) newsletters and posting on DPG listservs
- Pitching ideas to the local media (The Academy of Nutrition and Dietetics media guide, which is available from the Academy's website, is an excellent resource [12].)
- Posting social marketing messages (Many institutions now have Facebook pages and Twitter accounts. Discuss with marketing if you can use these media to advertise your services and whether these methods will effectively reach your target markets.)

Finally, remember that providing an outstanding service is fundamental to growing your business. Positive word of mouth is gold from a marketing standpoint (13).

Section 6: Service or Product Line

This section should describe in detail the product or service your business offers. Be sure to emphasize the benefits customers receive from your product or service, how it differs from the competition's offerings, and the specific need it fills for your target customers. In addition, provide information about which developmental stage your product or service is in (eg, concept, pilot program, or completed program). Also describe in this section how the product or service will be sold, any anticipated copyright or patent filings, and any plans for future product or service lines.

Section 7: Strategy and Implementation

Be specific in the section on strategy and implementation. Identify management responsibilities, establish concrete goals, lay out the anticipated timelines for tasks, and provide budgets. Make sure your strategy includes how you plan to track results.

Section 8: Financial Analysis

The following are some key items that belong in the financial analysis section (see also Chapter 2):

- **Fixed costs**: Costs that do not change depending on your business volume, such as rent, telephone, office furniture, utilities, postage, marketing, and some staff salaries. Also referred to as "overhead."
- **Variable costs**: Costs directly related to the products or services you provide (cost of goods sold), which increase or decrease depending on the volume of service that you produce or sell—for example, each cookbook that you sell has costs associated with it for (at minimum) printing and binding; the more cookbooks you sell, the more money you spend on these costs. The salaries of part-time staff would be included as variable costs if the number of hours they work depends on the volume of your revenue-generating service.
- **Gross profit**: The difference between sales revenue and variable costs. For example, if you sell a cookbook for $10 and it costs $2 to produce, the gross profit is $8.
- **Net income**: The difference between the revenue brought in from the product or service and the money spent on variable and fixed costs. A **net profit** means revenues exceed costs. A **net loss** means revenues are less than costs.
- **Break-even analysis**: Process used to calculate the minimum price you must charge for your service to meet all of your business costs, both fixed and variable. Included in this analysis is a calculation of the number of service units you are realistically able to provide in a given timeframe. Be sure to discuss with your facility leaders expectations for the amount of time needed to reach the break-even point, so you can be sure everyone is on the same page.

A financially sound business plan should include at least the following financial projections:

- A break-even analysis that shows income and expense estimates for a year or more.
- A profit-and-loss forecast (pro forma) that shows a formal, month-by-month projection of your business's net income for at least the first year of operations (pro formas are more refined than break-even analyses).

- A start-up estimate of the money that must be initially invested to launch the business—for example, if you are starting an outpatient MNT program, you might include estimated costs for educational materials and laptops, brochures, salaries, expanded liability insurance, and expanded telephone lines.
- A cash-flow projection that identifies how much cash you anticipate will be coming in during each month versus each month's anticipated expenditures; this analysis helps you plan for adequate funding during months when the cash coming in is likely to be less than the cost of doing business.

Be sure that sales revenue, gross profit, and net income are prominently featured in this section of the business plan.

As you create your financial projections, do not underestimate possible expenses and be conservative about your revenue expectations. Remember that your staff will not generate revenue during every hour of the work day. Your projections must include realistic assessments of the time required for non-revenue activities and how much time is left for revenue generation. When in doubt, be less optimistic. This conservatism will make it easier for you to defend your projections.

For example, if you plan to earn revenue from billable patient encounters, be sure to take into account the typical patient no-show rate for your institution or for the type of service provided. Also consider how much time is spent in indirect, non-billable activities, such as preparation and documentation for outpatient MNT. (See Chapter 6 for more information on productivity and time management.) If you are developing an advanced practice program, key components of your financial analysis might include revenue from participant fees; the cost of additional staff labor required; costs for staff continuing education to maintain their expertise in a particular clinical specialty; costs for participant meals and parking (unless these expenses are the responsibility of the participant); and marketing and printing costs.

Implementing Your Plan

Creating an Operational Plan

Once your business plan has been approved and you have the green light to move forward, it is time to put your plan into operation. The first step is to expand upon your business plan to establish more detailed internal work/operational plans, which identify concrete goals, responsibilities, and a timeline for accomplishing tasks. For example, if you are starting an outpatient counseling program, steps in your operational plan might include the following:

- Learn all variables affecting reimbursement: payers, practice settings, types of MNT
- Obtain Medicare provider status
- Set up reimbursement codes and billing requirements
- Select hours of operation (eg, do you want to offer weekend or evening hours?)
- Create a physician referral process, including set-up of electronic or paper forms that capture essential information

- Establish patient scheduling and insurance verification processes
- Plan the timeline for office set-up
- Document your customer service standards for timeliness of appointment scheduling and patient communication
- Implement MNT protocols and associated staff training
- Purchase patient education materials and business cards
- Write a specific marketing plan with assignments and timelines

If you are starting an advanced practice training program, operational plan components might include the following:

- Development of competency assessment forms
- Detailed rotation schedules
- Assignment of preceptors
- Development of evaluation tools and process
- A curriculum development timeline
- Marketing to targeted DPGs
- Development of a brochure with information on area restaurants and accommodations for participants
- The communication process with applicants
- The billing process

Regulatory and Documentation Considerations

As noted earlier in this chapter, your business must be compliant with regulations to succeed. If you want to be reimbursed for MNT, you must have at least a basic understanding of CMS requirements, including answers to the following questions:

- What types of patients can you see under Medicare guidelines?
- What types of services can you offer eligible patients?
- What does the physician referral need to say?
- What documentation do you need to provide to referring physicians?
- Do you and your staff need your own National Provider Identifier (NPI) numbers?

Note: The need for NPI numbers is often a particular point of confusion for hospital-based MNT programs. When filing for reimbursement, hospitals often use their own NPI numbers rather than using the NPI of the RD who provided the service. The "Frequently Asked Questions" section about the National Provider Identifier posted on the Academy's website is an excellent resource on this subject (14).

Other regulatory and reimbursement issues to consider include requirements related to the retention of patient records:

- How long do you need to keep these records? For example, Maryland state law requires that charts be retained for 5 years.

- Do you have the option of scanning financial information and inactive charts, and where should this information be stored?

As you set up operational processes, take care that you are meeting HIPAA requirements related to the protection of patient health information (PHI). It is a good idea to review your plan for protection of PHI and record storage with your health information management department to ensure that the plan is HIPAA-compliant. If you plan to use smartphones, tablets, or laptop computers in your program, take particular care to understand your facilities' policies regarding documentation of PHI on mobile devices.

Also work with your health information management and compliance departments to determine what outpatient health record documents need to be completed, where they will be stored once completed, their format (electronic or paper), and whether the documentation requirements for telepractice differ from those for face-to-face counseling. Be sure to take into consideration that patients now have a right to access outpatient electronic health record information.

In addition, determine what documentation needs to be provided to referring physicians and in what format. As you plan your documentation processes, aim to make them efficient, effective, secure, and appropriate for all constituents, and make sure the documentation itself is easily stored.

Technology Needs

The technology required for your initiative may already be covered in your business plan, but review your needs again during the implementation stage to be sure you have not forgotten anything. Set timelines to purchase or lease equipment such as fax machines, scanners, copiers, and computers. List the types of software needed and determine whether staff will need training in these programs. If you are starting an MNT program, determine what interfaces or electronic communication processes are necessary to connect with the hospital scheduling systems.

Assessment of Effectiveness

The effectiveness of all revenue-generation programs needs to be measured using valid methods. Outcomes assessment is particularly important for MNT programs. To demonstrate the effectiveness of MNT, the outcome must be a measurable, positive change—such as improvement in the patient's clinical or functional status, demonstrable financial benefits, or a shortened time period for treatment/care—that is a direct result of the MNT (2). The implementation of the Nutrition Care Process and creation of the standardized International Dietetics and Nutrition Terminology have greatly enhanced the ability of RDs to capture outcomes data directly related to the care they provide (15). Documentation should show whether the nutrition diagnosis was resolved and note changes in the signs and symptoms identified in the PES (problem, etiology, signs and symptoms) statement as well as improvement in overall nutrition-related health outcomes, such as weight, blood pressure, and lipid levels (15).

Documenting MNT outcomes is not difficult and is essential for the following reasons:

- Managed care demands positive outcomes. Insurance will reimburse only those health care services that are proven to produce positive outcomes in a cost-effective manner.
- Consumers also demand outcomes information. Patients expect to see results and may ask about your track record before they come to see you.
- Outcomes are the basis for standardized MNT protocols.
- Positive outcomes demonstrate the effectiveness of RDs to physicians, which in turn generates referrals that can generate revenue for your facility.
- Emerging reimbursement models, such as medical homes and bundled services, will also put outcomes data "under the microscope" to ensure that programs are cost effective and benefit patients.

CNMs launching new programs who have not yet had the opportunity to collect outcomes data may find information that is useful for shaping their outcomes predictions in *MNT Providing Return on Investment* (16) and the Academy's Evidence Analysis Library (http://andevidencelibrary.com). Have a plan in place to collect MNT outcomes-related data at the initial patient visit and then at regularly timed intervals thereafter, and be prepared to report and market positive outcomes to insurers, hospital administrators, and physicians, as well as your community, colleagues, and prospective customers. See Figure 10.2 for an example of a format for collecting outpatient outcomes data.

To evaluate the effectiveness of non-MNT programs, you will need to track different kinds of data. For example, if you implement a series of cooking classes, your measures of effectiveness could include the following:

- Survey data about participants' understanding of the class content, their satisfaction with the classes, and whether they intend to move toward healthier lifestyles
- The number of repeat customers
- Changes in overall numbers of participants

Marketing Your Business

As you begin your business opportunity, expand on the marketing plan from your business plan to provide more specific details about the steps to be taken, who will be involved, and when you expect the tasks to be completed. For example, if you are launching a series of heart-healthy cooking classes for your community, you might use a marketing plan like the one provided in Figure 10.3 (page 218).

Ask staff from your facility's marketing department to review your revised plan so you can draw from their knowledge of what has worked best in your particular market in the past. Also, identify ways to measure the effectiveness of marketing efforts. For example, what can you do to find out how patients or customers learned about your programs (eg, ads, social networking, or physician referrals)? Are certain

Outcomes Data Worksheet

Outpatient Location: _____

Outpatient RD	Patient Initials	Referring Medical Diganosis	Initial Visit Date	Patient Medical Outcome(s) Targeted for Change	Initial Anthropometric Data and Date	Initial Laboratory Data and Date	Follow-up Anthropometric Data and Date	Follow-up Laboratory Data and Date	Nutrition Diagnosis	Nutrition Diagnosis Resolved? Yes, No, or Progress Made, and Date

Figure 10.2 Sample Outpatient Outcomes Data Form

Heart-Healthy Cooking Program's Marketing Plan

Task	Due Date	Person Responsible
1. Meet with hospital marketing to share ideas and determine what services the marketing team will provide and what we will be responsible for. Obtain costs from marketing for any services they may be providing. Obtain facility approval if incentives such as prizes are going to be given out and approval to advertise prizes.		
2. Develop flyer advertising services.		
3. Obtain flyer approval if necessary.		
4. Determine number of hard copies needed and where flyer can be e-mailed.		
5. Distribute flyers to doctor's offices, employee break room, local libraries, and grocery stores.		
6. Provide information to be included in community newsletters, community websites, the health event section in local newspapers, and radio listings of local events on stations best suited to our target market.		
7. Provide phone number to call for reservations and more info. Be sure people answering phone can provide the appropriate information.		
8. Determine how registrants will be kept on mailing list/database for notification of future classes.		

Figure 10.3 Sample Marketing Plan for Cooking Class

physicians your main referral sources? Do employee health fairs at other companies result in increased consults? Once you answer these questions, maximize the efficiency of your marketing efforts by spending time on the strategies that produce results.

Summary

The upheaval in the current health care environment is leading CNMs to reexamine how they provide and are paid for services at their institutions. Opportunities to increase the value of RD services and generate revenue are emerging as preventive care and chronic disease management become greater priorities for health care facilities. By analyzing your market, identifying opportunities, and utilizing tools such as a sound business plan, you can capitalize on these opportunities and provide added revenue and value to your institution.

References

1. Academy of Nutrition and Dietetics. *MNT Works Tool Kit*. www.eatright.org/members/mntworks. Accessed August 1, 2013.
2. Overview of the Medicare MNT Benefit. Excerpt from *CMS Guide to Medicare Preventive Services*; pages 126–134. www.eatright.org/Members/content.aspx?id=7326. Accessed November 10, 2013.
3. Nelson J, Zeratsky K. More food trends for 2011. www.mayoclinic.com/health/food-trends/MY01645. Accessed February 9, 2011.
4. The Hartman Group. Looking Ahead: Food Culture 2012. www.hartman-group.com/publications /white-papers/looking-ahead-food-culture-2012. Accessed August 1, 2013.
5. Pakroo P. *The Women's Small Business Start-Up Kit: A Step-by-Step Legal Guide*. Berkeley, CA: Nolo Publishing; 2010.
6. Bangs DH. *Business Plans Made Easy*. 3rd ed. New York, NY: McGraw-Hill; 2005.
7. US Small Business Administration. Small Business Development Centers. www.sba.gov/content /small-business-development-centers-sbdcs. Accessed July 31, 2013.
8. Palo Alto Software Inc. Do I Need a Business Plan? www.powerhomebiz.com/bplan/businessplan3.htm. Accessed August 1, 2013.
9. Karsh E, Fox AS. *The Only Grant-Writing Book You'll Ever Need*. 3rd ed. New York, NY: Basic Books; 2009.
10. Academy of Nutrition and Dietetics. *State Reimbursement for Telehealth*. www.eatright.org/Members /content.aspx?id=7341. Accessed November 10, 2013.
11. Academy of Nutrition and Dietetics. MNT Provider newsletter. www.eatright.org/mntprovider. Accessed August 1, 2013.
12. Academy of Nutrition and Dietetics Media Guide. www.eatright.org/Media/content.aspx?id =6442451145. Accessed August 1, 2013.
13. Gross M, Ostrowski C. Getting started in private practice: a checklist to your entrepreneurial path. *J Am Diet Assoc*. 2008;108(1):21–24.
14. National Provider Identification Frequently Asked Questions. www.eatright.org/coverage. Accessed August 1, 2013.

15.　Academy of Nutrition and Dietetics. *International Nutrition and Dietetics Terminology Reference Manual.* 4th ed. Chicago, IL: Academy of Nutrition and Dietetics; 2013.

16.　Academy of Nutrition and Dietetics. MNT Providing Return on Investment. www.eatright.org /members/mntworks. Accessed August 1, 2013.

Appendix to Chapter 10

Sample Outpatient Nutrition Services Business Plan

Executive Summary

Since Mercy Medical Center opened one year ago, the priority of the Clinical Nutrition Department has been implementing processes to ensure efficient and quality inpatient care. We would like to expand our services by offering outpatient nutrition counseling services. Analysis of the present market indicates high demand for these services and strong potential for profitability.

The objective for this program is to provide medical nutrition therapy to Mercy Hospital outpatients through physician referral. The benefits are:

- Increased physician satisfaction
- Increased patient satisfaction
- Support for hospital chronic disease management initiatives through provision of outpatient nutrition counseling as a key component of overall lifestyle management
- Potential decrease in hospital readmissions
- Provision of a service that is already available at four out of six Mercy Hospital competitors
- Revenue generation

The program will be housed in the clinical nutrition department and use a part-time registered, licensed dietitian to provide direct patient care services and market the program in conjunction with the clinical nutrition manager. Part-time registered dietitian hours will be flexed to accommodate changes in patient volume. Market analysis indicates high demand for this service and strong potential for profitability. Frequent requests from physicians for this service indicate they will be supportive.

We would like to begin offering these services effective September 1, 2014. The initial service provided will be individual nutrition counseling. There is the potential to expand services to include prenatal nutrition and bariatric nutrition classes. Marketing materials and an implementation plan have been developed.

We estimate that the cost of developing the program and staff training will be $5,044. The program is expected to reach profitability by October 2014 and continue to generate revenue on an ongoing basis.

Market Analysis

Mercy Medical Center has 670 employees and 309 active physicians on staff. In the surrounding area, four main hospitals offer outpatient nutrition counseling services to the community and at least five commercial businesses offer weight-loss nutrition services.

Since August of 2013, we have received approximately four phone calls per week for nutrition counseling from both physician's offices and patients, indicating a definite need/interest in this service. In addition, Dr. Adams, Dr. Shah, Dr. Smith, and other MDs have asked repeatedly for this service to be made available to their patients.

Attached you will find a draft of an outpatient nutrition counseling services brochure. Furthermore, we can include a link to our services on the Mercy Hospital website, and nutrition counseling services can be included on the ancillary department outpatient referral form.

Department Description

The Mercy Hospital Clinical Nutrition Department is comprised of Sally Hall, CNM, four RDs, and a part-time diet clerk/administrative assistant. Present services include inpatient medical nutrition therapy (MNT) and community nutrition education. Measured by volume, the top-three inpatient diagnoses are cardiovascular disease, gastrointestinal disease, and diabetes. A part-time RD will be added to provide outpatient MNT services; this RD will work flexible hours based on patient volume. Sally Hall will partner with the outpatient RD to market and manage the outpatient services.

Organization and Management

The Mercy Hospital CNM is proposing to hire a part-time licensed/registered dietitian. Part-time RD staff hours will be increased as outpatient appointment volume grows to ensure that there is corresponding revenue to cover costs and no increase in net costs.

An additional consultation office on the third floor has been secured to meet patient privacy and HIPAA guidelines. A counseling table has been provided by the bariatric program coordinator. Standardized charge codes are in place to enable MNT billing in 15-minute increments. The fax/scanner machine in the inpatient dietitian's office can be moved to the third-floor consultation office. A computer and printer will be needed to assist with patient scheduling, patient e-mail correspondence, and printing of various educational resources for patients. A desk for the computer/printer/fax machine will also be needed. The anticipated start date of outpatient nutrition services is September 1, 2014.

The new part-time RD will require approximately one week of training. This training will include spending two days with another health care system outpatient RD, who will provide training on the system's outpatient counseling and billing process and complete a competency assessment of the new RD.

A tentative nutrition program has been determined for preoperative and postoperative bariatric patients. The anticipated start date for this service is November 1, 2014.

Products/Services

Medical nutrition therapy: Individualized nutrition counseling that in most cases includes a one-hour initial consultation with a registered and licensed dietitian. Most patients will leave with a personalized diet plan based on medical history. Additionally, supplemental materials such as a list of websites, recipes, and tips for success will be provided. Follow-up appointments, generally 30-minute sessions, will be scheduled at the end of each session. Various counseling techniques, such as motivational interviewing, will be used.

Other potential services include prenatal nutrition and bariatric nutrition classes.

Strategy and Implementation

1. Marketing materials and strategy are scheduled for implementation July 1, 2014.

    ◊ July–Sept: physician and community marketing campaign
    ◊ Website activated: August 1, 2014

2. Billing process has been developed. Charge code activation and registration office training scheduled for August 1, 2014.
3. Recruiting for part-time RD scheduled to begin May 1, 2014.
4. Target date for hire of part-time RD: August 1, 2014
5. RD training anticipated: August 2014
6. Office equipment and computer purchase: July 1, 2014
7. Educational materials purchase: July 1, 2014

Financial Analysis

Estimated Charges and Anticipated Gross Revenue

Month	Patients/Month	Patient Charge/Hour	Gross Revenue
September	17	$200	$3400
October	23	$200	$4600
November	25	$200	$5000
December	25	$200	$5000
January	30	$200	$6000
February	25	$200	$5000
March	30	$200	$6000
April	28	$200	$5600
May	30	$200	$6000
June	30	$200	$6000
July	30	$200	$6000
August	30	$200	$6000

Net Revenue

It is anticipated that 70% of charges will be reimbursed, based on 2013 audit with finance department for outpatient MNT reimbursement at other Mercy system hospitals providing this service. Revenue would include patients who pay cash as well as insurance payments.

Month	Patients/ Month	Patient Charge/Hour	Gross Revenue	Net Revenue
September	17	$200	$3,400	$2,380
October	23	$200	$4,600	$3,220
November	25	$200	$5,000	$3,500
December	25	$200	$5,000	$3,500
January	30	$200	$6,000	$4,200
February	25	$200	$5,000	$3,500
March	30	$200	$6,000	$4,200
April	28	$200	$5,600	$3,920
May	30	$200	$6,000	$4,200
June	30	$200	$6,000	$4,200
July	30	$200	$6,000	$4,200
August	30	$200	$6,000	$4,200

Costs

Start Up

- RD training salary and benefit cost for 40 hours/week: $1,344.00
- IT/Computer/Printer: $2,200.00
- Table: $800.00
- Marketing: $500.00
- Educational materials: $200.00
- **Total start-up cost: $5,044.00**

Ongoing Costs

- RD salary and benefits at 16 hours/week (average weekly work hours) with hourly rate of $28.00 per hour = $2,257.92 month
- Educational materials: $500 (for 12 months); $42.00/month
- RD education/continuing education: $600 for 12 months; $50.00/month
- **Total monthly ongoing costs for year 1: $2,349.92**

Month	Patients/ Month	Patient Charge/Hour	Gross Revenue	Reimbursement/ Net Revenue	Cost	Profit
Sept	17	$200	$3,400	$2,380	$7,393.92*	($5,013.92)
Oct	23	$200	$4,600	$3,220	$2,349.92	$8,70.08
Nov	25	$200	$5,000	$3,500	$2,349.92	$1,150.08
Dec	25	$200	$5,000	$3,500	$2,349.92	$1,150.08
Jan	30	$200	$6,000	$4,200	$2,349.92	$1,850.08
Feb	25	$200	$5,000	$3,500	$2,349.92	$1,150.08
Mar	30	$200	$6,000	$4,200	$2,349.92	$1,850.08
Apr	28	$200	$5,600	$3,920	$2,349.92	$1,570.08
May	32	$200	$6,400	$4,480	$2,349.92	$2,130.08
Jun	33	$200	$6,600	$4,620	$2,349.92	$2,270.08
Jul	30	$200	$6,000	$4,200	$2,349.92	$1,850.08
Aug	30	$200	$6,000	$4,200	$2,349.92	$1,850.08

*September includes start up costs.

## 11

Getting Involved
in Research Opportunities

Susan Renee Roberts, MS, RD, LD, CNSC

Introduction

Does the thought of conducting research excite you and your staff, or does research seem like a daunting endeavor? Many registered dietitians (RDs) think research can only be conducted by people with doctorates or in academic settings. However, there are many types of research, and RDs can incorporate research activities into their practice, no matter where they are working, as long as they have an inquisitive nature and a desire to solve a problem or answer a question. The intent of this chapter is to help you and your staff increase your understanding of and comfort level with research. Over time, you may even develop a passion for researching issues related to your practice.

Why Is Research Important and Why Should RDs Conduct It?

Research is important and necessary for a number of reasons. Think about all the amazing advances in science, technology, medicine, and nutrition that have been possible only because someone was willing to commit to researching a new method or different treatment. By collecting and analyzing evidence, researchers allow us to confidently and successfully identify processes and interventions that improve patient outcomes and achieve other important objectives. The Academy of Nutrition and Dietetics believes "that research is the foundation of the profession, providing the basis for practice, education, and policy" (1) and therefore promotes RD participation in research activities. The importance of research is also emphasized in Standard 4 of the Standards of Professional Practice (SOPP) for Registered Dietitians, which states that the RD "applies, participates in, or generates research to enhance practice" (2). The rationale for including research activities in the SOPP is to "promote improved safety and quality of nutrition and dietetics practice and services" (2), which is a practical and relevant goal for those of us practicing clinical nutrition. Within Standard 4, the following five indicators describe ways that the RD can demonstrate the standard in practice (2):

- 4.1: Accesses and reviews best available research/evidence for application to practice
- 4.2: Utilizes best available research/evidence as the foundation for evidence-based practice
- 4.3: Integrates best available research/evidence with best practices, clinical and managerial expertise, and customer values
- 4.4: Contributes to the development of new knowledge and research in nutrition and dietetics
- 4.5: Promotes research through alliances and collaboration with food and nutrition practitioners and other professionals and organizations

As you can see, the first three indicators direct practitioners to stay up to date on research and to use the best evidence in their practice environment. The last two indicators advance the RD's role as an active participant in research activities, which is the primary focus of this chapter.

Hopefully, you are now convinced that research is essential to the advancement of the dietetics profession. Additionally, it is important to consider the specific professional and personal benefits that you and your staff may gain by engaging in research activities. These benefits include professional development, interdisciplinary collaboration, enhanced respect for yourself and your staff, justification of the need for additional staffing, expanded career opportunities, and greater job satisfaction. Robien (3) and I have each asked clinical RDs about how their participation in research has enriched their career and benefited them or their practice. As reflected in the responses featured in Box 11.1, many RDs find that research gives them a great sense of accomplishment, helps them keep abreast of developments in the science of nutrition, elevates their critical thinking skills, and improves patient care.

Box 11.1 Quotes from RDs Who Participate in Research

"I get great joy and satisfaction from compiling the results and discussing them with colleagues. It's a tremendous feeling of accomplishment and completion when you finish a project that seems so huge when you first start out. Continuously having to read the literature in the area of study is also a great educational benefit to research."

—Faculty member, large state university*

"The research process has helped me become a critical thinker and given me the confidence to defend my synthesis of the literature, thereby allowing me to provide the best clinical consultations I can as a dietitian. It has also enhanced my acceptance by academic medicine people

(continues)

Box 11.1 *(continued)*

and provided me with opportunities for networking with other health care professionals in my field."

— Clinical nutrition manager, large pediatric hospital*

"Research can be very difficult, but it is so rewarding to see a project come to fruition, especially if you can design an experiment that answers a question that has not been answered before. It [research] will make you a greater asset to the medical team and sharpen your critical thinking skills. In the end, you will be a better clinician."

—Intestinal rehabilitation program director, large tertiary-care academic hospital*

"Research has benefited my career most by broadening my scope of practice, and my job satisfaction has been improved because I am more familiar with why I practice the way I do. I see the evidence behind it [my practice], and I am able to better represent our career to a multi-disciplinary staff by being informed by current research. Also, I enjoy seeing the outcomes of research; it is rewarding to see something that you have worked so hard on for so long, end up being an example for other RDs all around the country."

—Clinical dietitian specializing in trauma, large tertiary-care academic hospital**

"I have enjoyed doing research, especially when it has led to sharing the results at the national level. It's been great to share what we've done with others to help enhance their practices, too. Specific to the nutrition protocol pilot study, this is a great project to be involved in because it directly affects our scope of practice and allows more independence in the care of our patients. We can show the doctors and other disciplines that we are capable of managing our patients safely and effectively."

—Clinical dietitian specializing in hematopoietic stem cell transplant,
large tertiary-care academic hospital **

"The research helped to change our clinical practice in the neonatal intensive care unit and the literature reviews/peer reviews helped me be aware of the latest research and improve my own clinical practice, making me a better RD for my patients."

—Clinical dietitian specializing in neonatal intensive care,
large tertiary-care academic hospital **

Source: Quotes marked with * are from reference 3. Quotes marked with ** are from the author's personal communications.

Overcoming Barriers to Participation in Research

Despite the benefits and value of research to our patients and profession, participating in and publishing research are not typical parts of most clinical dietitians' activities (4). You will find that the benefits of research, such as increased recognition and opportunities to present and publish, can help motivate your staff to participate, but you must also help them identify and overcome barriers to participation. In one study using focus groups of clinical dietitians (5), researchers found that the most frequently identified barriers to research involvement were lack of support from the administration, lack of time, and insufficient understanding of research methodology. These barriers may be difficult to overcome, but they are not insurmountable.

Lack of Support from Administrators

If you do not have adequate financial support from your facility's administration to conduct a large study, consider starting with a small pilot project. If this project suggests that your research could lead to cost savings, an improvement in the quality of care, or increased patient safety, you may increase your odds of getting funding from the administration for additional staffing or monetary incentives for the researchers. Another strategy to enhance the administration's interest in your research is to ask a nurse or physician leader to join you in championing and presenting the research project.

Lack of Time

If you and your staff RDs perceive lack of time to be your main obstacle, consider whether any of the following strategies would work for you:

- Start with a small project that combines clinical care and data collection (eg, collect data in the intensive care unit [ICU] on the days that patients begin nutrition support to determine whether early feeding is consistently being done).
- Break the research project into manageable pieces with specific and realistic timelines.
- Spread the research workload among a team of RDs.
- Involve students or interns in the project to assist with the literature review, data collection, preliminary analysis, and draft report.
- Determine whether any of the researchers' clinical or administrative activities could be temporarily or permanently delegated to other individuals.
- If you have a large staff, establish a rotating "project day" in which one RD conducts research while other RDs cover the patient care responsibilities, thereby allowing the researchers to commit a block of time to their project without the department incurring the additional cost of supplemental staff.

Lack of Knowledge or Expertise

If the RDs on your staff avoid research because they are not knowledgeable about research methodology, direct them to books (eg, references 6 and 7) and online resources about the topic, or ask a physician or another clinician with research experience to serve as a mentor (6,7). RDs who are Academy members can also learn about and get more involved in the research process by joining the Academy's Dietetics Practice Based Research Network (DPBRN), which was established to "conduct, support, promote, and advocate research in practice-based settings" in order "to address questions of importance to the dietetics profession and to improve the delivery of food and nutrition services to enhance the health status of individuals, families, and communities" (8). A number of studies based on research conducted by the DPBRN have been published, including articles on nutrition diagnosis, critical thinking skills in professional practice, pediatric obesity, and adult weight management (9–12). RDs can participate in DPBRN in a variety of ways, such as sharing ideas for research, participating on the advisory committee that determines which research projects to conduct, collecting data, and disseminating results. Since no research experience is required to participate, DPBRN membership is a good way for RDs who are interested but not confident about research participation to get exposure and gain know-how (8).

Research has shown that RDs with a graduate degree and those with more knowledge of and affinity for evidence-based practice (EBP) are more likely to be involved in research (13). As a clinical nutrition manager (CNM), you can increase the probability of research activities occurring in your organization by hiring individuals with graduate degrees and by including research opportunities or expectations in job descriptions for CNMs and staff (see Chapter 1 for more information on writing job descriptions and hiring staff).

You can also foster your staff's knowledge of EBP in a number of ways, such as the following:

- Have regular journal club sessions led by staff members where your team discusses required readings on EBP topics and explores why EBP is important in clinical nutrition (14).
- Encourage your staff to use the Academy's Evidence Analysis Library (www .andevidencelibrary.com), which is an Academy member benefit.
- Refer RDs to other online EBP resources, such as information about EBP posted on the Academy website (15).

Finally, you and your staff may be reluctant to conduct research because you do not feel prepared to handle the statistical analysis requirements. While many RDs have taken a course in statistics as an undergraduate or graduate student, most of us are not experts in statistics. To overcome this barrier, keep in mind that we cannot be experts in all areas. Lack of advanced knowledge and expertise in statistics should not deter you from participating in research. Instead, look for ways to collaborate with others who have these skills and take the initiative to learn a bit about the statistics relevant to your particular research study (see Box 11.2 on page 234 for online resources). For example, Parrott (16) suggests the following ways to become more comfortable with and competent in statistical analysis:

- Learn the basics by talking with colleagues about what resources/statistical software they would recommend, obtaining a book about statistics designed for nonstatisticians, taking a course in statistics, and exploring different software and accompanying instruction manuals.
- Become familiar with the types of statistical tests generally used in the type of research you plan to conduct (from the research you reviewed in the literature review phase).
- Don't go it alone—rather, get involved with others who are skilled researchers.

In particular, you can overcome the barrier of insufficient statistical knowledge by involving a statistician early in the research process. He or she can help with determining the necessary sample size and analysis, which in turn can affect the research question and study design.

Box 11.2 Helpful Statistics-Related Internet Sites

The following are some websites that J. Scott Parrott, PhD, an associate professor in the Department of Nutritional Sciences at Rutgers University who teaches statistical methods, and his students have found helpful:

- **Statistical Associates Publishing**: www.statisticalassociates.com. "This is one of my favorite statistics websites for using SPSS. While it is focused on SPSS, it has good background on the concept behind different types of statistics. Very thorough. Some of the articles can be a little technical."
- **Web Pages That Perform Statistical Calculations, by JC Pezzullo**: http://statpages.org. "This page links to a dizzying number of online statistics calculators. Helpful for finding a calculator if something is missing from a statistical program you are using."
- **Institute for Digital Research and Education, University of California, Los Angeles**: www.ats.ucla.edu/stat. "The UCLA statistics department has an impressive Help website that is very well organized. They have different sections for the different statistical software packages. Note, in particular, the link to the 'What statistics should I use?' page: www.ats.ucla.edu/stat/mult_pkg/whatstat/default.htm."
- **A New View of Statistics, by WG Hopkins**: www.sportsci.org/resource/stats/index.html. "Similar to many other statistics websites, this site gives a brief overview of different statistics concepts. One of the notable things about this website is that the left navigation bar is populated by statistical terms. It's easy to browse through the list to find what you are looking for."
- **Karl Weunsch's Statistics Lessons, East Carolina University Department of Psychology**: http://core.ecu.edu/psyc/wuenschk/StatsLessons.htm. "A psychology professor at East Carolina University has posted his lecture notes for download. I've found his lectures unusually clear, and he covers a pretty good range of statistics topics."
- **StatSoft Electronic Statistics Textbook**: www.statsoft.com/textbook/stathome.html. "The range of topics covered in this online textbook is impressive. The length of the pages would make it very cumbersome to print, and the background logo makes it difficult to read. But the hyperlinked nature of the text can take you directly to another portion (in case the text makes reference to a statistic you need to brush up on). The right navigation bar is particularly helpful."
- **HyperStat Online Statistics Textbook, by D Lane, Associate Professor of Psychology, Statistics, and Management at Rice University**: www.davidmlane.com/hyperstat/index.html. "This site contains a web-friendly statistics textbook (short pages) and covers the basics in a pretty general fashion. The site itself is a bit cluttered, but it has a number of different gadgets and a list of free online statistics software."
- **Internet Glossary of Statistical Terms**: www.animatedsoftware.com/statglos/statglos.htm#index. "A glossary of statistical terms. Very simple. Scroll down past the ads on the first page."
- **Statistics Glossary, by VJ Easton and JH McColl**: www.stats.gla.ac.uk/steps/glossary. "A statistics glossary that is almost dictionary-like in the brevity of its definitions, which can be helpful when you are hit with a completely unfamiliar term."

Source: Personal communications between author and Parrott.

The Research Process

The research process involves choosing a question to answer, designing and implementing the study, analyzing the data, and disseminating the results. The following sections touch briefly on these issues, but the research process is certainly more complex than what can be described in this chapter. Other references should be explored for more information on this topic (6,7).

Choosing the Research Question and Designing the Study

The research process begins with the identification of a concern or question that is both relevant and important. To define your research question, you must begin by being knowledgeable about the published literature in the area of interest so you can focus your research efforts on an issue that is lacking evidence or requires further confirmation. A good research question can be described using the acronym FINER, which is short for "feasible, interesting, novel, ethical, and relevant" (see Box 11.3) (7). The question you develop is very important because it drives the rest of the research process. Creating a specific and measurable question will help you to use time and resources more effectively and assist with determining what research design is most appropriate. See Table 11.1 on page 236 for examples of ways to narrow down the research question.

Box 11.3 Using FINER to Help Define a Research Question

- **F = Feasible**: If you want to compare resting energy expenditure (REE) of critically ill patients as measured with indirect calorimetry to REE calculated using a predictive equation, you need a metabolic cart and someone to operate it correctly to make this study feasible. Another important consideration is your required sample size (the minimum number of subjects required to produce a statistically appropriate study group) and the length of time required to obtain it. If you have funding for 1 year but need 5 years to accrue the required sample, the study is not feasible as designed; you must restructure it or find additional funding. Consider collaborating with others who have expertise in the area to make your study more feasible and your subject pool more diverse.
- **I = Interesting**: The research topic should be of interest to you but also to the dietetics profession and other stakeholders, such as administrators, potential funding groups, physician or nurse leaders, and your staff. Their interest in your topic can assist in making the project more successful, and interesting research is more likely to be selected for presentation and/or publication.
- **N = Novel**: Research should lead to new evidence that answers a question. However, it is not always necessary (or possible) to ask a completely original question. In the area of nutrition, there is also opportunity for additional research to determine whether findings from previous research can be confirmed or validated. If you review evidence-based guidelines, such as those on the Academy of Nutrition and Dietetics Evidence Analysis Library, you will notice that many of the recommendations do not have a Strong rating because more evidence is needed.

(continues)

Box 11.3 *(continued)*

- **E = Ethical**: Research practices must always be ethical. To present and publish research outside of your organization, approval of the research protocol from an authorized institutional research board (IRB) is required prior to any data collection. The role of the IRB is to protect human and animal research study participants from potential harm and unethical research practices. For example, an IRB would not approve a study comparing the potential benefits of feeding patients versus starving them. In this context, keep in mind the burdens (eg, time, discomfort, invasion of privacy, and risks) on participants as you are planning your research study.
- **R= Relevant**: A research question must be relevant. Apply the "So what?" test to your question. For example, if you propose to research whether feeding a specific type of formula to oncology patients results in higher albumin levels, you may be selecting an endpoint that is not relevant enough to justify the effort. An outcome that involves quality of life, financial costs, or medical complications may be more relevant and more applicable to clinical practice. In addition, you must be able to use a valid instrument (eg, a scale for weight changes or a validated quality of life survey instrument) to measure what you are studying.

Table 11.1 Focusing a Research Question

Broad Topic	Narrowed Topic	Focused Topic	Research Question[a]
Women	Women and breast cancer	Postmenopausal women and breast cancer	Do postmenopausal women with a breast cancer diagnosis alter their dietary intake of fat from baseline (pre-cancer diagnosis)?
Critically ill patients	Critically ill patients and enteral feedings (EF)	Obese critically ill patients and EF	As compared to eucaloric EF, does hypocaloric EF in obese critically ill patients result in improved glycemic control after 5 ICU days?
Outpatients	Outpatients with hyperlipidemia	Overweight outpatients with hyperlipidemia who are not on statins	Does intensive nutrition counseling of overweight outpatients with hyperlipidemia help them attain and maintain healthful fasting serum lipid levels, thereby avoiding treatment with statins?

[a]Question should be very focused and measurable.

Once you have identified your research question, you must design a study that will answer it. Steps include choosing the type of study design, identifying primary and secondary outcomes, determining the specific population to be studied, selecting a sample size, establishing research methods, planning which data will be collected, and pretesting and revising the study protocol.

As you design the study, you will need to set expectations regarding the study logistics and publication. For example, the responsibilities of all study personnel should be clearly outlined from the start. Before any data collection begins, it is essential to establish who does what, how they will receive credit (eg, author order in publications), and how they will be compensated (eg, days off, time off, or monetary rewards).

Different types of study designs produce different types of evidence, with varying levels of quality and reliability (see Figure 11.1 and Box 11.4) (17,18). Randomized controlled trials (RCTs) and systematic reviews provide the highest level of evidence, but these types of research are not always feasible due to factors such as a lack of resources, insufficient expertise, or ethical concerns. Although observational studies (eg, cohort studies, case-control studies, case series, and reports) produce a lower level of evidence than RCTs, these types of research are often a good way for clinicians to become involved in and more comfortable with the research process, especially if time and expertise are limited. Furthermore, evidence from descriptive and correlational studies can be useful in determining whether an RCT is warranted.

- Highest level of evidence
  - Systematic review of randomized controlled trials
  - Randomized controlled trial

- Intermediate level of evidence
  - Cohort study
  - Case control study

- Lowest level of evidence
  - Case series and case reports
  - Clinical observation and expert opinion

Figure 11.1 Levels of Evidence for Various Research Study Designs. Study designs with more rigor are associated with a higher quality of evidence as well as less chance for bias and confounding factors. Source: Data are from reference 17.

Box 11.4 Selected Types of Research Studies

Descriptive study design:

- Research that examines and describes a group of patients, a situation, or an area of interest in a systematic manner; usually as a precursor to a quantitative study (which includes an intervention or randomization).
- Types of descriptive research include qualitative studies, case studies, and survey research.
- Examples:

  ◊ Nutritional status of critically ill patients (descriptive)
  ◊ Use of a focus group of individuals with celiac disease to understand their perceptions about the etiology of their gastrointestinal complaints and how they manage them (qualitative)
  ◊ Nursing staff's beliefs about the value of measuring gastric residual volumes in enterally fed patients (survey)

Correlational study design:

- Research that predicts the association or correlation between two or more variables. Note that a correlation and causation are very different, and a correlational study cannot imply a causal relationship.
- Types of correlational research include case control studies (comparison of two different groups of patients who have the same diagnosis but different treatment) and observational studies (comparison of two groups that does not involve an intervention or controls over the two groups).
- Examples:

  ◊ Comparison of the complication and readmission rates of head and neck cancer patients who receive nutrition support with a percutaneous endoscopic gastrostomy tube versus rates for those who do not receive nutrition support via a feeding tube (case control)
  ◊ Comparison of the risk of vitamin D deficiency in individuals who have undergone gastric bypass surgery versus those who had a gastric sleeve procedure (observational)

Experimental or analytic study design:

- Research involving application of an intervention to establish a cause and effect.
- Types of experimental/analytic research include randomized controlled trials or cross-over trials (study participants are randomly assigned to one or more groups exposed to a treatment or intervention or to a control group that is not exposed to the treatment or intervention).
- Examples:

  ◊ Differences in hospitalization rates for exacerbation of congestive heart failure (CHF) for individuals with CHF who are randomly assigned to receive nutrition counseling from a RD or receive an educational handout only
  ◊ Incidence of diarrhea as measured by frequency and stool consistency in enterally fed patients on a standard isotonic formula randomly assigned to receive a probiotic, a fiber supplement, or a placebo

Source: Data are from references 17 and 18.

Prospective Versus Retrospective Study Designs

As you think about the appropriate research design for your research question, consider whether data should be collected prospectively or retrospectively. Each approach has benefits and limitations. Examples of prospective research include RCTs and cohort studies. A cohort study involves two or more groups, one or more of which has a risk factor, prognostic feature, or specific intervention that one group does not. The groups are then followed prospectively and observed for specific predetermined outcomes. With cohort studies, confounding variables cannot be easily controlled, which can make it difficult to attribute the outcomes to a specific factor or intervention. However, if the groups are well matched and individuals with confounding variables are excluded, the researcher can be more confident that the factor/intervention is truly related to the outcome (17). RCTs are less affected by confounding factors because these trials are designed to use the principles of control, randomization, and replication. When key confounders are mitigated in an RCT, the researcher can conclude from statistically significant results that there is a cause-and-effect relationship between the intervention and outcomes. The limitations of these types of prospective studies are that they are typically expensive to conduct, require a relatively large sample size, and can take longer to complete.

Case studies, case series, and most case-control studies are conducted retrospectively. Such retrospective studies are a good place for novice researchers to start. These studies are usually faster to complete and less expensive than prospective studies, and they can be an effective way to gather the data about a population or group of patients needed to design a prospective trial. However, retrospective data collection can be hampered by selection bias, missing information from a database or medical record, or poor recall by study subjects.

Outcomes Research

Outcomes research focuses on maximizing the quality of care and is conducted in a practice site or real-world setting. The outcomes studied can be clinical (eg, ventilator-free days, infectious complications, or mortality), functional (eg, quality of life or patient satisfaction measures), and/or economic (eg, cost of services). The aim of an outcomes study is to determine "the impact of an intervention on one segment of the sample (intervention group) compared with the impact on a segment of the sample not receiving the intervention (comparison or control group)" (19). Because many variables in the practice setting can influence outcomes, the "selected intervention should be one that can be tested realistically within the dietetics professional's span of control and can be expected to show measureable difference if implemented" (19). Box 11.5 on page 240 guides you through the steps of an outcomes project. The PICO (patient group, intervention, control/comparison group, outcome) format is recommended to organize your research question for an outcomes project (19).

Box 11.5 Steps in an Outcomes Research Project

Step 1: Develop the practice question.

- Typically, a desirable question is one that is not answered by existing evidence or the evidence available is not very strong, or is conflicting.
- The question should be stated in PICO format, where P = patient group; I = intervention; C = control or comparison group; and O = outcome(s). For example:

  ◊ Do inpatients on tube feedings (P) who are monitored daily by the RD (I) compared to inpatients on tube feedings who are monitored twice a week by the RD (C) receive more of their nutrition prescription and have a shorter hospital length of stay (O)?

  ◊ Do inpatients with congestive heart failure (P) who receive nutrition education provided by an RD (I) compared to members of the same patient population who receive nutrition education provided by a nurse (C) have better dietary compliance and fewer hospital readmissions (O)?

Step 2: Conduct an exhaustive literature review.

- What has already been done in the area you are researching?
- Are there gaps in the evidence?
- What methodologies and research techniques are used and accepted?

Step 3: Determine study design.

- Define the comparison by identifying which intervention will be tested and what type of care the comparison group will receive.
- Establish the necessary sample size (discuss with a statistician), a description of the participants, and inclusion/exclusion criteria.
- Plan appropriate data collection methods. Data should include patient characteristics, information about the intervention (Did it happen consistently? Was it carried out by only one individual or multiple individuals?), outcome indicators, how the outcomes are being measured, and any covariates or confounders that could also influence the outcomes. Establish the frequency of data collection, and confirm that all individuals collecting data will follow the same procedure.

Step 4: Institute study methods.

- Prepare to enroll participants. Enrollment includes recruitment, screening for eligibility (be prepared to keep records of how many participants were screened but not enrolled), informed consent procedure, and assignment of participants to the intervention or control group.
- Standardize procedures by using a study manual and data collection forms and tools. Take care to identify potential sources of bias and, if possible, remove them.
- Obtain commitment to the study from all participating sites.
- Secure institutional review board approval from the primary site followed by approval from other sites.

(continues)

Box 11.5 *(continued)*

- Provide appropriate training for staff involved in the study.
- If appropriate, conduct a pilot study before launching a larger study.
- Plan a method to check the accuracy of data collection during the study.

Step 5: Data analysis and reporting.

- Create a database for data entry. There are some free software programs for download into spread-sheets. If you are using multiple sites, a central, blinded data collection site is preferred.
- Identify a coding method. Statistical analysis usually requires the data to be entered as a number, so a number must be assigned to "word" data (eg, if you are collecting information on diagnoses, the various diagnosis categories need to be assigned their own numbers for entry into the database and you need to keep a record of what each code means).
- Engage the help of a statistician (if needed) to conduct the statistical analysis.
- Prepare results for presentation and publication. Dissemination of the evidence is essential to promote the dietetics profession and enhance knowledge. The results should be used to demonstrate to department and organization leaders the value of nutrition interventions and the RD as well as to change practice to improve patient care.

Source: Adapted from reference 19: Biesemeier C. Outcomes research in nutrition support. *Support Line.* 2003;25:7–13. Copyright © 2003 *Support Line*, Dietitians in Nutrition Support, a dietetic practice group of the Academy of Nutrition and Dietetics. Used with permission.

Outcomes research that evaluates and documents the benefits of interventions provided by the RD can help you and your staff improve performance, gain respect, and increase funding and revenues, and it can advance the dietetics profession more generally. When conducting outcomes research, focus on measuring outcomes that can demonstrate the value of our profession to patients, payers, and administrators. Ideally, the evidence/data you collect should be used to ensure quality of care, patient safety, and/or cost savings.

Outcomes research using an existing database, such as the electronic health record (EHR), is a good way for a clinical dietitian or CNM to begin participating in research activity. The EHR can help you learn about specific practice patterns (eg, initiation of enteral feedings in the ICU or nutrition interventions used for patients with pressure ulcers). Ask your facility's information technology personnel whether they can assist with building reports that capture the desired data. This type of research requires approval from the institutional review board (IRB).

The Institutional Review Board Process

Before you initiate any research study, you should understand its legal and ethical dimensions, including those related to the institutional review board process. In the

United States, health care and medical research is regulated by the federal government through the Department of Health and Human Services as well as through the Food and Drug Administration. US regulations have established the IRB as one way to ensure the protection of the rights and welfare of humans who participate in research (20). The principles of IRB can be traced to the Nuremburg Code, which was developed in reaction to the coerced human experiments conducted by the Nazis in World War II, and the Belmont Report, released in the 1970s, which declared that acceptable and ethical human research must embrace "respect for persons, beneficence, and justice" (20,21). To demonstrate respect for persons, researchers are obligated to ensure that all study participants involved in research have voluntarily consented to participate and understand the risks and benefits associated with the study. Researchers must also protect the participants' privacy and confidentiality and offer greater protections for vulnerable populations, such as children or those with disabilities. The application of beneficence requires that any possible benefits of research be maximized and risks minimized. Justice involves the equitable selection of subjects.

As a CNM, you will need to understand whether it is mandatory for your proposed research study to undergo the research approval process. You will also need to ensure that any staff involved with the research study complete training on how to conduct research appropriately. The IRB will not grant study approval until all study personnel have completed the training.

To achieve IRB approval of your study, seek out and collaborate with the IRB staff at your organization. They can advise you about the IRB process and provide specific instructions and templates, which are often dictated by regulations, to assist you through the process. The IRB will typically have specific dates that they meet to review and approve research studies. Take care to learn what the timeline is, ask whether pre-review of a study is possible, pay close attention to the directions and deadlines, and call the IRB staff if you have questions or have not heard back about your study when you anticipated. Box 11.6 lists documents that the IRB requires to review and approve a research study.

Not all organizations have their own IRB. If your facility does not have one, you can seek approval for your research from another organization's IRB or a central IRB.

The necessity for IRB approval will depend on the nature of the project. If the project's aim is quality or performance improvement and the findings will not be published or presented outside your organization, IRB approval may not be needed. However, you should still obtain project approval from upper management or the organization's administration. For example, suppose you wish to study whether your ICU patients on mechanical ventilation are positioned with the head of the bed inclined 30 degrees, and then use the data to determine the need for an intervention (eg, nursing inservices) to ensure that beds at your hospital are positioned correctly. Your study probably does not need IRB approval as long as you do not plan to share the results outside of your hospital. However, if you designed a study to randomly assign ICU patients on mechanical ventilation to be positioned in beds with the heads inclined 30 degrees or left in a supine position in order to compare the incidence of ventilator-acquired pneumonia, your study would need IRB approval, even if the

---

Box 11.6 Potential Documentation Required for Institutional Review Board (IRB) Approval

---

- Research proposal/protocol, including how you plan to obtain informed consent
- Grant application, if applicable
- IRB application (will differ among organizations)
- Documents related to informed consent, such as a sample consent form or consent cover letter or an appeal for a waiver of consent
- Advertisements for recruitment of subjects and plans/tools for recruitment
- Printed information provided to subjects
- Background information related to study-related use of drugs, devices, or procedures
- Qualifications of research staff
- Specific information about the study site to demonstrate it is an appropriate setting for the study
- Financial incentives for either researchers or subjects
- Survey instruments, if applicable, with validity and reliability statistics
- Data collection tools

Source: Adapted from reference 20: Cothran EH. Institutional review board review: a collaborative process. *Support Line.* 2010;32:22–27. Copyright © 2010 *Support Line*, Dietitians in Nutrition Support, a dietetic practice group of the Academy of Nutrition and Dietetics. Used with permission.

---

intent was to keep the results internal, because the research poses a risk to the patient and cannot be classified as merely a performance improvement project.

In general, if you plan to present or publish research outside of your organization, you will need to obtain IRB approval for the study or project. Some studies can fall under an exempt status, meaning informed consent is waived. However, the criteria to meet this exemption are strictly defined by federal regulations. All of the following criteria must be met to get approval from the IRB for a waiver of consent (20):

- The research involves no more than minimal risk to the subjects.
- The study will not adversely affect the rights and welfare of the subjects.
- The research could not practicably be carried out without the waiver or alteration.
- Whenever appropriate, the subjects will be provided with additional pertinent information after participation.

Prior to submitting a request for a waiver of consent, contact the IRB staff to discuss whether your study design meets the criteria listed here and ensure that you can provide the appropriate documentation to obtain the waiver.

The review process and associated obligations extend beyond the initial study approval. Annually, at a minimum, a report on the status of the study is required. If subjects enrolled in the study experience any adverse events, these must be reported to the IRB within a certain time frame, even if the adverse event is not related to the study intervention. Other types of information that must be reported include protocol deviations, patient complaints, and loss of data. The standards for submission of this type of information vary. Take care to familiarize yourself with your organization's specific rules and reporting procedures (20).

Communicating and Publishing Results

Once you have completed a study and analyzed the results, the next step is to communicate the information to others, both internally as well as externally to other groups who will benefit from learning about your research. After all of your hard work conducting the research, the process of communicating your results brings a great sense of accomplishment and adds to the much-needed body of knowledge related to clinical nutrition—so don't skip this step!

First, determine what groups within your organization should hear about your research because their goals or practice are related and the information could make a significant impact. In other words, if you share your study results with them, can you influence their actions or gain support for an initiative or change in practice to improve patient care? Think about including committees involved with quality improvement, patient safety, or a specific service line (eg, intensive care, surgical, or cardiovascular units). Also consider the value of reporting your findings to the pharmacy and therapeutics committee or nursing leadership committee. These committees often have physician and nursing champions who can drive change related to their discipline. Be sure you know the composition of the group (eg, identify potential supporters and opponents of your ideas), how long you have to present the information, and if there is a specific format for the presentation. Depending on the type of research study, you may want to share the results in an internal newsletter or publication to disseminate the information to a wider audience at your organization.

Submitting an abstract for an oral or poster presentation at a state or national meeting is a good initial way to share your study results outside of your organization. Frequently, the organization hosting the meeting will identify specific topics of interest for their meeting. Prior to submitting an abstract, you should review these topics and take care to understand and follow the abstract submission guidelines. Each author is typically required to declare his or her role in the conduct of the research (design, data collection, writing, etc) and complete a conflict of interest statement as part of the abstract submission. Ask a colleague experienced in abstract submission to review your abstract and provide suggestions for improvement prior to submission. Once the abstract is accepted, be sure you understand and follow all instructions related to the presentation, whether it is a poster or an oral session.

Publishing your research results is also important but will take more time and effort than the previously described communication strategies. When looking to publish your findings, the first thing to determine is which journal or publication is most appropriate for the type of research design you used, as well as the focus of your research (22). For example, consider the journals that published the research you used in your literature review; some of these journals likely reach audiences who will be interested in your research. The publications of the various dietetic practice groups of the Academy of Nutrition and Dietetics are a good place to showcase pilot research, especially if the study is your initial effort or if the study is lower on the hierarchy of study designs.

Once you have selected your target journal or publication, obtain a copy of its author and submission guidelines and follow these carefully. Also, you might want to read other articles published in the journal or publication to get ideas about how to format your manuscript (23).

Regardless of where you decide to publish, be aware that publishers require a review and editing process for all manuscripts that they find worthy of consideration for publication. Do not be discouraged by the reviewers' comments and suggestions. Instead, take a deep breath and put the manuscript aside for a day or two to gain perspective. The reviewers' comments and your subsequent revisions will only make the manuscript stronger. You do not have to incorporate all of the comments and suggestions into your manuscript. However, you will want to address each of the reviewer comments, and if you opt not to make a suggested change, explain why. At this time, you may want to contact a mentor who has published before. He or she may be able to help you discern which changes are more important to ensure that your manuscript is accepted for publication.

Additionally, if your manuscript is rejected by a publisher, do not give up on publication. Perhaps the first journal you tried was not the right fit for your manuscript. Re-evaluate your article, discuss your options with a mentor, and then submit your manuscript to another, more appropriate journal. Keep in mind that the author and submission guidelines of the new journal will likely be different from those of the first journal, so some reformatting and rewriting may be necessary.

Embracing the Research Process

Now that we have progressed through the steps of the research process, from formulating the question to publishing the results, let's briefly consider an example of how your staff might progress from preliminary research to a complex trial. Imagine that your staff becomes worried about diarrhea in tube-fed patients and wants to identify interventions that will decrease the incidence of this adverse effect. You decide to conduct a descriptive study to identify how many patients on enteral feedings have diarrhea. The descriptive study shows that the incidence is high, so you decide to perform a correlational study to determine whether the incidence of diarrhea is associated with certain formulas, fiber supplements, or probiotics, or whether it correlates with certain medications or conditions, such as infectious complications in the gastrointestinal tract. That study finds a negative association between the incidence of diarrhea and the use of a probiotic (ie, the incidence of diarrhea is lower in patients who are receiving a probiotic). Based on this evidence as well as a review of published research, you explore the idea of conducting an RCT in which enterally fed patients are randomly selected to receive a probiotic or a placebo. Ideally, the study would be double-blind, meaning neither the patient nor the study investigators would be aware of which patients were receiving the actual treatment versus the placebo. Before launching a large RCT, your team of researchers carries out a pilot study. This small-scale study helps the team fine-tune the research design and determine that the larger trial is logistically and financially feasible. Building on the pilot study, your team designs the RCT, gets it approved by the IRB, and conducts the trial. Upon completion, you communicate the results to key decision makers in your facility and publish the results in a leading nutrition journal. At this point, you find yourself asking new questions or looking for more evidence . . . and the research cycle begins again.

Resources

Because there is a great deal more to research than can be covered in the scope of this chapter, selected additional resources are listed in Box 11.7.

Box 11.7 Research-Related Resources

Academy of Nutrition and Dietetics: www.eatright.org

Offers many research-related resources, including many that are available to Academy members only.

Academy of Nutrition and Dietetics Evidence Analysis Library: www.andevidencelibrary.com

The Academy's site for evidence-based practice guidelines, evidence analysis projects, and related publications and tools.

American Society for Parenteral and Enteral Nutrition: www.nutritioncare.org

Resources include a research toolkit (member benefit).

CINAHL (Cumulative Index to Nursing and Allied Health Literature): www.cinahl.com/

Requires subscription to access (web address will vary by subscriber).

An index of English-language and selected other-language journal articles about nursing, allied health, biomedicine, and health care.

Cochrane Library: www.thecochranelibrary.com

Cochrane Reviews and other evidence-based health care resources.

Critical Care Nutrition: www.criticalcarenutrition.com

Site includes information about participating in the International Nutrition Survey project and other research led by this Canadian group.

National Guidelines Clearinghouse: www.guidelines.gov

A public resource for evidence-based practice guidelines; hosted by the US Department of Health and Human Services, Agency for Healthcare Research and Quality.

NutritionDay: www.nutritionday.org

NutritionDay is an international effort to collect facility data about malnutrition. Site includes information about how to participate in this research initiative. (See Chapter 8 for additional information.)

PubMed: www.ncbi.nlm.nih.gov/pubmed

Essential database for conducting literature reviews.

Summary

Research is an exciting part of clinical nutrition. If you have not yet "dipped your toes" into this particular activity, I heartily encourage you to do so for several reasons. Primarily, RDs need to be proactive in demonstrating how our interventions can improve outcomes. If we do not accomplish this task, we may find at some point that our roles are not valued or supported in the clinical setting. No one else is going to make the case for us. Second, you and your staff will gain additional clinical knowledge, professional skills (eg, writing, presentation, and leadership), recognition from others, including physicians and administrators, and job satisfaction. So take action! You can undoubtedly name a number of problems or questions that need addressing in your organization, and a research study, even if simple and small in scope, is the solution.

References

1. Academy of Nutrition and Dietetics. Research Philosophy. www.eatright.org/Members/content .aspx?id=8339. Accessed December 26, 2011.
2. Academy of Nutrition and Dietetics Quality Management Committee. Academy of Nutrition and Dietetics: Revised 2012 Standards of Practice in Nutrition Care and Standards of Professional Performance for Registered Dietitians. *J Acad Nutr Diet.* 2013;113:S29–S45.
3. Robien K. Making research happen: the real world of clinical nutrition research. *Support Line.* 2003;25:3–6.
4. Eck LH, Slawson DL, Williams R, Smith K, Harmon-Clayton K, Oliver D. A model for making outcomes research standard practice in dietetics. *J Am Diet Assoc.* 1998;98:451–457.
5. Slawson DL, Clemens LH, Bol L. Research and the clinical dietitian: perceptions of the research process and preferred routes to obtaining research skills. *J Am Diet Assoc.* 2000;100:1144–1148.
6. Monsen ER, Van Horn L, eds. *Research: Successful Approaches.* 3rd ed. Chicago, IL: American Dietetic Association; 2008.
7. Hulley SB, Cummings SR, Browner WS, Grady DG, Newman TB. *Designing Clinical Research.* 3rd ed. Philadelphia, PA: Lippincott Williams & Wilkins; 2007.
8. Academy of Nutrition and Dietetics DPBRN. www.eatright.org/Members/content.aspx?id=8336. Accessed December 28, 2011.
9. Enrione EB. Content validation of nutrition diagnoses. *Topics Clin Nutr.* 2008;23:206–319.
10. Trostler N, Meyers EF. Review of critical thinking in professional practice: application in making decisions to either measure or estimate resting metabolic rate. *Topics Clin Nutr.* 2008;23:278–291.
11. Resnicow K. Study design and baseline description of the BMI2 trial: reducing pediatric obesity in primary care practices. *Pediatr Obes.* 2012;7:3–15.
12. Snetselaar L, Smith K, Hollinger D, Myers E, Murphy G, Qualls L. Registered dietitian wellness insurance benefit makes a difference in adult weight management: a pre-post study. *Food Nutr Sci.* 2011;2:1043–1047.
13. Byham-Gray LD, Gilbride JA, Dixon B, Stage FK. Predictors of research involvement among registered dietitians. *J Am Diet Assoc.* 2006;106:2008–2015.
14. Tappenden K, Zimmerman B. Evidence-based practice. In: *The A.S.P.E.N. Nutrition Support Core Curriculum: A Case-Based Approach—The Adult Patient.* Silver Spring, MD: American Society for Parenteral and Enteral Nutrition; 2007:783–790.
15. Academy of Nutrition and Dietetics Evidence-Based Practice. www.eatright.org/Members/content .aspx?id=7186. Accessed December 28, 2011.

16. Parrott JS. Why dietitians can be great researchers. *Support Line*. 2010;32:17–21.

17. Hoppe DJ, Schemitsch EH, Morshed S, Tornetta P, Bhandari M. Hierarchy of evidence: where observational studies fit in and why we need them. *J Bone Joint Surg Am*. 2009;91(Suppl 3):2–9.

18. Boushey C, Harris J, Bruemmer B, Archer SL, Van Horn L. Publishing nutrition research: a review of study design, statistical analyses, and other key elements of manuscript preparation, part 1. *J Am Diet Assoc*. 2006;106:89–96.

19. Biesemeier C. Outcomes research in nutrition support. *Support Line*. 2003;25:7–13.

20. Cothran EH. Institutional review board review: a collaborative process. *Support Line*. 2010;32:22–27.

21. National Institutes of Health. Regulations, Policies, & Guidance. Ethical Guidelines & Regulations. http://grants.nih.gov/grants/policy/hs/ethical_guidelines.htm. Accessed January 2, 2013.

22. Bliss DZ, Guenter PA, Heitkemper MM. From proposal to publication: are you writing research right? *Nutr Clin Pract*. 2000;15:299–305.

23. Gifford H, Ireton-Jones C. Taking your message to the street: presentation and publication. *Support Line*. 2010;32:16–19.

## 12

Creative Staff Development

Cindy Hamilton, MS, RD, LD, Robert S. DeChicco, MS, RD, LD, CNSC, Laura A. Jeffers, MEd, RD, LD, and Elizabeth Anne Pash, MS, RD, LDN

Introduction

Staff development helps employees attain new skills and knowledge, gain increasing levels of competence, and keep abreast of new technology and practice. It is usually an institution-based initiative designed to advance the goals of the company, but it benefits both individuals and the organization alike. Individuals can choose to develop their skills and knowledge independent of company-based programs, but staff development works best when the goals of the institution and individual are aligned and the activities transfer information or skills from the organization to employees to allow them to effectively perform their jobs. Institutions benefit from increased workforce productivity and decreased employee turnover. Individual employees benefit by improving existing skills or learning new skills, which results in increased job satisfaction, better job security, and more opportunities for career advancement.

Some organizations have expanded the definition of staff development to focus on improving the workplace environment and the health and well-being of the employees in ways that might not be directly related to their job tasks. Employees who have a good relationship with their direct supervisor and others who represent the employer feel appreciated and that their opinions matter. Employees who have opportunities for career and personal development may be more content, dedicated, and compassionate. For these reasons, many health care companies wish to develop strategies to strengthen and augment the traditional staff development program.

Implementation of these institutional initiatives is usually the responsibility of midlevel managers. In addition, managers can and should independently take steps to develop their staff and create a better work environment. This chapter discusses various staff development tools that can be used by clinical nutrition managers (CNMs) to enhance clinical practice as well as employee engagement, recognition, and wellness.

Competency-Based Education

Recent advances in medical science and technology are unprecedented, and health care is becoming increasingly complex. However, according to the Institute of Medicine (IOM), "The nation's health care delivery system has fallen short in its ability to translate knowledge into practice and to apply new technology safely and appropriately" (1). Among the solutions that IOM proposed for this problem is competency-based education (CBE) for health care professionals. Traditional education is teacher-based, with the focus on transferring knowledge that the teacher believes the learner should know to the student. Achievement is measured by the number of credit hours spent studying a subject. In most cases, the learner demonstrates acquisition of knowledge by answering a series of questions. The concern with regard to how this knowledge will be used to perform a job task is secondary. In contrast, CBE is worker-based and focuses on the ability of the learner to apply knowledge in a real-life situation. Knowledge and skills are assessed in simulated or real-life situations rather than with written tests. Because individual learners focus on the specific knowledge or skills required to perform a task and are not distracted by extraneous information, CBE is a more efficient learning method than traditional education, where all students are provided the same information, regardless of individual differences in pre-existing knowledge or experience.

The challenge with CBE is evaluation, which requires a trained observer who is considered an expert in the task being evaluated. Observers can use a variety of different methods to evaluate learners, including direct observation, simulation, return demonstration, verbalization, or review of documentation. Observers are usually senior staff clinicians or supervisors from the learner's team. Unfortunately, observers may be burdened by the demands of their own clinical duties and are not always given adequate training or time to perform the evaluations.

CNMs should incorporate CBE into their staff development program. Ideally, all training and evaluation should be competency-based, but it may be more practical to focus first on activities that are difficult to evaluate using standardized tests, such as performing an abdominal assessment or practicing motivational interviewing.

The first step in CBE is to identify individual tasks employees are expected to perform. This step can be accomplished by reviewing professional practice audits, standards of practice (SOP), and standards of professional performance (SOPP) for the focus area, if available. Additional information can be gleaned from reviewing job descriptions, discussing job tasks with the employees and their supervisors, and observing employees, both directly and indirectly, during the performance of their job.

Once the tasks are identified, a minimum acceptable level of performance, or competency, should be assigned to each task. For example, imagine the competency is to determine whether a central venous catheter is properly positioned for infusion of central parenteral nutrition from a chest radiograph. The employee should understand the proper position and be able to identify the location of the catheter tip within the vasculature using established landmarks. To demonstrate competency in providing diet education, the registered dietitian (RD) or dietetic technician, registered (DTR) should be able to provide individualized education appropriate for a specific patient's education level and cultural/religious factors, and also be able to determine the patient's understanding of the information provided and willingness to comply with the dietary advice.

Competencies can be subdivided into different levels of proficiency, from novice to expert. For example, the Academy of Nutrition and Dietetics SOPs/SOPPs for RDs practicing in nutrition support established three levels of practice: generalist, specialty, and advanced (2). As the SOPs/SOPPs are updated, the terms "competent," " proficient," and "expert" will be used in accordance with the Dietetics Career Development Guide (3). A competent RD is a novice who is able to perform the basic skills required for entry-level practice in nutrition support. RDs at the next level are considered proficient because they have developed a deeper understanding of nutrition support and are better able to apply evidence-based principles in practice and modify practice in unique situations. Advanced-practice RDs are considered experts who demonstrate complex decision-making abilities and superior clinical skills.

Different levels of proficiency are linked to specific tasks and scope of practice. For example, the SOP for evaluating access sites for RDs practicing in nutrition support is not listed as a competency for a competent RD, whereas the proficient RD is expected to be able to evaluate *existing* sites for the delivery of nutrition support, and the expert RD is expected to evaluate both *existing* and *potential* sites for the delivery of nutrition support (2). As compared with evaluating existing sites only, evaluating potential sites requires a deeper understanding of the anatomy and function of the vascular system and gastrointestinal tract, the types and features of intravenous and enteral access devices, placement techniques, and potential complications.

Individual institutions should develop competencies based on their organizational goals and patient population and use SOPs and SOPPs for their specialty areas, if available, as templates. Figure 12.1 (page 252) is a sample form used in the evaluation of competencies related to management of venous access devices by nutrition support dietitians. Each competency is listed separately along with the name of the evaluator and the method of validation. Different tasks can be evaluated by different people, including the employee's direct supervisor, a co-worker, or a trained observer, provided they are competent in the task(s) being evaluated. When direct observation is the method of validation for a task, the evaluator should ideally have consistent and intimate interaction with the employee during the daily performance of his or her job. However, direct observation during clinical simulation by a trained observer is an acceptable method for determining competency.

When you have new employees in training, plan to evaluate their competencies at regularly scheduled intervals until they become proficient at a task. After the training is complete, employees should be evaluated periodically, usually prior to their annual performance review, to ensure that they remain competent.

In a CBE program, each competency should have a list of learning objectives that will provide the knowledge and skills necessary for the learner to perform that task. For example, a competency of using a stethoscope to auscultate for bowel sounds requires a combination of knowledge and skills, including how to use a stethoscope, understanding the structure and function of the gastrointestinal tract, and identifying landmarks of the abdominal wall (see Table 12.1 on page 253). Accordingly, the

Nutrition Support Dietitian Competency Evaluation

Name: _____

Competency	Achieved: Date/Evaluator	Validation Method[a]
Venous access devices		
Recommend appropriate type of venous access device and number of lumens for short and long-term parenteral nutrition.		
Evaluate tip position of existing central venous access device for infusion of central parenteral nutrition using a chest radiograph.		
Evaluate venous access device exit site for signs of infection (eg, redness, tenderness, erythema, drainage).		
Recognize signs/symptoms of catheter-related blood stream infection.		
Understand steps in treating suspected catheter-related bloodstream infections in short- and long-term venous access devices.		

[a]Validation method: CS, clinical simulation; DR, direct observation; RD, return demonstration; ROD, review of documentation; V, verbalization.

Figure 12.1 Sample Nutrition Support Dietitian Competency Evaluation Form

learning activities to teach the objectives will involve multiple educational methods. Education about the physiology and anatomy of the gastrointestinal tract is best accomplished by reviewing a textbook or computer-based module or listening to a webinar or live lecture. Because different employees may learn differently, you might want to offer options for how to acquire this scientific information—for example, some people may prefer reading while others retain learning better by listening. Next, the employee could learn to use a stethoscope to auscultate for bowel sounds by simulation on volunteer subjects or at the bedside on real patients under the supervision of a trained instructor.

To encourage ongoing learning, consider a monthly or quarterly case study/chart review process. You could also invite professionals from other disciplines (eg, physicians, respiratory therapists, speech language pathologists, nurses, or pharmacists) to present on topics of interest to clinical RDs. These presentations could help your staff see how their roles intersect with those of experts in other disciplines and learn ways that they can collaborate to enhance patient care. A journal club is another avenue for elevating knowledge, improving critical thinking and research skills, and discussing evidence-based guidelines. If you choose to launch a journal club, you may wish to start with an introductory session that is moderated by an individual who is knowledgeable about how to critique research.

DTRs also need ongoing education related to their role. RDs can usually mentor DTRs and teach their education classes.

As a CNM you are responsible for annually surveying the educational needs of your staff and planning the necessary educational opportunities. CBE programs should be evaluated regularly and modified as necessary to reflect changes in technology and practice. For example, the focus in nutrition assessment has shifted from anthropometrics and laboratory tests toward physical examination and patient history. CNMs, in turn, need to adjust their training programs to reflect this change by offering educational pathways for RDs to learn these skills.

Table 12.1 Learning Objectives and Activities for Auscultating for Bowel Sounds

Learning Objective	Learning Activities
1. Identify parts and function of a stethoscope.	Review textbook or computer/web-based learning module.
2. Understand structure and function of the gastrointestinal tract.	Review textbook or computer/web-based learning module.
3. Identify location of bony landmarks and internal organs underlying abdominal wall.	Review textbook or computer/web-based learning module.
4. Demonstrate proper technique for auscultating for bowel sounds.	Review textbook or computer/web-based learning module; view demonstration by expert; return demonstration on simulated or live patient.
5. Identify hyperactive, normal, and hypoactive bowel sounds.	Review textbook or computer/web-based learning module including audio files; supervised practice on live patients.

Individual Development Plan

An individual development plan (IDP) can help employees identify their strengths, interests, and areas for improvement so they can meet job expectations and identify career goals. The IDP can align with the employee's Commission on Dietetics Registration (CDR) professional development portfolio as well as the goals of the employer.

The employee begins the IDP process by drafting his or her individual plan, completing any required paperwork, and then meeting with his or her supervisor or manager. The employee and manager should work together to make sure the IDP is realistic, attainable, and agreeable to both parties. The employee and manager should also plan to meet at least once (midyear) after they agree on the IDP to assess progress, identify any problems, and make any needed changes to the plan.

The IDP should identify the goal item(s) and establish the action plan, including resources that are needed, the expected time frame to accomplish the goal, and how the goal will be measured (see Figure 12.2). A good time to establish the initial IDP with the employee is during an annual performance review. As a CNM, you should provide direction for each goal that can ultimately lead to the employee's success.

Career Management and Ladders

As CNM, you should aim to help clinical dietetics staff identify and reach their long-term career goals. When you develop career paths or ladders for the RDs and DTRs on your staff, they feel recognized and appreciated, which helps you retain good employees who are engaged in their work, their department, and the organization. Career ladders can also be a part of succession planning, as they can prepare employees to transition to higher-level positions when they become available.

When developing career ladders, you may find it helpful to work closely with your human resources (HR) department. The HR team may know of other disciplines in the facility that have career ladders that you can use as a reference. Additionally, they may be able to help you use the Academy of Nutrition and Dietetics Career Development Guide (3) and SOP/SOPP to establish career ladders that make sense for your organization. In particular, HR may have suggestions about how you can translate the general descriptions and defined criteria for education, experience, and performance presented in the guide for various practitioner levels (from novice to advanced) into job descriptions for your department. For example, Figure 12.3 (page 256) is a job description created for an Advanced Practice II clinical dietitian that is derived from the Dietetics Career Development Guide (3) and reflects the Academy's view that an advanced practitioner exhibits the highest level of knowledge and skills along with leadership and visionary characteristics, and has a minimum of a Master's degree with board certification, if available.

In addition to establishing general career ladders for your department, you can also provide individualized career management guidance to each member of your staff. Begin by helping them identify the following:

Individualized Career Development Plan

Name: *Donna Dietitian*_____   **Date:** *January 2, 2014*_____

Job Title: *Advanced Practice Dietitian*_____

	Goal 1	Goal 2
Development goal	*Publish review article in peer-reviewed professional journal.*	*Obtain specialty credential: Certified Specialist in Oncology (CSO).*
Action plan (Work that must be done to reach goal)	*Determine subject matter; identify potential journal. Collaborate/determine other authors (co-workers). Review literature, establish outline, draft manuscript, and submit.*	*Study for certification exam. Submit application to take exam.*
Resources needed (Identify tools or support required)	*Guidance from manager.*	*Reimbursement monies after passing the exam.*
Time frame (Completion date)	*December 31, 2014*	*June 6, 2014*
Measure (Define success: How will you know you achieved your goal?)	*Acceptance of article in a peer-reviewed journal.*	*Passed examination and awarded CSO.*

Figure 12.2 Sample Individual Development Plan

Job Description

Job Title: REGISTERED DIETITIAN ADVANCED PRACTICE II

Job Summary: Utilizing expert skills and knowledge, provides individualized medical nutrition therapy to assigned patient population. Assesses patients' nutritional needs, develops and implements nutrition programs, and evaluates and reports the results. Nationally recognized within the nutrition profession as having mastered the highest degree of skill and knowledge in a clinical area. Functions as the department's expert in area of focus and will mentor peers to share knowledge.

Job Responsibility 1: Provides direct patient care using medical nutrition therapy for an assigned patient population. Serves as an expert in using the Nutrition Care Process (assessment, diagnosis, intervention, and monitoring and evaluation) in patient care.

Job Responsibility 2: Develops and conducts education programs for patients, physicians, nurses, allied health professionals, students, peers, and the public. Functions as a preceptor/class instructor in support of the dietetic internship program.

Job Responsibility 3: Leads and designs departmental initiates relative to patient care. Leads committees and projects.

Job Responsibility 4: Develops programs and services to market and expand departmental services and generate revenue. Markets nutrition services to potential and current referral sources; develops and implements services in response to clients' needs. Designs, implements, and publishes research and presents research findings. Publishes in peer-reviewed literature.

Education: Masters or PhD degree in nutrition, dietetics, or related field. Must possess clinical specialty credential, if available.

Licensure: Current license to practice dietetics in the state. Completion of an Academy of Nutrition and Dietetics–approved dietetic internship (or equivalent dietitian-qualifying experience) and current certification as a registered dietitian.

Required Experience: Minimum of eight (8) years of experience as a registered dietitian in therapeutic nutrition, with responsibility for nutrition assessment and development and implementation of nutrition care plans. Recognized expert in nutrition field through national presentations, publications, and leadership roles in professional organizations. Demonstrated personal and organizational leadership.

Source: Data are from reference 3.

Figure 12.3 Sample Job Description for Advanced Practice Registered Dietitian

- **Their core interests**: eg, direct patient care, managing people and solving problems, educating patients, training new staff, or technology
- **Their core values**: eg, autonomy, salary, or title
- **Their strengths/skills**: eg, research or grant writing, project development, or interpersonal relationships

As you advise your employees about their career plans, ask them to think about what they want the most. Are they primarily interested in higher wages, more prestige, or a different job title? Are they excited by the idea of new challenges, or are they looking to increase their repertoire of skills? When you understand the employee's specific motivating factors, you can provide the best guidance.

For career ladders and plans to be effective, you need to establish procedures to continually evaluate whether employees are progressing as expected and determine if they meet the defined criteria of higher level positions. Figure 12.4 (page 258) is an example of an application form completed annually by the clinician and provided to the CNM to justify maintenance of the advanced level of practice.

Employee Engagement

Health care organizations and other employers are increasingly recognizing the importance of employee engagement for their overall success. Engaged employees are fully involved in and enthusiastic about their work. They have an emotional attachment to their job, co-workers, and organization, and they act in ways that advance their organization's interests. In contrast, "non-engaged" employees may be productive but they are not psychologically committed to the workplace, and "actively disengaged" employees are psychologically absent or unhappy at work and may even actively resist or sabotage departmental goals and initiatives. Unsurprisingly, employee engagement seems to lead to decreased employee turnover rates, increased productivity, and greater profitability. In the case of health care, engaged employees are more likely than non-engaged employees to be committed to a higher standard of care; they are also more productive and focused on their patients' care and treatment, and they create a superior patient experience overall (4).

Employee engagement programs are typically established within a business by HR or through a consulting company that focuses on organizational performance and improvement. National organizations such as Gallup Consulting use annual surveys to evaluate the level of engagement of employees at a particular business (4). The surveys ask employees about recognition, progress/development, opportunities, and quality of work. Questions might include the following:

- Have you recently been recognized for your work?
- Do you feel someone at work (supervisor/co-worker) cares about you?
- Do you feel your opinions count?
- Do you have the materials and equipment to do your work correctly?

Advanced Practice Dietitian II Application

Name: _____   Date: _____

I would like to submit my application to be considered for the Registered Dietitian, Advanced Practice II position.

I fulfill each of the job requirements in the following manner:

Serves as an expert in a focused area in the provision of nutrition care:

_____

_____

Develops techniques, protocols, and programs to provide comprehensive nutrition care and markets to expand services and generate revenue:

_____

_____

Proactively communicates and provides education, consultation, and guidance to physicians, allied health care professionals, dietitians, and students:

_____

_____

Designs, implements, publishes, and presents research:

_____

_____

Actively contributes to department committees and participates in professional growth activities:

_____

_____

Meets two of three criteria:

- ☐ Participates as a committee member of a national professional organization.
- ☐ Speaker at national professional conferences (sought-after speaker).
- ☐ Publishes manuscripts in peer-reviewed journals and/or professional books. Is first author or corresponding author.

Advanced degree and specialty certification, if available (attach documentation):

_____

Eight years work experience as RD in a focused clinical area. At least 50% of work assignment is in declared focused area: _____

Excellent interpersonal and communication skills with groups and individuals. Known nationally as an expert clinician in a focused area: _____

Figure 12.4 Annual Renewal Form for Advanced Practice Dietitian

The results of these types of surveys offer evidence to a manager or supervisor about their employees' engagement level and can be used to identify changes that are needed or strengths that should be sustained.

Types of Initiatives and Tools

Efforts to improve or maintain employee engagement should be employee-driven. Consider assigning employees who are role models of exceptional customer interactions and who are committed to the concept and process of employee engagement to a work group that develops the engagement plans for your department. The program they create may involve more than one type of initiative or engagement method. For example, the work group might plan work outings (such as a summer picnic), start a softball team, sponsor charitable events (such as fundraisers), or organize volunteers to help at a local food bank or soup kitchen. The work group might also create an employee committee to lead departmental efforts in professional education. The committee volunteers could survey others in the department to determine topics of interest and arrange learning sessions that offer continuing professional education credits to participants. In another initiative, the nutrition support staff in your department could schedule regular meetings where they could express opinions, ask questions, and discuss issues of importance to their jobs.

Some teams use a "huddle" to foster a feeling of connection among employees on a regular basis during work hours. In a brief (eg, 10-minute) daily or weekly gathering, employees "huddle" together to discuss operational issues and recognize each other for work well done or acts of compassion. For example, the work leader might begin the huddle by saying, "A couple key operational issues today. Sam will not be in today, and Sarah is covering. The electronic medical record seems to be moving slow this morning; IT is aware and is working on it. Also, I want to note that I saw our colleague Elizabeth step off an elevator on Monday so a patient with crutches had room to step onto the elevator. This demonstrated compassion and exceptional service for our patients. Does anyone else want to recognize a colleague today?"

Employee Recognition

Employee recognition is an essential component of employee engagement and helps reinforce behavior consistent with an institution's mission and values. Employees can be recognized in a variety of ways, and the most appreciated type of recognition may vary among individuals. For example, some employees like to be praised in front of their colleagues, but others might feel embarrassed by the attention. To determine the type(s) of recognition desired by employees, solicit feedback during staff meetings or in one-on-one discussions.

Cleveland Clinic uses an online program, "Caregiver Celebrations," as a personalized and easy way to acknowledge employees for work that enhances patient care and supports fellow caregivers. The program encourages employees to recognize their peers and allows managers to give nonmonetary and monetary awards to staff who perform actions that have a substantial positive impact on performance or leadership and support Cleveland Clinic values, such as quality, innovation, teamwork, service, integrity, and compassion. Quarterly and annual awards are given to recognize notable acts that benefit the organization's business opportunities, demonstrate leadership, improve patient care, or support the institution's mission. For example, awards have been given to clinical nutrition personnel for the following accomplishments:

- A registered dietitian worked with a local community school district to analyze and adjust menus to meet the new proposed US Department of Agriculture guidelines for reduced sodium and fat and increased fruits, vegetables, and whole grains.
- Nutrition support team dietitians established processes with the pharmacy department to manage shortages of injectable electrolytes, vitamins, and minerals for patients receiving parenteral nutrition.
- Clerical nutrition personnel worked together to establish a cross-training schedule that led to provision of better services for the department.

Another way to recognize employees is through a regular communiqué, such as a printed or electronic newsletter. Useful for providing departmental updates or send reminders, a weekly or monthly newsletter can also be a place to recognize employee accomplishments, such as awards, certifications, new hires, retirements, research, and publications, and share celebratory personal information, such as birth or wedding announcements.

Some managers choose to hold annual recognition events to show their appreciation for their employees. If you plan such an event, offer awards to recognize performance in several categories that capture the variety of services normally provided by a clinical nutrition department. For example, you might recognize employees for the following:

- Clinical excellence—adults
- Clinical excellence—pediatrics
- Dietetic technical excellence
- Excellence in research
- Humanitarian efforts
- Administrative/clerical excellence
- Ambulatory care excellence
- Leadership

To maintain a fair and successful process, establish criteria for each award, allow employees to drive the nomination process, and ask a committee of employees to serve as judges. (See Figure 12.5 for a sample nomination form.) The awards you present can be simple (eg, a printed certificate), or you may wish to offer more elaborate awards, if your budget permits them.

Clinical Excellence Award

Center for Human Nutrition

Nominee: _____

Job Title:_____

DEADLINE: February 15

Purpose: The clinical excellence award is given to a clinician with extensive experience who is considered an expert in an area of clinical practice and who exhibits a range of highly developed clinical and technical skills, along with a high degree of proficiency and autonomy.

Instructions: Complete the following questions, citing specific examples. Use a separate piece of paper if more space is required.

1. **Displays extensive clinical knowledge and technical skills. Applies evidence-based guidelines in the care of patients.**

    _____

    _____

    _____

2. **Demonstrates a high degree of proficiency and autonomy.**

    _____

    _____

    _____

3. **Is recognized as a clinical leader by peers and colleagues (within and outside the clinic).**

    _____

    _____

    _____

4. **Displays knowledge of nutrition literature, research design, and methods. Implements research and/or publishes.**

    _____

    _____

    _____

Figure 12.5 Clinical Excellence Award Application Form. Source: Reprinted by permission of the author, Cindy Hamilton, MS, RD, LD.

Employee Wellness

When employees are involved in programs that improve or maintain their optimal health and well-being and enhance their quality of life, they tend to be more engaged in their work and can better serve patients (5). Studies have shown that worksite wellness programs can assist in controlling health care costs for employees, increase employee productivity, improve job satisfaction, lower absenteeism, promote a sense of community, and improve health behaviors and long-term health (5).

Wellness programs typically use incentives, such as lower rates for health care plans, to encourage employees to make healthful behavior changes or maintain healthy habits. For example, such programs might include smoking cessation, stress management, improving work-life balance, or nutrition and physical activity.

In addition to participating in their employer's wellness plan, nutrition employees may be able to take part in developing the nutrition programs used in the plan. In this way, wellness plans may enhance individual career development goals while promoting employee engagement. Employee nutrition programs generally address weight management and overall healthy eating habits; when they are part of a wellness initiative, they should be associated with exercise programs. Goals are usually measured by monitoring changes in body mass index, blood pressure, cholesterol, triglycerides, and/or blood glucose (5).

Many health care workers struggle to maintain a healthy work-life balance and avoid professional burnout, particularly if they work in stressful environments, such as critical care, or handle large volumes of work. Whether or not the employer offers an employee wellness plan, CNMs can promote wellness among their staff by encouraging them to participate in organization-sponsored events, such as charity runs or walks. Managers can also encourage physical fitness on a departmental level by organizing activities such as runs/walks, walking groups, weight-loss contests, exercise groups, and sports outings (eg, golf or bowling).

Psychological issues such as depression, financial concerns, and family/marital issues may not be addressed by wellness initiatives, but they can deeply affect the employee's health and well being. Managers should therefore be prepared to offer resources to employees for these types of problems. Employee assistance programs (EAPs) are available as a resource in most institutions.

Summary

Staff development is the responsibility of CNMs, and its scope is no longer limited to the simple transfer of information from the organization to the employee. CNMs must ensure that their employees have the necessary knowledge and skills to perform their jobs and also create a supportive work environment where employees are happy and productive and have opportunities for career advancement. The complex process of staff development is easier when the employer's administration is supportive, provides the necessary time and resources for development, recognizes and rewards staff excellence, and aims to retain clinicians who are capable of advanced practice. However, even in the absence of administration support, CNMs can foster staff development in their departments by asking employees about their perceptions of their jobs, inviting staff suggestions about how to improve the work environment, developing action plans to address these issues, and then monitoring and adjusting these plans as needed. CNMs can also establish a system for recognizing and rewarding good workers on an individual or small-group basis. Acknowledgment might be offered one-on-one from the manager to employee or be built into a work group activity. Employee wellness is also directly linked to organizational success. Wellness activities increase the likelihood that employees will be engaged in their work. Participants in such activities may be happier, more productive, and more likely to exhibit behaviors consistent with the organization's mission and values. Ultimately, engaged and healthy employees provide better patient care.

References

1. Institute of Medicine. *Crossing the Quality Chasm: A New Health System for the 21st Century.* 2001. http://iom.edu/Reports/2001/Crossing-the-Quality-Chasm-A-New-Health-System-for-the-21st-Century.aspx. Accessed June 19, 2011.
2. American Society for Parenteral and Enteral Nutrition and American Dietetic Association: Standards of Practice and Standards of Professional Performance for Registered Dietitians (Generalist, Specialty, and Advanced) in Nutrition Support. *J Am Diet Assoc.* 2007;107:1815–1822.
3. Academy of Nutrition and Dietetics. Dietetics Career Development Guide. www.eatright.org/Members/content.aspx?id=7665. Accessed November 29, 2011.
4. Gallup. Employee Engagement. http://www.gallup.com/strategicconsulting/en-us/employeeengagement.aspx. Accessed September 11, 2013.
5. Merrill R, Aldana S, Garrett J, Ross C. Effectiveness of a workplace wellness program for maintaining health and promoting behaviors. *J Occup Environ Med.* 2011;53:782–787.

Index

Page number followed by *b* refers information in a box, *f* indicates a figure, and *t* refers to a table.